Evaluating and Communicating Subsistence Seafood Safety in a Cross-Cultural Context: Lessons Learned from the *Exxon Valdez* Oil Spill

Other titles from the Society of Environmental Toxicology and Chemistry (SETAC):

Endocrine Disruption in Invertebrates: Endocrinology, Testing, and Assessment
deFur, Crane, Ingersoll, Tattersfield, editors
1999

Reproductive and Developmental Effects of Contaminants in Oviparous Vertebrates
Di Giulio and Tillitt, editors
1999

Multiple Stressors in Ecological Risk and Impact Assessment
Foran and Ferenc, editors
1999

Linkage of Effects to Tissue Residues: Development of a Comprehensive Database for Aquatic Organisms Exposed to Inorganic and Organic Chemicals
Jarvinen and Ankley
1999

Ecotoxicology and Risk Assessment for Wetlands
Lewis, Mayer, Powell, Nelson, Klaine, Henry, Dickson, editors
1999

Uncertainty Analysis in Ecological Risk Assessment
Warren-Hicks and Moore, editors
1998

Ecotoxicological Risk Assessment of the Chlorinated Organic Chemicals
Carey, Cook, Giesy, Hodson, Muir, Owens, Solomon, editors
1998

Sustainable Environmental Management
Barnthouse, Biddinger, Cooper, Fava, Gillett, Holland, Yosie, editors
1998

Ecological Risk Assessment Decision-Support System: A Conceptual Design
Reinert, Bartell, Biddinger, editors
1998

Principles and Processes for Evaluating Endocrine Disruption in Wildlife
Kendall, Dickerson, Giesy, Suk, editors
1998

For information about any SETAC publication, including SETAC's international journal,
Environmental Toxicology and Chemistry,
contact the SETAC Office nearest you:

1010 N. 12th Avenue
Pensacola, Florida, USA 32501-3367
T 850 469 1500 F 850 469 9778
E setac@setac.org

Avenue E. Mounier 83, Box 3
1200 Brussels, Belgium
T 32 2 772 72 81 F 32 2 770 53 86
E setac@ping.be

http://www.setac.org

Evaluating and Communicating Subsistence Seafood Safety in a Cross-Cultural Context: Lessons Learned from the *Exxon Valdez* Oil Spill

Edited by

L. Jay Field
National Oceanic and Atmospheric Administration

James A. Fall
Alaska Department of Fish and Game

Thomas S. Nighswander
Alaska Native Medical Center

Nancy Peacock
National Oceanic and Atmospheric Administration

Usha Varanasi
National Oceanic and Atmospheric Administration

SETAC Technical Publications Series

SETAC Liaison
William A. Stubblefield
ENSR Consulting & Engineering

Current Coordinating Editor of SETAC Books
Christopher G. Ingersoll
U.S. Geological Survey, Midwest Science Center

Publication sponsored by the Society of Environmental Toxicology and Chemistry

SETAC PRESS

Cover design by Michael Kenney Graphic Design and Advertising; original photograph used with kind permission of Natalie Fobes Photography, Seattle, WA.
Indexing by IRIS

Library of Congress Cataloging-in-Publication Data

Evaluating and communicating subsistence seafood safety in a cross-cultural context: lessons learned from the *Exxon Valdez* Oil Spill / edited by L. Jay Field. . . [et al.].
p. cm. -- (SETAC technical publications series)
Includes bibliographic references and index.
ISBN 1-880611-29-5
1. Oil spills--environmental aspects--Alaska--Prince William Sound Region 2. Exxon Valdez (Ship) 3. Oil pollution of the sea-Environmental aspects--Alaska--Prince William Sound. 4. Aquatic animals--Effect of oil spills on--Alaska--Prince Williams Sound Region. 5. Subsistence economy--Alaska--Prince William Sound Region. 6. Prince William Sound Region (Alaska)--Economic conditions.
I. Field, L. Jay, (Lawrence Jay), 1947-
II. Series.
TD427.P4E93 1999 99-12327
363.19 ' 2--dc21 CIP

International Standard Book Number 1-880611-37-6
Printed in the United States of America
06 05 04 03 02 01 00 99 10 9 8 7 6 5 4 3 2 1

∞ The paper used in this publication meets the minimum requirements of the American National Standard for Information Sciences—Permanence of Paper for Printed Library Materials, ANSI Z39.48-1984.

Reference Listing: Field LJ, Fall JA, Nighswander TS, Peacock N, Varanasi U. Evaluating and communicating subsistence seafood safety in a cross-cultural context: lessons learned from the *Exxon Valdez* oil spill. Pensacola, FL: Society of Environmental Toxicology and Chemistry (SETAC). 338 p.

The SETAC Technical Publication Series

The SETAC Technical Publications Series was established by the Society of Environmental Toxicology and Chemistry (SETAC) to provide in-depth reviews and critical appraisals on scientific subjects relevant to understanding the impacts of chemicals and technology on the environment. The series consists of books on topics reviewed and recommended by the SETAC Board of Directors and approved by the Publications Advisory Council for their importance, timeliness, and contribution to multidisciplinary approaches to solving environmental problems. The diversity and breadth of subjects covered in the series reflect the wide range of disciplines encompassed by environmental toxicology, environmental chemistry, and hazard and risk assessment. These volumes attempt to present the reader with authoritative coverage of the literature, as well as paradigms, methodologies, and controversies; research needs; and new developments specific to the featured topics.

SETAC Technical Publications are useful to environmental scientists in research, research management, chemical manufacturing, regulation, risk assessment, and education, as well as to students considering or preparing for careers in these areas. The Series provides information for keeping abreast of recent developments in familiar subject areas and for rapid introduction to principles and approaches in new subject areas.

Contents

List of Figures

List of Tables

Acknowledgments and Dedication

This book represents exceptional efforts by many individuals and organizations too numerous to mention here. The book would not have been possible without the support and long-term commitment of David Kennedy, Director, Office of Response and Restoration, National Ocean Service, NOAA. As NOAA's Scientific Support Coordinators for the *Exxon Valdez* Oil Spill, John Robinson (retired), formerly Chief of Hazardous Materials Response and Assessment Division, and David Kennedy recognized the importance of the subsistence issues and made the subsistence program a priority in NOAA's response to the spill.

Sin-Lam Chan, Donald Brown, and many other individuals from NOAA's National Marine Fisheries Service Environmental Conservation Division provided high-quality analyses and interpretation of data under a demanding schedule, which required setting aside ongoing research projects.

John Middaugh, State Epidemiologist, Alaska Department of Health and Social Services, played a major role in the initiation and development of the Oil Spill Healt Task Force (OSHTF) and expert committee.

Steve Lewis, a senior toxicologist for Exxon Biomedical, directed Exxon's response to subsistence seafood safety and served as their primary representative on the OSHTF and the expert committee. Although Exxon provided the funding for the combined subsistence seafood safety study and was an active participant in the OSHTF, the company declined to participate in this publication.

Robert Wolfe, Research Director of the Division of Subsistence, Alaska Department of Fish and Game, played a critical early role in helping to define the role of the OSHTF, design the studies, and develop a credible message. As oil spill coordinators for the Division of Subsistence, Philippa Coiley and Rita Miraglia provided important staff support for the OSHTF. Also, Andy Williams worked as a publications specialist for the Division to write the first several OSHTF newsletters and also wrote and produced the informational video for the OSHTF.

During OSHTF meetings, Len Vining and Mara Kimmel ably represented the Alaska Native communities of Prince William Sound and Lower Cook Inlet through The North Pacific Rim. Brenda Schwantes did the same for the Kodiak Area Native Association.

Ann Hayward Walker (SEA, Inc., under contract to NOAA) coordinated NOAA's initial response to subsistence issues. Gary Winston (toxicologist, Lousiana State University, under contract to NOAA) participated in the expert committee and played an important role in the village meetings in the fall of 1989. Lori Harris (NOAA) provided technical editing throughout the process. Al Hielscher, Dean Dale, and John Murphy of Genwest Systems provided graphics and information-management support.

We would like to acknowledge the important contribution of Mike Bolger and the rest of the expert panel (see list of panel members in Appendix 2).

Finally, we also would like to acknowledge the following reviewers of this book: Keith Cooper, Rutgers University; Richard Di Giulio, Duke University; and Ruth Yender, NOAA Office of Response and Restoration.

This book is dedicated to the memory of Chief Walter Meganack and to the people of Prince William Sound, Lower Cook Inlet, Kodiak Island, and the Alaska Peninsula whose subsistence food resources and traditional way of life were affected by the 1989 *Exxon Valdez* oil spill.

Foreword

The *Exxon Valdez* oil spill of March 1989 has been characterized as one of the worst environmental disasters in American history. The spill had a critical human dimension as well. Prince William Sound, Lower Cook Inlet, Kodiak Island, and the Alaska Peninsula are home to thousands of people, including an indigenous Alaska Native population. Soon after oil entered the waters of Prince William Sound, many residents of spill-area communities questioned whether the oil was contaminating the fish, shellfish, birds, and mammals that they depended upon as subsistence foods. Large numbers of animals, including sea otters, seabirds, and shellfish, were killed by the oil and washed up on the beaches. Newspaper headlines and television news dramatized the spread of the "black tide." The closure of most of the commercial salmon and other fisheries contributed to local residents' concerns that these resources were no longer safe to eat.

The Oil Spill Health Task Force (OSHTF) formed soon after the spill in response to a variety of human-health related issues, and it soon focused on addressing subsistence concerns as it became apparent that subsistence food safety was a problem that was not being adequately addressed as part of the general response. Recognition of the problem was an important first step, but it was not accompanied by a clear path to a solution. Time passed as the OSHTF, while recognizing the seriousness of the subsistence concerns, struggled to define the problem and develop an organized response. The OSHTF, with its diverse interdisciplinary membership, had to "start from square one." There were no ready-made answers. No guidance manuals or accepted guidelines were available, and information on the approach to seafood safety from other spills provided limited guidance. Each step created a new set of questions: What information do we need? Who should do the study? How do we interpret the results? What is the best way to communicate the findings to the Alaska Native and other local communities? How are local observations and traditional knowledge brought into the process?

The response involved the collection and chemical analysis of an unprecedented number of samples of fish, shellfish, bird, and marine mammal tissues. Experts were brought in to review the results and evaluate the potential risk to consumers of subsistence seafood in the spill area. However, the OSHTF did not anticipate the persistence of the subsistence concerns; like the oil on some protected beaches, fears about the safety of subsistence foods persisted for years after the spill.

The intent of this book is to describe the OSHTF response to the concerns about subsistence food safety and the lessons that were learned in order to guide others preparing for similar challenges at future oil spills. The book includes contributions from several members of the OSHTF and others involved in the efforts to address concerns about subsistence seafood safety and communicate health advice in a cross-cultural setting. As a retrospective and introspective examination of the OSHTF effort, the chapters identify both what worked well and what could have been done better.

Preface

Coping with the Time When the Water Died

Walter Meganack Sr.*

The Native story is different from the white man's story of oil devastation. It is different because our lives are different, what we value is different, how we see the water and the land, the plants and the animals, is different. What white men do for sport and recreation and money, we do for life: for the life of our bodies, for the life of our spirits, and for the life of our ancient culture.

Our lives are rooted in the seasons of God's creation. Since time immemorial, the lives of the Native peoples harmonize with the rhythm and the cycles of nature. We are a part of nature. We don't need a calendar or a clock to tell us what time it is.

When the days get longer, we get ready. Boots and boats and nets and gear are prepared for the fishing time. The winter beaches are not lonely anymore, because our children and our grown-ups visit the beaches in the springtime and they gather the abundance of the sea: the shellfish, the snails, the chitons. When the first salmon is caught, our villages are excited. It is an annual ritual of mouth watering and delight.

When our bellies are filled with the fresh new life, then we put up the food for the winter. We dry and smoke and can. Hundreds of fish to feed a family.

Much has happened to our people in recent centuries. We have clocks and calendars in our homes. Some of us go to an office in the morning. The children go to school in the morning. But sometimes the office is empty and locked. Sometimes the child is absent from school. Because there are more important things to do. Like walking the beaches. Collecting the chitons. Watching for the fish.

The land and the water are our sources of life. The water is sacred. The water is like a baptismal font, and its abundance is the Holy Communion of our lives. Of all the things that we have lost since non-Natives came to our land, we have never lost our connection with the water. The water is our source of life. So long as the water is alive, the Chugach Natives are alive.

It was early in the springtime. No fish yet. No snails yet. But the signs were with us. The green was starting. Some birds were flying and singing. The excitement of the season had just begun. And then we heard the news. Oil in the water. Lots of oil. Killing lots of water. It is too shocking to understand. Never in the millennium of our tradition have we thought it possible for the water to die. But it is true.

*The late Walter Meganack Sr. was chief of the Native village of Port Graham from 1959 to 1989. This essay is an edited version of remarks he prepared for a conference of mayors who met 27 June 1989, in Valdez to review the *Exxon Valdez* oil spill's impact. The speech was read by the village council secretary, Elenore McMullen, who later succeeded Meganack as the village chief. Reprinted with the kind permission of Elenore McMullen, Port Graham Tribal Chief, and the *Anchorage Daily News*, 5 August 1989.

We walk our beaches. But the snails and the barnacles and the chitons are falling off the rocks. Dead. Dead water. We caught our first fish, the annual first fish, the traditional delight of all — but it got sent to the state to be tested for oil. No first fish this year. We walk our beaches. But instead of gathering life, we gather death. Dead birds. Dead otters. Dead seaweed.

Before we have a chance to hold each other and share our tears, our sorrow, our loss, we suffer yet another devastation. We are invaded by the oil company. Offering jobs. High pay. Lots of money. We are in shock. We need to clean the oil, get it out of our water, bring death back to life. We are intoxicated with desperation. We don't have a choice but to take what is offered. So we take the jobs, we take the orders, we take the disruption.

We start fighting. We lose trust for each other. We lose control of our daily life. Everybody is pushing everyone. We Native people aren't used to being bossed around. We don't like it. But now our own people are pointing fingers at us. Everyone wants to be boss; we are not working like a team. We lost control of our village.

Our people get sick. Elders and children in the village. Everybody is touchy. Everybody is ready to jump you and blame you. People are angry. And afraid. Afraid, and confused. Our elders feel helpless. They cannot work on cleanup, they cannot do all the activities of gathering food and preparing for winter. And most of all, they cannot teach the young ones the Native way. How will the children learn the values and the ways if the water is dead?

The oil companies lied about preventing a spill. Now they lie about the cleanup. Our people know what happens on the beaches. Spend all day cleaning one huge rock, and the tide comes in and covers it with oil again. Spend a week wiping and spraying the surface, but pick up a rock and there's four inches of oil underneath. Our people know the water and the beaches. But they get told what to do by ignorant people who should be asking, not telling. We fight a rich and powerful giant, the oil industry, while at the same time we take orders and a paycheck from it. We are torn in half.

Will it end? After five years, maybe we will see some springtime water life again. But will the water and the beaches see us? What will happen to our lives in the next five years? What will happen this fall, when the cleanup stops and the money stops? We have lived through much devastation. Our villages were almost destroyed by chicken pox and tuberculosis. We fight the battles of alcohol and drugs and abuse. And we survive.

But what we see now is death. Death—not of each other, but of the source of life, the water. We will need much help, much listening in order to live through the long barren season of dead water, a longer winter than before.

I am an elder. I am chief. I will not lose hope. And I will help my people. We have never lived through this kind of death. But we have lived through lots of other kinds of death. We will learn from the past, we will learn from each other, and we will live. The water is dead. But we are alive. And where there is life, there is hope.

Chapter 1

The March 1989 *Exxon Valdez* Oil Spill: A Case Study in Responding to Subsistence Seafood Safety Issues

Nancy Peacock, * *L. Jay Field*

Background of the *Exxon Valdez* Oil Spill

The events of the March 1989 *Exxon Valdez* oil spill (EVOS) in Prince William Sound, Alaska stand out in the minds of most Americans as a major environmental disaster. The aftermath of the spill captured the public's attention for months, and the mass media fueled this attention with images—on television and in news magazines and newspapers—of oil-blackened beaches, of rescuers trying to clean oil-smothered birds and sea otters, and of swarms of cleanup crews in ominous-looking decontamination suits aiming high-pressure hoses on the beaches. This was the first major U.S. spill that had occurred in a remote wilderness of spectacular beauty and biological richness, despite the fact that Valdez, Alaska was the Alyeska oil terminal of the 800-mile Trans-Alaska pipeline and the major port for a fleet of more than 70 tankers carrying Prudhoe Bay oil to refineries outside Alaska. Overnight, the picture-postcard beauty and seemingly pristine character of Prince William Sound had been abruptly besmirched not only by the highly visible oil from the *Exxon Valdez* but also by impacts of the cleanup activities carried out by thousands of cleanup workers and the noise and exhaust from equipment, vessels, and aircraft (Mearns 1996) (Figure 1-1). Heightening the sense of outrage were the circumstances surrounding the grounding of the 980-foot tank vessel *Exxon Valdez* on Bligh Reef just after midnight on 24 March 1989 and the perception that corporate negligence played a major role.

Yet, while Americans thousands of miles away were cutting up their gasoline credit cards in protest, the human dimensions of the disaster for the subsistence-based Alaska Natives—to whom Prince William Sound and the larger spill area had been

*Nancy Peacock has been a journalist and editor in environmental science and policy for nearly 20 years. She has worked with NOAA for most of those years, both for the National Marine Fisheries Service and the National Ocean Service.

Evaluating and Communicating Subsistence Seafood Safety in a Cross-Cultural Context: Lessons Learned from the Exxon Valdez Oil Spill
L. Jay Field et al., editors. © 1999 Society of Environmental Toxicology and Chemistry (SETAC). ISBN 1-880611-29-5

Figure 1-1 Cleanup activities following the *Exxon Valdez* oil spill

home for thousands of years—were somehow lost in the flurry of post-spill activity and media coverage. Many residents of Prince William Sound, Lower Cook Inlet, Kodiak Island, and Alaska Peninsula villages were left to question whether their traditional subsistence shellfish, fish, and marine mammal resources were contaminated with oil from the spill and no longer safe to eat. Further, these people were in great fear that their physical environment and subsistence food resources, and the culture and spirituality that were inextricably linked to these resources, would never be the same. Even 10 years later, this dimension of the spill remains the least understood.

The contributors to this book have come together to address this gap in understanding by sharing their firsthand experiences as members of the Alaska Oil Spill Health Task Force (OSHTF) in tackling the questions of subsistence seafood safety arising from the *Exxon Valdez* disaster and reflecting on the important lessons learned. The objectives of the OSHTF—chaired by an Indian Health Service physician and composed of representatives from the National Oceanic and Atmospheric Administration (NOAA) and other state and federal agencies, Alaska Native organizations, and Exxon (see list of OSHTF members)—were to assess the levels of oil observed in the villagers' subsistence resources and the potential health risks from consuming these resources and to develop the best ways to communicate the results and their implications to the local communities. Although the focus of this book is on the complexities of assessing and communicating risk in a cross-cultural context, many of these cross-disciplinary issues apply broadly to any seafood safety assessment involving local communities following an oil spill.

Lingering controversies

Oil spills are known to heighten public concern compared with other, more frequent and familiar hazards (Lowden 1997), and much of it has to do with the avoidable nature of oil spills and the fact that "negligent corporations" often can be blamed for them. Ten years later, controversy still roils among Exxon, commercial fishermen, subsistence communities, scientists, and environmental advocates about the amount of oil actually remaining in the spill area, the adequacy of the spill cleanup and restoration of damaged resources and services, and the recovery status of marine mammals, birds, fish, and other resources. For example, although many shorelines in southwestern Prince William Sound are clean, on some beaches pockets of crude oil remain beneath large rocks and boulders and dense mussel beds (Broderson et al. 1999; EVOS 1999).

The out-of-court settlement for lost subsistence harvests accepted by the Alaska Native class in July 1994 was based almost entirely on the available data on subsistence harvests for pre-spill years and for 1989 through 1992 collected by the Alaska Department of Fish and Game (ADF&G) (see Chapter 4). The settlement assumed only very minor continuing impacts—to end entirely in 1995 (Duffield 1999). Yet household interviews with subsistence users in 1998 indicated that subsistence harvests still have not fully recovered from the effects of the spill (EVOS 1999; Chapters 4 and 11, this volume). Although concerns about food safety and lifestyle effects have lessened, scarcity of important subsistence resources, particularly harbor seals, herring, clams, and crab, is a continuing concern. Thus, increases in pounds of subsistence seafood harvested in 1998 reflect greater harvest effort than that before the spill (e.g., traveling further, spending more time and money) and a greater reliance on fish in the subsistence diet than on shellfish and marine mammals.

The human dimension of oil spills

The EVOS is not only the largest and most expensive spill in U.S. waters but also is certainly the most intensely documented spill in recent U.S. history. An extensive body of scientific literature covers nearly every aspect of the effects of the spill and subsequent cleanup operations on fisheries and wildlife and the shoreline environment as well as on the longer-term restoration efforts and environmental recovery processes. Much new knowledge about the fate and effects of oil, the consequences of various cleanup procedures, and the rate of biological recovery from an oil spill, new methodologies for long-term biological monitoring; and research and development of new cleanup technologies have been generated by the *Exxon Valdez* oil spill and shared among researchers, response and natural resource agencies at state and federal levels, and the oil industry.*

Since the 1989 EVOS, new and amended legislation, including the Oil Pollution Act of 1990 and amendments to the existing Clean Water Act, have established an area-level planning and coordination structure that did not exist in 1989, calling for more local citizen oversight of terminal facilities and crude oil tankers and development of area contingency plans for future spills. There has also been a grassroots movement among Alaska Native communities to more directly involve their people, and their traditional ecological knowledge, in oil spill prevention and response. The 1999 EVOS Symposium Abstracts is full of examples of such programs.

Yet oil spill responders still have much to learn about the human dimensions of oil and other hazardous materials spills, not only for local subsistence-based communities in the case of the EVOS, but for any local populace. This learning, by necessity, must be heavily experiential and must incorporate both scientific and sociological knowledge and approaches. The EVOS is only one of many oil spills in which "expert outsiders," i.e., spill responders and scientists, including the spiller, have converged on a local community only to find that their perceptions and agendas are often in conflict with those of the local people, not to mention with other responder groups. For example, following the recent *Kuroshima* spill in Dutch Harbor, Alaska in November 1997, local residents criticized the responders for failing to involve the community or to consider local knowledge and concerns in the response decision-making and planning process; for appearing to downplay health concerns resulting from petroleum contamination of subsistence resources by emphasizing paralytic shellfish poisoning as a greater risk; and for poor communication about the risks of contamination of subsistence seafood (Ruth Yender, NOAA Office of Response and Restoration, Hazmat Div., Seattle WA, personal communication, Jan. 1999).

This is symptomatic of the difficulty in learning the human-relations lessons from previous spills so as not to repeat mistakes. In sharing the experience of the OSHTF, this book is one attempt to establish a knowledge base about working successfully with the local community to address their concerns not only about the safety of their seafood, in both the short and longer term, but also about the welfare of their way of life following an oil spill. Recovery, as acknowledged by the *Exxon Valdez* Oil Spill Trustee Council (1999), must be understood to include the restored confidence by local people that the resources are safe to eat and, in the case of subsistence users, that the cultural values provided by gathering, preparing, and sharing food can be

*For examples, see Piper 1993; ASTM 1993; Wells et al. 1995; Alaska Sea Grant 1995; Mearns 1996; and Rice et al. 1996. See also symposia and research funded by the *Exxon Valdez* Oil Spill Trustee Council, most recently, its 10-year anniversary symposium in March 1999; annual Arctic Marine Oil Pollution (AMOP) Program seminars sponsored by Environment Canada; and the annual proceedings of the International Oil Spill Conferences cosponsored by the U.S. Coast Guard, the American Petroleum Institute, the U.S. Environmental Protection Agency, the International Maritime Organization, and the International Petroleum Industry Environmental Conservation Association.

reintegrated into community life. Hopefully, this book also serves as a reminder that a sensitivity by outside experts to the deeper sociocultural impacts of such disasters can go a long way toward meeting the cleanup and recovery objectives of all interested parties.

The Path and Behavior of Spilled Oil among Coastal Subsistence Communities in Prince William Sound, Lower Cook Inlet, and the Gulf of Alaska

On Friday, 24 March 1999, the *Exxon Valdez* released approximately 10.8 million gallons (~ 35,500 metric tons) of North Slope crude oil into Prince William Sound. North Slope, or Prudhoe Bay, crude oil is relatively heavy and tends to form a fairly stable water-in-oil emulsion. By Saturday night, the area containing the spilled oil had grown to 50 square miles. A major windstorm three days after the spill enhanced the oil's emulsion, creating what is called a "mousse" that triples the volume of the floating oil and makes it highly viscous and adhesive, thus more likely to stick to animals and beach material. This windstorm dramatically changed the appearance, character, and distribution of the oil (Galt et al. 1991), moving and mixing it and rupturing contiguous slicks into bands and streaks spread over a significantly larger area. Figure 1-2 shows the spatiotemporal movement of the spilled oil from day 1 to day 56.

The estuarine system of Prince William Sound, a circular complex of fjords 15 times the size of San Francisco Bay, presents a particularly dynamic set of atmospheric and oceanic energetics that complicates predictions of oil behavior and spill trajectories as well as cleanup strategies (Galt et al. 1991). The Sound also just happens to sit on one of the world's most active seismic zones, evidenced by the March 1964 earthquake, one of the most destructive geologic events ever measured. Although the two main passageways from the Gulf of Alaska to Prince William Sound are less than 15 miles across, in wintertime the high winds from the Gulf, generated by the Aleutian Low, can stir up large and chaotic waves in the Sound. As described by Wheelwright (1994), these winds can be locally unpredictable because they are bent by the steep and broken terrain that hems in the Sound between the mountains and the sea. The huge Alaska Coastal Current enters the Sound via Hinchinbrook Entrance (see Figure 1-3), transporting 50 to 100 million gallons of water every second, circulates counterclockwise, and leaves the Sound by way of Montague Strait. Hinchinbrook Entrance is also the route taken by oil tankers entering and exiting the Sound. The Alaska Coastal Current was the dominant process transporting the spilled oil from Prince William Sound (Galt et al. 1991).

Wheelwright (1994) describes the Sound as an ecosystem that "reels and rebounds" from a pattern of unrelenting and often overlapping disturbances that set off many physical and biological changes. These disturbances cause wide fluctuations in the

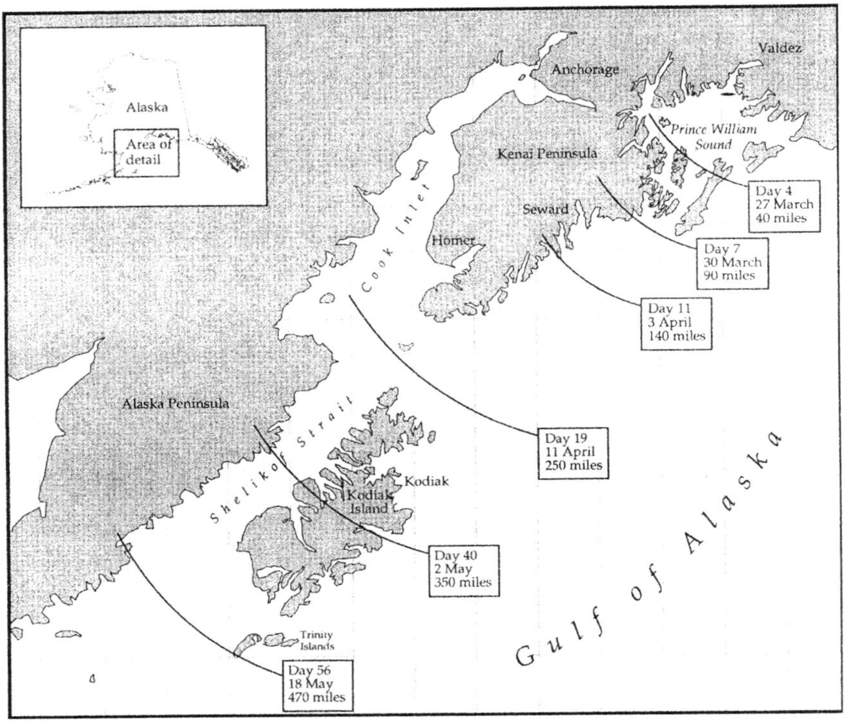

Figure 1-2 Spread of oil from the *Exxon Valdez* spill 24 March to 20 June 1989 (USCG 1993)

numbers of a profusion of species, both from season to season and year to year, including the following: seabirds, sea otters, salmon, herring, killer whales, jellyfish, and eagles. This biological flux is caused by the turmoil of the atmospheric/oceanic elements, changes in availability of food, incidence of disease, and shifts in predator to prey relationships.

This flux is important to our discussion because the subsistence villagers of Prince William Sound have coevolved with the dynamics of these waters for many centuries and are skilled at "reading," even predicting, these disturbances and biological fluxes and at coadapting their fishing, hunting, and gathering activities. These natural dynamics, however, had not prepared them for the abrupt and drastic changes wrought by an oil spill, changes that were unlike any natural physical or biological event they had witnessed in their history. Villagers stated that even the powerful earthquake of 1964 and the accompanying tsunami that destroyed the village of Chenega in Prince William Sound, forcing a total evacuation for 20 years until the village was relocated to Evans Island in 1983, was less traumatic than the *Exxon Valdez* spill.

During the weeks following the spill, the oil in the Sound was spread southwestward by winds and currents along shorelines of the Kenai Peninsula. After about two

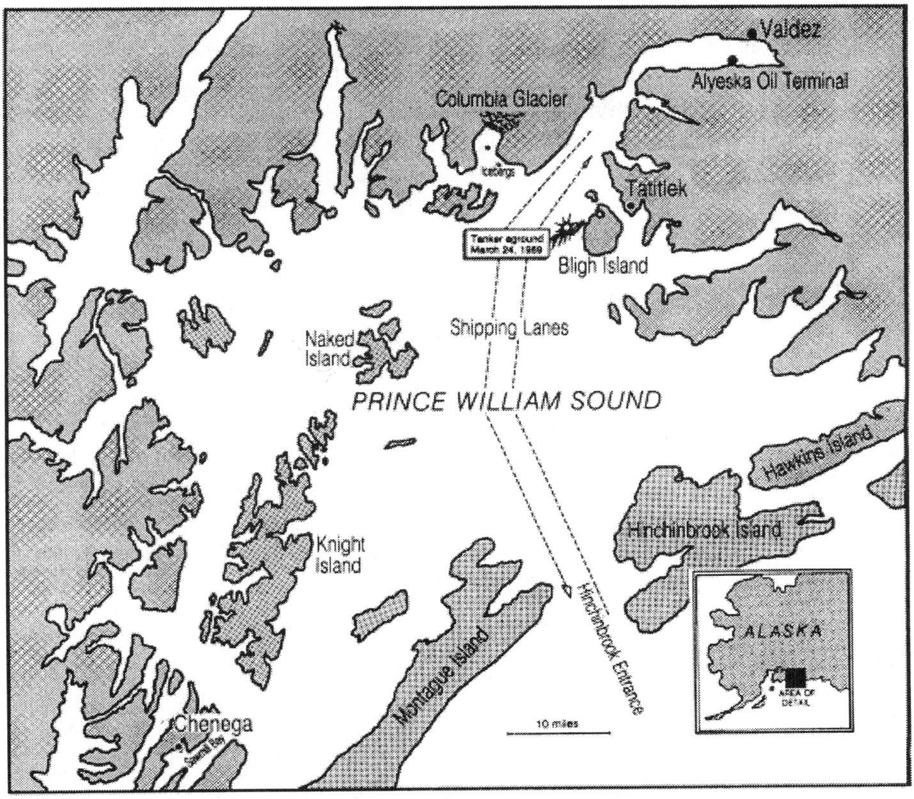

Figure 1-3 Prince William Sound and tanker grounding location (from NRT 1989)

weeks, the oil was pushed beyond the Sound and out through Montague Strait. The heaviest shoreline impacts were seen on beaches of the numerous island groups in southwestern Prince William Sound that face predominant currents and winds (Galt et al. 1991). For example, the subsistence harvest areas of the Alaska Native village of Chenega Bay on Evans Island were among the hardest hit (see Chapter 4). Once through the Strait, the oil moved further southwestward into the Gulf of Alaska, past Lower Cook Inlet, and flowed between Kodiak Island and the Alaska Peninsula. In all, about 1750 km of shoreline were oiled (Wolfe et al. 1994), including some of the harvest areas of 15 predominantly Alaska Native villages. Once out into the strong currents of the Gulf, widely scattered patches of oil comprised of "tarballs" (small pieces of mousse) met with strong convergence patterns in the currents, coalescing the tarballs and mixing them with debris and flotsam to form a continuous line of mousse that appeared to reconstitute the oil (Galt et al. 1991). One convergence zone at the mouth of Cook Inlet coalesced the scattered tarballs into a large band of oil that trapped many birds sleeping on the water at night.

As the oil was transported by currents and winds, it was constantly transforming; repeatedly deposited, refloated, and redeposited on affected shorelines as local winds and tides shifted. Alaska Native harvest areas along the southwestern path of the moving oil include Windy Bay on the outer Kenai Peninsula, Nanwalek and Port Graham on the tip of the Kenai Peninsula in Lower Cook Inlet, six Kodiak Island village areas, and five villages on the Alaska Peninsula (Chapters 2 and 4; Rice et al. 1996) (Figure 1-4).

The Unique Concerns of Alaska Native Villages After the Spill

Areas used for subsistence by 15 predominantly Alaska Native villages were in the path of the spill. These people, whose ancestors had used the area for hunting, fishing, and gathering for at least 7000 years, watched as their homeland and their way of life—focused on the shorelines and the sea—were devastated by the oil and the cleanup operations. Their homeland was turned upside down for six months after the spill by the more than 10,000 people in and around the Sound and the Gulf of Alaska working on cleanup operations and sampling.

The *Exxon Valdez* was the first major oil spill to affect Native American communities dependent on subsistence foods for a major portion of their diet, equivalent to an amount exceeding the average household purchases of meat, fish, and poultry in the U.S. (see Chapter 2). Cash income is limited in these villages, jobs are scarce, and commercial fishing among the villages is generally no longer as lucrative or as reliable an income source as it was in the past. As Piper (1993) states, “Subsistence is how people eat.” But more than that, as Fall (Chapter 2) and Picou and Gill (1996) explain, subsistence economies are structured not around monetary capital but rather around the primary economic objectives of maintaining life, social organization, and culture.

The Alaska Natives’ concerns about the short- and long-term effects of the spilled oil were much more holistic, and thus significantly more complex, than those of any other interest group. Not only did the spill endanger their ancestral harvest areas, it disrupted the seasonal cycle of subsistence harvests of a diverse range of wild foods (including not only fish and shellfish but also land and marine mammals, birds, and plants) around which their lives are organized. The value of their subsistence harvests could not be expressed in terms of dollars but rather as the first stage in a complex of traditional subsistence rituals that were woven into their social fabric. As described by Kroll-Smith and Couch (cited in Picou and Gill 1996), community equilibrium among subsistence peoples is maintained through the network of exchange relationships with their biophysical environment and their collective interpretation of these relationships. This collective interpretation is expressed in cultural traditions of harvesting, consuming, exchanging, and maintaining renew-

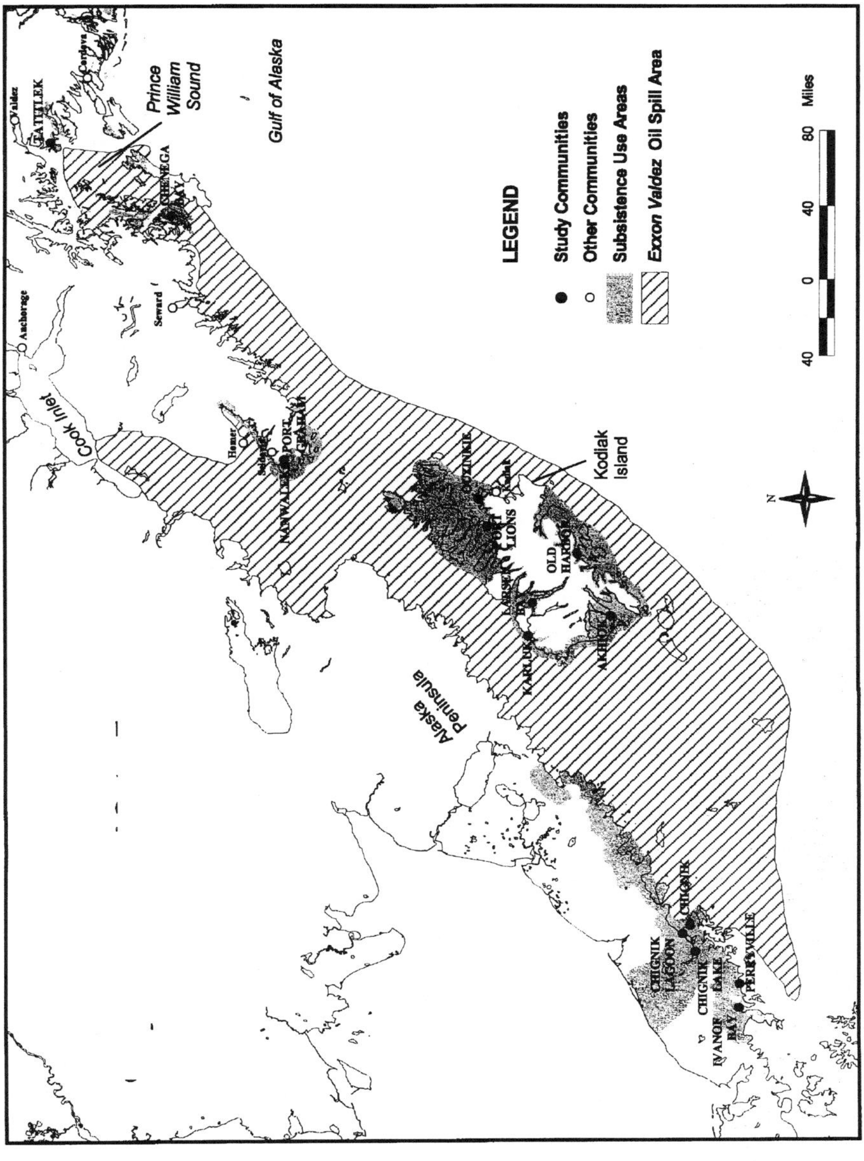

Figure 1-4 Subsistence harvest areas of communities and outer extent of the *Exxon Valdez* oil spill

able subsistence resources. Thus, these were a people whose very maintenance of life, social organization, and culture was threatened by the spill's contamination of their environment and the intrusion of response activities.

Initial Response Efforts Following the Spill

A team of scientists from NOAA's Hazardous Materials Response Branch (HAZMAT) was at the scene within hours of the *Exxon Valdez* spill. HAZMAT Scientific Support Coordinators (SSCs) provide scientific advice and coordination of scientific resources during oil spills in support of the Federal On-Scene Coordinator, the U.S. Coast Guard for spills in the coastal zone. The SSCs play a leading role in the on-site effort by providing information on a variety of issues during the spill response, including the following:

- the physicochemical properties of oil over time,
- analysis of the spill trajectory,
- resource protection priorities,
- assessment of shoreline impacts,
- different countermeasures that can be used, and
- consequences of different cleanup strategies.

Although NOAA had responded to hundreds of oil spills, concerns about subsistence seafood safety had never played a major role in previous spill responses. Issues relating to fisheries and aquaculture occasionally arose at previous spills, but these were primarily concerns about tainting and gear contamination. At the 1979 IXTOC I spill in the Gulf of Mexico (Hooper 1981), consumer confidence in seafood was addressed by sensory monitoring of the shrimp catch in multiple locations. Most human-health issues at other oil spills focused on potential effects on cleanup workers. The lack of a precedent meant that no comprehensive approach had been developed or included in contingency planning, and no summary of relevant literature was readily available.

The initial response to the *Exxon Valdez* spill focused on developing critical shoreline cleanup priorities (FOSC 1993). At a teleconference on March 27, "high subsistence use areas" were among sensitive resources identified as important shoreline cleanup priorities. In addition, areas used by Native residents of the village of Chenega Bay were given high priority for protection from floating oil. However, identifying subsistence-use areas as priority areas for protection or cleanup did not address the concerns of the communities in the spill path about potential contamination of subsistence resources. Although identified early on as important, the responders greatly underestimated the magnitude of the issue and the degree of concern in the villages. The perception among the villages was that "oil was poisoning Prince William Sound," and the feeling was that their concerns were not taken seriously, particularly in regard to subsistence.

The subject of subsistence food safety was addressed in the Report to the President prepared by the National Response Team in May 1989 (NRT 1989):

> To ensure food safety properly over the long term, however, a system involving both organoleptic and chemical analytic testing needs to be developed. [U. S. Food and Drug Administration (USFDA)] and other agencies and experts are obtaining information on the characteristics of crude oil, accumulation and dissipation of oil components in fish and shellfish, analytical methodology, organoleptic detection in fish and shellfish, and toxicity data relative to long-term consumption of oil components. Information developed from these sources will be evaluated, particularly in terms of the type of food safety program needed.

Addressing subsistence concerns clearly required an interagency approach. More than a month after the spill, the Subsistence Division of the ADF&G began collecting a variety of subsistence resources from identified subsistence harvest areas in Prince William Sound and Lower Cook Inlet for sensory testing, with chemical analysis to be conducted by a USFDA laboratory. This was later referred to as the "pilot study." However, there was considerable skepticism among the villages about the value of sensory testing, and results from the chemical analyses were not returned for several months. Consequently, the villagers' level of concern continued to increase and was vigorously expressed to the U.S. Coast Guard, NOAA, Exxon, and state and federal agencies at village outreach meetings. It became increasingly clear that advisories about food safety based on sensory testing were not sufficient to satisfy these concerns and that a more comprehensive approach was needed to address the issue of subsistence seafood safety.

Exxon began planning a study in June 1989 that expanded the ADF&G Pilot Study to include field collection of fish and shellfish from subsistence areas in Prince William Sound, Lower Cook Inlet, and Kodiak Island. NOAA considered conducting a separate study, primarily because of concerns about establishing the credibility of an Exxon study among villagers. However, NOAA decided that conducting a joint study with Exxon, within the framework of the OSHTF, would provide the most comprehensive and credible study possible.

By the third week of July (in the middle of the first cycle of sample collection), Exxon and NOAA had signed an agreement (see full text in Appendix 5) to undertake a joint study of the degree of oil contamination in subsistence resources. The principal element of this agreement was that all chemical analyses of subsistence seafood resources would be conducted at NOAA's Northwest & Alaska Fisheries Center in Seattle, Washington, an internationally recognized laboratory (now known as the Northwest Fisheries Science Center). Because of the laboratory's extensive experience in analyzing tissue samples for petroleum hydrocarbons and other contaminants, appropriate analytical methods were already in place so that analysis could begin immediately. It was also agreed that NOAA would participate in the sample collections along with Exxon's sampling team (provided by Dames & Moore, a biological consulting firm under contract with Exxon) and that all results would be immediately released to the OSHTF. Although Exxon was funding the sample collection and tissue analysis, the agreement was designed to ensure an unbiased, comprehensive, and credible study.

The Challenges Facing the Oil Spill Health Task Force

The OSHTF was formed one month after the spill out of a recognition that the concerns of Alaska Native villagers about the safety of their subsistence seafood were not being adequately addressed in the existing spill-response organizational structure. At the time of the spill, there were no specific provisions in the National Contingency Plan for dealing with fisheries or human-health effects, nor did the USFDA have any established guidelines for seafood safety relative to oil contamination. Thus the OSHTF was charting new territory, not only because of the lack of established protocols and the information gap relative to seafood contamination, but also in dealing with the inherent communication barriers between the scientific establishment and Native subsistence communities.

The OSHTF had to start out playing "catch up" at the same time that they were on a steep learning curve about which scientific methods to use, what health advice they could reasonably provide, the nature of the audience they were trying to reach, and how best to reach them. The OSHTF's initial objectives were to collect and evaluate information that could be used to assess the safety of subsistence resources and to communicate this information to the villagers to enable them to make their own informed judgments about whether to collect subsistence resources from their traditional harvest areas. At community meetings organized to communicate the results and interpretation of the chemical analyses of subsistence seafood, the OSHTF was met by a wide range of demands by Native villagers for answers and information. Some people simply wanted a straightforward answer to the question, "Are the fish safe to eat?" The answer to this question, "yes," was provided immediately and almost unequivocally, except in the case of obvious tainting detectable by sensory testing, which the villagers were encouraged to rely on to determine for themselves the safety of a harvesting site or a resource. Others wanted to know actual concentrations in specific resources and locations and demanded the most sophisticated laboratory testing possible to make these determinations. The OSHTF thus had to stretch its communication efforts to address this range of questioning.

Opposing world views

In carrying out its sampling design, laboratory analyses, and interpretive and communication roles, the OSHTF had its work cut out for it. The first obstacle they faced was the need to bridge two opposing world views: the western European, Cartesian, empirical scientific view, and the Native American social-natural view. According to an analysis by Wright (1992), the western European stance is that of the critical observer of "objective" nature, a social-natural nonparticipant committed to knowledge of nature that is validated exclusively on the observer's terms, through manipulation, explanation, and predictability. Wright contends that this Enlightenment system of knowledge has disconnected itself from the legitimating aspects of any social criteria, separate from the world of language, nature, and social life. In contrast, the Native world of nature is a sociable and human world, in which people are social-natural participants through their commitment to tradition, and for whom the validity of knowledge is an issue of sustaining social life. Clearly, there was no separating the Alaska Natives from their personal, social, and cultural connection to their oil-damaged environment in an attempt to convince them to trust the expert outsiders' perspective.

Further, the OSHTF conducted a scientific analysis—a process that is inherently difficult to describe in lay terms—while trying to articulate their methods and results so that they could be understood and trusted by the villagers. For example, when the scientists designed their studies to collect and provide information about contaminant levels in customary village harvesting areas rather than targeting the most heavily oiled beaches, some villagers were suspicious that this was a ploy to minimize the contaminant levels in their results (Piper 1993). And, although villagers were demanding the scientific testing of seafood samples, some were uncomfortable with the fact that these samples were being analyzed in a federal laboratory thousands of miles away in Seattle, using techniques and instruments that are incomprehensible to most Americans, let alone to people from a remote, rural environment and coming from a very different world view.

The post-spill psychological setting

Another obstacle facing the OSHTF was in dealing with communities of people who already felt let down by the cleanup itself. As explained by Smith (1992), the Alyeska Pipeline Service Company's oil-spill contingency plan, approved by the State of Alaska, promised that the company would respond to a 200,000-barrel spill at Bligh Reef within two to five hours and that it would recover 50% of the oil. The actual first response to the *Exxon Valdez* came 14 hours later, and efforts during the first week recovered less than 4% of the oil. The Exxon Corporation quickly stepped in and took over responsibility for the cleanup effort, effectively abandoning the contingency plan agreed to by Alyeska and the state and causing confusion and skepticism by state agencies and residents alike. After two years, less than 20% of the spilled oil had been recovered. The villagers were also embittered by the millions of dollars that were immediately poured into wildlife rescue while subsistence issues did not receive comparable attention.

The Alaska Natives of the impacted fishing communities were also under severe psychological stress from the spill and its aftermath, exhibiting relatively high levels of depression (Palinkas et al. 1992 cited in Picou and Gill 1996), intrusive stress, and avoidance behaviors, compared with control communities (see Chapter 10 for a broader discussion of the stressors from technological disasters that can hinder effective communication.) There were also intracommunity stressors brought on by the fact that some Alaska Natives, particularly boat owners, profited from the spill by getting contracts for cleanup work (Russell et al. 1996). Friends and neighbors argued over the inequities in opportunity, over money lost and gained in the cleanup. An "environment of opportunism" prevailed (Russell et al. 1996) in which the morality of accepting money from Exxon became a bone of contention. Village social roles were altered, since nearly all able-bodied adults worked on the cleanup in one capacity or another, such as monitoring the spill path from boats, rescuing oiled birds and other wildlife, collecting dead and dying animals, or assisting in sample collection for the subsistence studies.

The litigation-sensitive environment

Communication was also complicated by the preparations for litigation between the villages and Exxon and between the state and federal trustees and Exxon in the natural resource damage assessment, all of which tended to foster adversarial relationships and inhibit open exchange of information. As mentioned earlier, the formal agreement between NOAA and Exxon (and later between the state and Exxon) mandated immediate public release of all data collected in the study of subsistence resources. This was not the case, however, in the studies conducted by the trustee agencies, including NOAA, and Exxon to gather evidence of injury to resources—evidence that would serve as the basis for resolving liability questions under the Comprehensive Environmental Response, Compensation, and Liability Act of 1980 (CERCLA) and the Oil Pollution Act of 1990. Whereas damage-assessment studies tended to focus on heavily oiled areas to document the worst-case scenario for adverse effects, the subsistence seafood study focused on known subsistence harvest areas (without regard to the degree of oiling) to provide health advisories as quickly as possible to subsistence users (see Shaw and Bader 1996 for a discussion of these conflicting goals). Most of the data collected as part of the damage assessment, which might have provided additional relevant information for the subsistence seafood study, was considered litigation-sensitive information and was kept secret for several years. The fact that all of this sampling was taking place without any release of information, even to the OSHTF, cast doubts on the credibility of the OSHTF while fueling the general perception that information was being withheld.

Slow release of risk information

The villagers' stress was further exacerbated by the delay in getting any quantitative information (i.e., results of chemical analysis) at all until almost five months after the spill (August 1989), when much of their main subsistence harvest season was already past. By then, notes Piper (1993), "Doubts had solidified into skepticism." Pamphlets and newsletters and a video circulated among the villages and aired on the rural TV network seemed to do little to allay many villagers' distrust. Thus, the first obstacle to the OSHTF's effectiveness—to establish trust—had apparently not been overcome. Also, the central and highly visible role played by "the spiller," Exxon, in the subsistence seafood safety studies and village meetings only added to the villagers' wariness. All this stress and discord undermined the OSHTF's attempts to establish trust with the villagers so that its efforts would be received, understood, and acted upon.

Why Still So Little Information about Subsistence Seafood Safety?

Questions about assessing and communicating the safety of seafood resources—whether subsistence, recreational, or commercial in nature—following oil spills or hazardous materials releases continue to plague health and natural resource managers. A literature search conducted by NOAA shortly after the spill (see Chapter 3) found virtually no studies on judging the safety of subsistence foods nor any established standards for safe levels of hydrocarbon contamination in food. A decade after the *Exxon Valdez*, there is still little information on the risks to human health from consuming oil-contaminated food, and there is even less scientific literature on subsistence seafood safety issues.

Yet the potential worldwide for future spills that could directly affect local subsistence communities is significant. Although the USFDA published its risk assessment on the *Exxon Valdez* subsistence study and presented its analysis at the 1992 Anchorage Symposium and at an ASTM meeting in Atlanta in 1993 (see Chapter 9), the debate continues over seafood tainting and both potential and perceived human-health effects. Because this debate has been prolonged by knowledge gaps and uncertainties about oil contamination and recovery of seafood resources, clear guidelines are still lacking on fishery closures and reopenings. There is also confusion about how, within a crisis atmosphere and a cross-cultural setting, to most effectively analyze these risks and communicate them to a local populace that is highly dependent on subsistence resources, as both a source of protein and a way of life.

It seems to the contributors to this book that the experience and knowledge gained during the *Exxon Valdez* spill response have not been adequately included in the broader debates about seafood safety during and after spill-response efforts.

Undoubtedly, there has been more study and discussion in Canada and Alaska (see Usher et al. 1995). Commercial seafood safety issues and criteria for commercial fishery closures and reopenings following oil spills have been discussed at various workshops (e.g., see Mearns and Yender 1997). Subsistence issues have been under-represented at these workshops, in part because commercial seafood-safety issues are driven by potentially enormous economic impacts of fishery closures, locally and regionally, on commercial and recreational fishing, seafood processing, and entire coastal communities, not to mention the human-health risks from seafood that is distributed to a wide consumer base.

In contrast, Alaska Native subsistence seafood users live in small, isolated coastal villages where they harvest and exchange subsistence resources among kinship groups. A subsistence way of life such as theirs simply does not fall within the western economic value system. The OSHTF understood from the start that simply replacing wild foods with processed substitutes misses the point. The social cohesion provided by subsistence harvesting, food preparation, and sharing is not easily understood by non-Natives, nor is the profound disruption in the lives of these people caused by the oil spill and the doubts it cast on the safety of harvesting and consuming traditional subsistence foods.

Another possible reason that information about subsistence seafood issues has not been widely discussed is that it requires a cross-disciplinary venue, even more so than do commercial fishery issues that do not encompass anthropological, social, psychological, and cross-cultural components. This cross-disciplinary venue involves toxicology and epidemiology, human health, marine biology, environmental chemistry, risk assessment (itself a synthesis of disciplines), cultural anthropology and ecology, social psychology, sociologies of science and technology, and cross-cultural communication.

The effective discussion and analysis of Alaska Native subsistence issues must reflect an understanding, by all concerned, of the conflicting scientific paradigms of western European versus Native American (observational, experiential) world views, and of the ongoing evolution in recent decades of the traditional western scientific paradigm (Kuhn 1970). In particular, this western paradigm shift has eroded the historical insulation of scientific communities from the demands of the laity and everyday life (Kuhn 1970). Indeed, the situation that experts faced in addressing the subsistence issues following the *Exxon Valdez* oil spill, and in analyzing and discussing them in the years since, has forced them to incorporate the vocabulary of the social sciences, chiefly because their approach to the research "problem" (assessing and communicating risk) was driven by the social importance of achieving a solution and achieving it quickly. As Picou and Gill (1996) assert, true restoration of environmental damage from a disaster such as the *Exxon Valdez* must include the reestablishment of a social equilibrium between the biophysical environment and the human community.

Clearly, the lessons of the *Exxon Valdez* oil spill point to the need for more detailed study and greater understanding of the psychosocial significance of technological disasters. Specifically, understanding of how these events shatter the cultural and social links to the biophysical environment that define land-based, resource-dependent cultures is needed. Throughout this book, we have taken a self-evaluative approach in describing how the OSHTF tried to answer the critical subsistence questions being raised by Alaska Native villagers. Obviously, our answers were based on the state of the knowledge and the prevailing cross-cultural awareness that we were able to bring to those questions at the time. This book is an expression of the need to provoke greater interdisciplinary discussion and, through research, to reach for greater understanding of the issues and processes of risk analysis and risk communication. Most urgently, however, this book is intended to help spill-response and public-health professionals anticipate and prepare for similar challenges at future oil spills.

Syllabus of This Book

Tom Nighswander, chairman of the OSHTF, describes in detail (in Chapter 3) the stages of the OSHTF's planning, evaluation, and decision-making processes, including 1) sampling of subsistence resources, 2) analytical testing for levels of contaminants in the samples, 3) full-scale assessment of the risk of consuming oiled seafood based on the laboratory analyses, and 4) communication of actual risk to the villagers through a multipronged community outreach program. The following chapters are structured around those processes, examining from several disciplinary perspectives the OSHTF's overall response to the issues surrounding subsistence food safety, most importantly the cross-cultural approaches to risk analysis and risk communication. Following are some of the issues examined:

- the historical importance of subsistence resources to Alaska Native communities in the areas affected by the spill (Chapter 2) and subsequent changes in patterns of subsistence use following the spill (Chapter 4);
- the OSHTF's response to concerns about subsistence seafood safety, emphasizing the questions raised by the Alaska Native communities and the decision-making process that subsequently unfolded (Chapter 3);
- the interactions among Exxon, the OSHTF, and the Native communities over subsistence seafood issues from the point of view of Exxon's primary liaison with the villages (Chapter 5);
- the sampling strategy used to determine the degree of contamination in important subsistence harvest areas and resources (Chapter 6);
- the analytical protocols, results, and implications of the multi-year laboratory analyses of aromatic hydrocarbon residue in shellfish, fish, and marine mammals (Chapter 7, Chapter 8, Appendix 1);

- the quantitative assessment of the human-health risk of consuming petroleum-contaminated seafood, based on harvest data and laboratory analyses of the subsistence seafood samples (Chapter 9);
- the risk-communication methods used and an analysis of their effectiveness in addressing the villagers' concerns about subsistence seafood safety, particularly given the cross-cultural context (Chapter 10); and
- the lessons learned from the OSHTF's response efforts and its recommendations for confronting the gaps in knowledge and understanding—both scientific and sociological—that continue to hinder post-spill efforts to address the specific seafood-safety questions of a local populace (Chapter 11).

Acknowledgments—Many thanks for the support and encouragement of David Kennedy and Jean Snider, Office of Response and Restoration (OR&R); the spirit of collaboration among Jay Field, Tom Nighswander, James Fall, and myself; and the thoughtful review by Ruth Yender of OR&R.

References

Alaska Sea Grant. 1995. Prevention, response, and oversight five years after the *Exxon Valdez* oil spill. Proceedings of an international conference; 23–25 March 1994; Anchorage, AK. Fairbanks AK: Alaska Sea Grant College Program. AK-SG-95-02. 392 p.

[ASTM] American Society for Testing and Materials. 1993. Symposium on environmental toxicology and risk assessment; 26 April 1993; Houston TX. Philadelphia PA: ASTM.

Broderson C, Short J, Holland L, Carls M, Pella J, Larsen M, Rice S. 1999. Evaluation of oil removal from beaches 8 years after the *Exxon Valdez* oil spill. In: Proceedings, Twenty-second Arctic and Marine Oil Spill Program (AMOP) technical seminar; 2–4 June. 1999; Calgary, Alberta, Canada. Ottawa, Ontario, Canada: Environment Canada. p 325–336.

Duffield JW. 1999. The economic impacts of the *Exxon Valdez* oil spill on Alaska natives: a ten-year retrospective. Paper presented at the symposium Legacy of an Oil Spill: 10 Years after *Exxon Valdez*, 23–26 March 1999; Anchorage AK. Missoula MT: University of Montana.

[EVOS] *Exxon Valdez* Oil Spill Trustee Council. 1999. Legacy of an oil spill: 10 years after *Exxon Valdez*. Abstracts of the Symposium; 23–25 March 1999; Anchorage AK: Alaska Department of Fish and Game.

[FOSC] Federal On-Scene Coordinator. 1993. *T/V Exxon* Valdez Oil Spill. Federal On-Scene Coordinator's Report. Final Report 24 March 1989 to 10 June 1992. September 1993.

Galt JA, Lehr WJ, Payton DL. 1991. Fate and transport of the *Exxon Valdez* oil spill. *Environ Sci Technol* 25(2):202–209.

Hooper CH, editor. 1981. The IXTOC oil spill: The federal scientific response. NOAA Special Report. Boulder CO: NOAA Hazardous Materials Response Project.

Kuhn TS. 1970. The structure of scientific revolutions. Second edition. Chicago IL: University of Chicago Press.

Lowden G. 1997. Identifying the factors that heighten public concern over oil spills. 1997. In: Proceedings/International Oil Spill Conference. Washington DC: American Petroleum Institute. p 747-751.

Mearns AJ. 1996. *Exxon Valdez* shoreline treatment and operations: implications for response, assessment, monitoring, and research. *Am Fish Soc Symp* 18:309–328.

Mearns AJ, Yender R. 1997. Workshop on managing seafood problems during the response phase of an oil spill. In: Proceedings, Twentieth Arctic and Marine Oil Spill Program (AMOP) technical seminar. Vancouver BC, Canada: Environment Canada. p 203–214.

[NRT] National Response Team. 1989. The *Exxon Valdez* Oil Spill. A Report to the President. Washington DC: National Response Team. May 1989.

Picou JS, Gill DA. 1996. The *Exxon Valdez* oil spill and chronic psychological stress. *Am Fish Soc Symp* 18:879–893.

Piper E. 1993. The *Exxon Valdez* oil spill. Final report, State of Alaska response. Anchorage AK: Alaska Department of Environmental Conservation. 184 p.

Rice SD, Spies RB, Wolfe DA, Wright BA, editors. 1996. Proceedings of the *Exxon Valdez* Oil Spill Symposium; Anchorage AK, 2–5 February 1993. Bethesda MD: *Am Fish Soc Symp* 18.

Russell, JC, Downs MA, Petterson JS, Palinkas LA. 1996. Psychological and social impacts of the *Exxon Valdez* oil spill and cleanup. *Am Fish Soc Symp* 18:867–878.

Shaw DG. 1992. The *Exxon Valdez* oil spill: ecological and social consequences. *Environ Conserv* 19:253–258.

Smith C. 1992 The unthinkable happens: oil in Prince William Sound. In: Smith C, editor. Media and apocalypse. Westport CT: Greenwood Press.

[USCG] U.S. Coast Guard. 1993. Oil progression from day 4 to day 56 following the spill. Federal On Scene Coordinator's Report T/V *Exxon Valdez* Oil Spill, Volume I. Washington DC: U.S. Government Printing Office. p 36.

Usher, PJ, Baikie M, Demmer M, Nakashima D, Stevenson MG, Stiles M. 1995. Communicating about contaminants in country food: the experience in aboriginal communities. Ottawa, Ontario, Canada: Research Department, Inuit Tapirisat of Canada.

Wells, PG, Butler JN, Hughes JS, editors. 1995. *Exxon Valdez* oil spill: fate and effects in Alaskan waters. Philadelphia PA: American Society for Testing and Materials. STP 1219. 955 p.

Wheelwright J. 1994. Degrees of disaster. Prince William Sound: how nature reels and rebounds. New York: Simon & Schuster.

Wolfe DA, Hameedi MJ, Galt JA, Watabayashi G, Short J, O'Claire C, Rice S, Michel J, Payne JR, Braddock J, Hanna S, Sale D. 1994. The fate of the oil spilled from the *Exxon Valdez*. *Environ Sci Technol* 28(13):561A–568A.

Wright W. 1992. Wild knowledge: science, language, and social life in a fragile environment. Minneapolis MN: University of Minnesota Press.

CHAPTER 2

Patterns of Subsistence Uses of Fish and Wildlife Resources in the Area of the *Exxon Valdez* Oil Spill

*James A. Fall**

The *Exxon Valdez* oil spill of March 1989 fouled waters and beaches used for subsistence hunting, fishing, and gathering by 15 predominantly Alaska Native communities of Prince William Sound, Lower Cook Inlet, the Kodiak Island archipelago, and the Alaska Peninsula of south-central and southwest Alaska (Figure 2-1). Alaska's people have used this area for subsistence purposes for at least 7000 years (Clark 1984a). At the time of the spill, about 2000 people, most of Alutiiq descent and cultural heritage, lived in these 15 villages: Chenega Bay and Tatitlek in Prince William Sound; Nanwalek and Port Graham in Lower Cook Inlet; Akhiok, Karluk, Larsen Bay, Old Harbor, Ouzinkie, and Port Lions in the Kodiak Island Borough; and Chignik, Chignik Lagoon, Chignik Lake, Ivanof Bay, and Perryville on the Alaska Peninsula (Table 2-1). Today, the survival of these communities and their way of life continues to depend directly on the food that subsistence activities provide and the strength of the cultural traditions that subsistence activities support. Additionally, in 1989 another 13,000 people, who were eligible to engage in subsistence activities under state and federal regulations, lived in three larger communities of the region, Seldovia, Cordova, and Kodiak. In 1990, about 12% of the population of these three communities was Alaska Native (Fall et al. 1996). These communities are not discussed in this chapter, however.

Before the spill, the Division of Subsistence of the Alaska Department of Fish and Game had conducted baseline research in each of the 15 Alaska Native communities in the oil spill area. Created by Alaska statute in 1978, the Division is charged with collecting information on all aspects of subsistence uses of fish and wildlife in the state and disseminating this information to the public (Fall 1990). The results of this research appear in the Division's Technical Paper Series (Stanek 1985; Stratton and Chisum 1986; Schroeder et al. 1987; Morris 1987; Stratton 1990) and in the Community Profile Database (Scott et al. 1998). For each community, the Division has

*Dr. James Fall is a cultural anthropologist who serves as a regional program manager for the Subsistence Division of the Alaska Department of Fish and Game in Anchorage, Alaska. He was a member of the Alaska Oil Spill Health Task Force and supervised studies of post-spill effects on subsistence uses of fish and wildlife.

Evaluating and Communicating Subsistence Seafood Safety in a Cross-Cultural Context: Lessons Learned from the Exxon Valdez Oil Spill
L. Jay Field et al., editors. © 1999 Society of Environmental Toxicology and Chemistry (SETAC). ISBN 1-880611-29-5

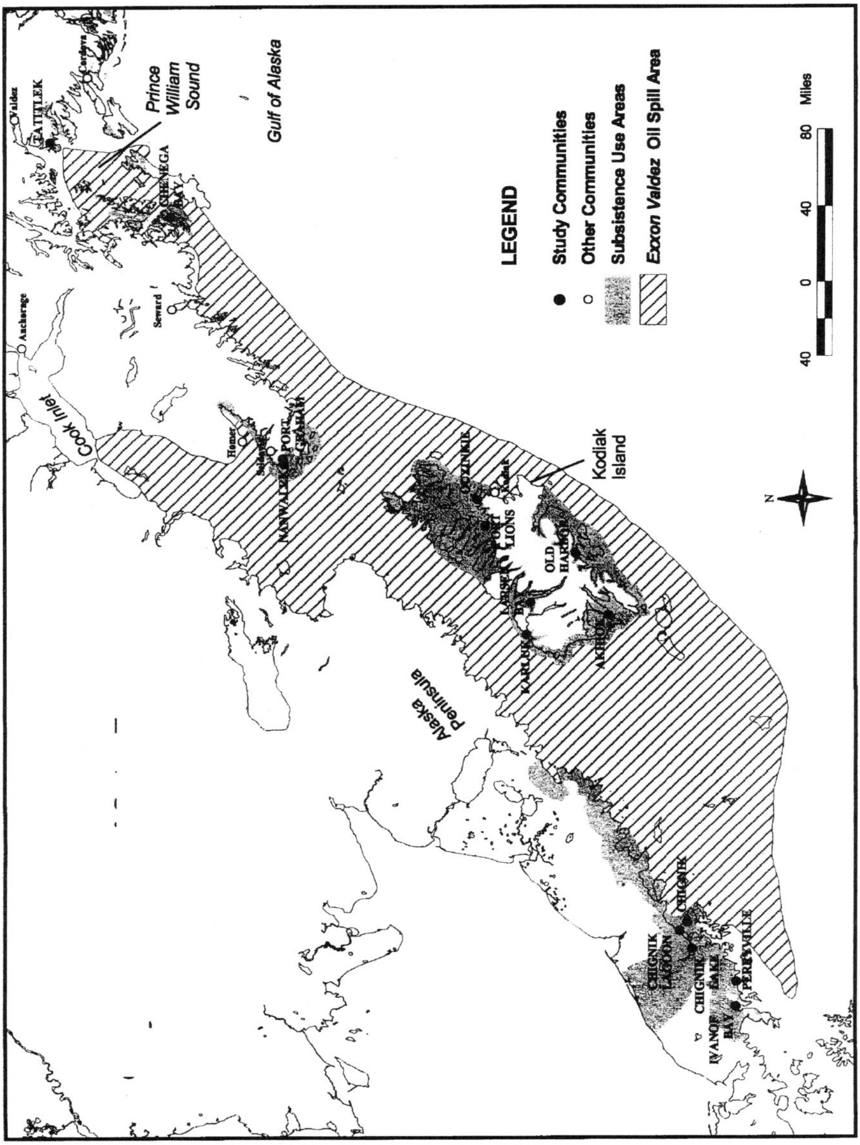

Figure 2-1 Subsistence harvest areas of communities and outer extent of the *Exxon Valdez* oil spill

Table 2-1 Population of *Exxon Valdez* study communities of south-central Alaska, 1990[1]

Community	Population	Percentage Alaska Native
Chenega Bay	94	69.1%
Tatitlek	119	86.6%
Nanwalek	158	91.1%
Port Graham	166	90.4%
Akhiok	77	93.5%
Karluk	71	91.5%
Larsen Bay	147	84.4%
Old Harbor	284	88.7%
Ouzinkie	209	85.2%
Port Lions	222	67.6%
Chignik Bay[2]	160	53.1%
Chignik Lagoon	53	56.6%
Chignik Lake	133	91.7%
Ivanof Bay	35	94.3%
Perryville	108	94.4%
Total	2036	82.3%

[1]Source: Alaska Dept. of Labor 1991.
[2]Population for Chignik Bay excludes 28 seasonal occupants of group quarters.

collected comprehensive information for at least one study year on harvest quantities; levels of participation in subsistence activities; the seasonal cycle of subsistence harvests; maps of areas used for hunting, fishing, and gathering; the distribution and exchange of subsistence products; methods and means of harvest; and techniques for preparing and preserving wild foods. Estimates of subsistence harvest quantities and levels of participation in subsistence uses are available for one pre-spill year for seven of the study communities and for two pre-spill years for the other eight communities. These harvest data were collected during systematic household interviews using a standardized questionnaire. Most interviews were conducted in the respondents' homes by Division personnel and by local assistants trained by Division researchers.

Historical Background and Contemporary Community Descriptions

All of the 15 Alaska Native communities of the oil-spill area lie within the region traditionally inhabited by Alutiiq-speaking people. Alutiiq, also called Sugpiaq, Sugcestun, Pacific Yup'ik, or "Aleut," is a language of the Aleut-Eskimo linguistic family most closely related to Central Yup'ik (Woodbury 1984). The Alutiiq way of life has always been oriented toward the shorelines and the sea, focusing on such subsistence activities as salmon and other fishing, marine mammal hunting, and marine invertebrate gathering (Clark 1984b). The Alutiiq people were among the first in Alaska to be subjected to European and American exploration, colonization, and attempts at economic and cultural subjugation. Despite more than 200 years of contact, the Alutiiq communities have maintained a way of life based upon subsistence uses of fish and wildlife resources and other Alaska Native cultural traditions (Davis 1984).

Although some of the contemporary Alutiiq communities have become established in their present locations relatively recently, most of these communities' families have lived in this region for many generations. Tatitlek is the oldest inhabited community of Prince William Sound, while Chenega Bay is the newest. It was founded on Evans Island in 1983 by former residents of the old village of Chenega, which had been destroyed by a tsunami following the great earthquake of Good Friday 1964; the *Exxon Valdez* spill also occurred on Good Friday, 25 years later. The Alutiiq families of Port Graham and Nanwalek on the southern tip of Cook Inlet are descended from inhabitants of several small villages in this area, such as Yalik and Nuka Bay. Nanwalek itself was the site of the first permanent Russian settlement on Alaska's mainland, called Alexandrovsk and founded in 1785, while the present community of Port Graham originated in 1912 with the construction of commercial fish processing facilities there (Stanek 1985). Old Harbor on Kodiak Island was established by early Russian traders in 1794, while Ouzinkie was founded in the 19th century as a retirement community for employees of the Russian-American Company. Larsen Bay, Karluk, and Akhiok are the sites of ancient Alutiiq settlements. Port Lions, like Chenega Bay, owes its origin to the 1964 earthquake, when the village of Afognak was destroyed. By 1965, survivors had resettled at Port Lions. On the Alaska Peninsula, Chignik Bay and Chignik Lagoon are the sites of prehistoric settlements. The community of Chignik Lake was founded in the 1950s by Alutiiq families who had formerly used the area seasonally; they originally came from local villages such as Chignik Lagoon, Kanatak, and Ilnik. Similar to Chenega Bay and Port Lions, Perryville's founding was the consequence of a natural disaster. The community was settled in 1912 by families whose villages of Katmai and Douglas were destroyed in a volcanic eruption. Finally, Ivanof Bay was founded in 1965 by families originally from Perryville and Chignik Lake.

None of these communities is on Alaska's road system, although at the time of the spill Port Lions was serviced by the Alaska Marine Highway ferry system, as was Chignik Bay a few times a year. The primary means of transportation to each village is by small plane. Poor and rapidly changing weather makes travel to all of these villages problematic at times. The costs of goods and services in these relatively remote communities are substantially higher than those of communities along Alaska's road system.

Patterns of Subsistence Uses Before the Spill

Before the spill, subsistence hunting, fishing, and gathering were of great economic, social, and cultural significance in each of the 15 study communities. Accordingly, they are good examples of communities with mixed subsistence/cash economies that exist in much of rural Alaska today (Wolfe and Walker 1987). Table 2-2 summarizes subsistence uses in the study communities in the 1980s, based on Division of Subsistence research. Although the same general categories of subsistence resources are available in the four regions, specific species of fauna and flora vary among the regions. Examples of the variety of subsistence resources throughout the study area are

- five species of salmon;
- other fish such as halibut, Pacific cod, rockfish, herring, and Dolly Varden;
- marine invertebrates such as clams, chitons, crabs, and octopus (Figure 2-2);
- land mammals such as deer in Prince William Sound and the Kodiak Island area, black bear and mountain goats in Prince William Sound and Lower Cook Inlet, moose in Lower Cook Inlet and the Alaska Peninsula, and caribou on the Alaska Peninsula;
- marine mammals (primarily harbor seals and Steller sea lions) (Figure 2-3);
- birds (including ptarmigan, waterfowl, and sea birds and their eggs); and
- wild plants.

In the 1980s, subsistence harvests in the study communities were relatively large and diverse. For example, in the study years before the spill (1987 to 1988 and 1988 to 1989), households in Tatitlek used on average 19.1 specific kinds of wild resources (Table 2-2). In 1987, households in Nanwalek used an average of 25.0 kinds of wild foods, and neighboring Port Graham households averaged 21.5 kinds (Table 2-2). Subsistence harvests in these communities ranged from about 200 lbs per person per year to over 600 lbs per person annually. That subsistence harvests provided a large portion of each community's food supply is shown by comparing these harvest levels with average purchases of meat, fish, and poultry in the U.S. In the late 1970s, the average family in the western U.S. purchased about 222 lbs per person of meat, fish, and poultry. Subsistence harvests in the study communities nearly matched or exceeded this average. These subsistence harvests were also much higher than those of more populated, urbanized areas of Alaska (Wolfe and Walker 1987).

Additionally, participation in subsistence uses and harvesting was virtually universal in these communities before the spill. Almost every household used wild foods, and the vast majority attempted to harvest and successfully harvested subsistence resources (Table 2-2). Furthermore, most harvesters shared portions of their subsistence takes with other households. Such sharing often took place along lines of kinship. In a case study from Nanwalek, a typical example, one harbor seal was shared among an extended family of eight households with 25 people (Stanek 1985).

Table 2-2 Characteristics of uses of subsistence resources in the Alaska Native study communities before the 1989 *Exxon Valdez* oil spill

	Pre-spill annual averages						
Community	Per capita harvest (lbs)	Mean number of specific kinds of resources used per household	Percentage of households that:				
			Used resources	Attempted harvest	Harvested resources	Received resources	Shared resources
Chenega Bay[1]	346.6	18.8	100	97	97	97	88
Tatitlek[2]	483.4	19.1	100	100	100	100	98
Nanwalek[3]	288.8	25.0	97	94	94	94	94
Port Graham[3]	227.2	21.5	100	100	100	98	82
Akhiok[4]	325.9	12.6	95	91	91	57	66
Karluk[4]	618.1	17.0	100	95	95	97	84
Larsen Bay[4]	309.5	15.4	99	88	87	91	72
Old Harbor[4]	456.3	15.2	100	99	99	83	79
Ouzinkie[4]	389.3	18.3	97	94	94	85	67
Port Lions[4]	307.2	14.0	99	94	94	85	76
Chignik Bay[5]	187.9	12.5	100	84	84	95	79
Chignik Lagoon[5]	220.2	10.4	100	88	88	82	71
Chignik Lake[5]	279.0	16.2	100	100	100	96	83
Ivanof Bay[5]	455.6	18.5	100	100	100	100	83
Perryville[5]	391.2	21.2	100	100	100	100	100

[1]mean of 1984/1985 and 1985/1986 data; [2]mean of 1987/1988 and 1988/1989 data; [3]1987 data only; [4]mean of 1982/1983 and 1986; [5]1984 data only

Sources: Scott et al. 1998; Fall et al. 1995, 1996; Schroeder et al. 1987; Stanek in press.

Figure 2-2 Harvests of chitons or "bidarkies" (top) and cockles (bottom) at Ivanof Bay

Figure 2-3 A villager removes fat from a seal skin at Tatitlek. The fat will be rendered into oil and the skin will be used for crafts and clothing.

In addition to sharing with relatives, subsistence foods are also shared with the elderly and others in need.

Kinship also shaped the composition of subsistence harvesting and processing groups in these Alutiiq communities in the 1980s. Extended families often worked together to harvest and process wild foods. These family activities provided the context in which young people learned the skills and values linked with the subsistence traditions of their communities (Stanek 1985).

In the 1980s, each community followed a patterned seasonal cycle of subsistence harvest activities that was shaped largely by the cycle of resource availability. Table 2-3 depicts the seasonal cycle of subsistence harvesting and use in the Prince William Sound communities of Chenega Bay and Tatitlek. Here, the cycle of subsistence harvests begins in the spring (March, April, May), a period of renewed activities, when herring and herring spawn, clams, birds, eggs, and other resources are harvested. Summer is traditionally the busiest time of year, when people harvest and preserve large quantities of salmon for winter use. Autumn is also important for salmon fishing, as well as for land mammal hunting, marine mammal hunting, waterfowl hunting, and marine invertebrate gathering. Subsistence activities in winter may include marine mammal hunting, land mammal hunting, and trapping (Stratton and Chisum 1986; Stratton 1990). With mostly minor modifications, a similar seasonal pattern was followed by the communities of the other three regions (Lower Cook Inlet, Kodiak Island Borough, and Alaska Peninsula). One important difference is the availability of large numbers of caribou on the Alaska Peninsula harvested from August to April (Schroeder et al. 1987).

In addition to its support of social organization, the cultural importance of subsistence is evidenced by the traditional knowledge about animals, plants, geography, and weather that is shared and passed on during subsistence activities. For example, young women at Tatitlek learn how to identify ripe herring eggs and the appropriate kelp on which to harvest them when they accompany their mothers and grandmothers in the spring to herring spawning areas (Stratton 1990). A key element in the successful resettlement of Chenega Bay was the teaching about hunting and fishing areas to the younger men of the village by the older, former residents of Chenega (Stratton and Chisum 1986). Local place names, in either Alutiiq or of non-Native language origin, often do not appear on maps and must be learned during subsistence activities. These local names are generally concentrated at prime subsistence use areas (Stanek 1985).

Most often, subsistence hunting, fishing, and gathering take place within definable village harvest areas, sometimes corresponding closely to the territories of ancestral Alutiiq regional groups (Figure 2-1). For example, the contemporary core harvest areas used by Tatitlek within Prince William Sound are much like those used by the *Tititlarmiut* regional group from which Tatitlek families are descended (Stratton 1990). Hunting and fishing skills, and knowledge about local weather patterns,

Table 2-3 Seasonal cycle of subsistence harvest activities (average of pre-spill years) by households of Chenega Bay and Tatitlek, Prince William Sound, 1980s. Black bars = intensive harvest; gray bars = intermittent harvest. Source: Fall et al. 1996.

	Avg. % of households attempting harvest	
Resource	Chenega	Tatitlek
Herring	16.1%	30.6%
Chitons	35.5%	19.6%
Harbor seals	67.8%	55.3%
Clams	51.5%	31.4%
Halibut	80.7%	57.5%
Herring spawn	9.7%	71.5%
Smelt	25.8%	4.5%
Black bear	35.5%	9.6%
Seabird eggs	12.9%	39.2%
Cockles	29.0%	37.9%
Dolly Varden	12.9%	2.6%
Pacific Cod	19.4%	27.4%
King salmon	32.3%	50.6%
Sockeye	45.1%	62.8%
Shrimp	25.8%	26.1%
Wild plants	90.4%	97.7%
Pink salmon	71.0%	72.6%
Chum salmon	54.8%	69.4%
Coho salmon	54.8%	57.3%
Deer	74.2%	75.3%
Crabs	9.7%	12.8%
Octopus	25.8%	47.5%
Goat	25.8%	14.1%
Ducks	64.5%	57.0%
Sea lions	51.7%	26.9%
Rockfish	54.8%	47.0%

reliable harvest areas, and safe camping locations, are shared within kinship groups in these areas. The successful harvest and thorough use of a wide array of mammal, bird, fish, marine invertebrate, and plant species reflect the detailed knowledge of these areas that has developed and been shared over generations of subsistence use.

Further evidence of the cultural significance of subsistence uses today in these Alutiiq communities is reflected in the contemporary nomenclature of subsistence products. Although the primary language in most communities today is English, the Alutiiq language is used to designate important resources or groups of resources. For example, "oodiks" (Alutiiq *uutuk*) is the name frequently used for sea urchins. At Nanwalek and Port Graham, *uyangtaaq* are bottom-dwelling animals, such as crab, that are found in shallow waters of bays and intertidal areas. These animals are all designated by the single name *uyangtaaq* because they can be harvested by people of various ages and abilities at times of the year when other resources are scarce or when poor weather prevents extensive travel. *Tamuuq, uumatak,* and *ataneq* are products made from dried salmon that are staples in each community's diet (Stanek 1985). The nutritional and cultural significance of dried salmon and halibut is so great that at Nanwalek and Port Graham these foods are called in English "our bread" (Stanek 1982) (Figure 2-4).

Figure 2-4 Salmon and halibut drying in Nanwalek

In short, subsistence uses of wild, renewable resources are of fundamental economic, social, and cultural importance to the communities of the oil-spill area. It is not surprising, therefore, that the potential effects on fish, marine invertebrates, birds, and mammals of the 11 million gallons of oil spilled by the *Exxon Valdez* were of primary concern to the people and communities in the spill area who have traditionally relied upon these natural resources.

Acknowledgments—First and foremost, the author is sincerely grateful to the many people who took the time to participate in this research. I also thank the governments of each study community for granting approval of the studies. I thank my colleagues at the ADF&G who conducted the research upon which Chapters 2 and 4 are based, or who otherwise contributed to the Subsistence Division's oil spill response program, including Dave Andersen, Jeff Barnhart, Louis Brown, Janet Cohen, Philippa Coiley, Joe Dinnocenzo, Roger Dunbar, Gretchen Jennings, Vera Kinzer, Jim Marcotte, Rachel Mason, Susan McNeil, Leah Merritt, Rita Miraglia, Craig Mishler, Amy Paige, Brad Palach, Sverre Pedersen, Deborah Robinson, Lisa Hutchinson-Scarbrough, Jody Seitz, Jeniffer Sepez, Neil Shisido, William Simeone, Sandra Skaggs, Ronald Stanek, Lee Stratton, Lisa Tomrdle, Charles Utermohle, Vicki Vanek, Robert Walker, Andy Williams, Barbara Winkley, and Robert Wolfe. Residents of the study communities assisted in the research, including James Kvasnikoff, Nick Tanape Sr., Olga Fomin, Mary Malchoff, Violet Yeaton, Sheila Theriault, David Pestrikoff, John P. Moonin, Anne Metcalf, Tamara Squartsoff, Angeline Anderson, Jennifer Brown, Elmer Anahonak, Fedora Hedrick, Dick Moonin, Vera Rose, Nicholas Tanape, Marvin Agnot, Diane Selanoff, Robert Katelnikof, Lillian Elvsaas, Robert Nelson, Gladys Yuth, Laura Chase, and Brad Osborne. I also thank other field workers, including Don Callaway, Karen Gibson, and Tracy Andrews of the U.S. Minerals Management Service, Robert Stovall of the U.S. Fish & Wildlife Service, and Susan Savage of the National Park Service. Funding for these projects was provided by the ADF&G, the U.S. Department of the Interior, Minerals Management Service, and the U.S. Fish and Wildlife Service.

References

Alaska Department of Labor. 1991. Alaska population overview: 1990 census and estimates. Juneau AK: Division of Administrative Services.

Clark DW. 1984a. Prehistory of the Pacific Eskimo region. In: Damas D, editor. Handbook of North American Indians. Volume 5, Arctic. Washington DC: Smithsonian Institution. p 136–148.

Clark DW. 1984b. Pacific Eskimo: historical ethnography. In: Damas D, editor. Handbook of North American Indians. Volume 5, Arctic. Washington DC: Smithsonian Institution. p 185–197.

Davis NY. 1984. Contemporary Pacific Eskimo. In: Damas D, editor. Handbook of North American Indians. Volume 5, Arctic. Washington DC: Smithsonian Institution. p 198–204.

Fall JA. 1990. The Division of Subsistence of the Alaska Department of Fish and Game: an overview of its research program and findings: 1980-1990. *Arctic Anthropology* 27(2):68–92.

Fall JA, Hutchinson-Scarbrough LB, Coiley PA. 1995. Fish and wildlife harvest and use in five Alaska Peninsula communities, 1989. Juneau AK: Alaska Department of Fish and Game, Division of Subsistence. Technical Paper 202.

Fall JA, Stratton L, Coiley P, Brown L, Utermohle CJ, Jennings G. 1996. Subsistence harvests and uses in Chenega Bay and Tatitlek in the year following the *Exxon Valdez* oil spill. Juneau AK: Alaska Department of Fish and Game, Division of Subsistence. Technical Paper 199.

Morris JM. 1987. Fish and wildlife uses in six Alaska Peninsula communities: Egegik, Chignik, Chignik Lagoon, Chignik Lake, Perryville, Ivanof Bay. Juneau AK: Alaska Department of Fish and Game, Division of Subsistence. Technical Paper 151.

Schroeder RF, Andersen DB, Bosworth R, Morris J, Wright JM. 1987. Subsistence in Alaska: arctic, interior, south central, southwest, and western regional summaries. Juneau AK: Alaska Department of Fish and Game, Division of Subsistence. Technical Paper 150.

Scott CL, Paige AW, Jennings GB, Brown L. 1998. Community profile database catalog, 6 vols. Juneau AL: Alaska Department of Fish and Game, Division of Subsistence.

Stanek RT. 1982. Natural resource harvest at Port Graham and English Bay, 1982: an interim report. Juneau AK: Alaska Department of Fish and Game, Division of Subsistence. Technical Paper 32.

Stanek RT. 1985. Patterns of wild resource use in English Bay and Port Graham, Alaska. Juneau AK: Alaska Department of Fish and Game, Division of Subsistence. Technical Paper 104.

Stanek RT. In press. An update of wild resource use in Nanwalek and Port Graham. Juneau AK: Alaska Department of Fish and Game, Division of Subsistence. Technical Paper 176.

Stratton L. 1990. Resource harvests and use in Tatitlek, Alaska. Juneau AK: Alaska Department of Fish and Game, Division of Subsistence. Technical Paper 181.

Stratton L, Chisum EB. 1986. Resource use patterns in Chenega, Western Prince William Sound: Chenega in the 1960s and Chenega Bay 1984-1986. Juneau AK: Alaska Department of Fish and Game, Division of Subsistence. Technical Paper 139.

Woodbury AC. 1984. Eskimo and Aleut languages. In: Damas D, editor. Volume 5: Arctic, Handbook of North American Indians. Washington DC: Smithsonian Institution. p 49–63.

Wolfe RJ, Walker RJ. 1987. Subsistence economies in Alaska: productivity, geography, and development impacts. *Arctic Anthropology* 24(2):56–81.

CHAPTER 3

The Role of the Alaska Oil Spill Health Task Force Following the *Exxon Valdez* Oil Spill

*Thomas S. Nighswander**

The origin of the Alaska Oil Spill Health Task Force (OSHTF) was modest and spontaneous. At an unrelated breakfast with Elizabeth Ward, then Director of the State of Alaska Division of Public Health on 24 April 1989 (exactly one month after the *Exxon Valdez* oil spill), I suggested we meet with a few of our staff and pool our collective knowledge about health issues related to the oil spill and cleanup activities. I was representing the Alaska Native Medical Center, whose service area included the villages of Prince William Sound that were most heavily impacted by the oil spill. Coastal villagers were already expressing health concerns. The Division of Public Health had heard the same concerns, as well as questions about health and safety of the oil-spill cleanup workers.

On 26 April 1989 the first meeting of the OSHTF was held. At that time it was inconceivable to any of us that these meetings would continue until August 1993. Although the first meeting was to include only the Alaska Native Medical Center and the State Division of Public Health, the word about the meeting was out. Fifteen people crowded into our small office at the medical center. These included representatives of the National Institute for Occupational Safety and Health (NIOSH), the Subsistence Division of the Alaska Department of Fish and Game (ADF&G), the University of Washington Division of Occupational Medicine, the Laborers National Health and Safety Fund, three members of The North Pacific Rim (a regional Native corporation), and five representatives from the Alaska Division of Public Health.

The Situation

The issues raised at that initial meeting were to confront the OSHTF for the next four years (see Appendix 6). The Native villagers were concerned about the large influx of people taxing the water and sewer systems and available housing. There was mounting concern about the psychological impact of this monumental event;

*Dr. Nighswander has been an Indian Health Services Physician with the Alaska Native Medical Center in Anchorage and has worked with all the Prince William Sound villages since 1972. He chaired the Alaska Oil Spill Health Task Force.

Evaluating and Communicating Subsistence Seafood Safety in a Cross-Cultural Context: Lessons Learned from the Exxon Valdez Oil Spill
L. Jay Field et al., editors. © 1999 Society of Environmental Toxicology and Chemistry (SETAC). ISBN 1-880611-29-5

the oil spill had already disrupted subsistence collection activities. Many of the adults had left their homes and families to work on the oil spill cleanup activities, leaving behind children and elders in the villages.

There was a serious situation involving subsistence food. Most hunting and fishing had been suspended while Native villagers awaited some statement about subsistence-food safety. The subsistence harvest of salmon was to begin in mid-May, only a few weeks away. We needed historical health-effects information from previous oil spills and current information about food safety and oil toxicity from the U.S. Food and Drug Administration (USFDA) and NIOSH as quickly as possible.

With no official standing or funding, and with an unclear mission and vision for the future, the OSHTF decided to meet again. The most crucial need was for information about the immediate and long-term effects on seafood from past oil spills around the world, as well as studies of subsistence foods from the current spill. By our next meeting on 10 May 1989, the salmon runs had begun and it was reported from the villages that people were afraid of potentially contaminated salmon and were not eating subsistence foods. Chenega Bay, Tatitlek, Port Graham, and Nanwalek—all poor villages highly dependent on subsistence food—were not collecting subsistence foods at all. As the oil spread to the west, many people in Kodiak Island and Alaska Peninsula villages also ceased their subsistence activities.

The Subsistence Division of the ADF&G, which was very familiar with the villages from past research and had been in contact with many of them, had identified the lack of subsistence foods as a critical issue. They were successful in having non-oiled salmon areas opened for subsistence fishing by emergency regulations and planned to launch a pilot sampling study looking for contamination of sockeye salmon, halibut, and clams from traditional subsistence areas. There was the need for a rapid turnaround of these data to give timely reports to the villagers.

Although there was no in-state capacity for a quantitative analysis of hydrocarbons in food, the Alaska Department of Environmental Conservation (ADEC) was able to conduct a qualitative evaluation known as the organoleptic or sensory test (the look, smell, and taste of the fish) for oil contamination at their lab in Palmer, Alaska. By our 21 June meeting, the ADEC reported that all the ADF&G Subsistence Division samples tested negative for hydrocarbon contamination. Everyone on the OSHTF thought we were close to putting to rest the concerns about subsistence food only three months after the spill. In fact, this was just the beginning, and trouble had already started well over a month before.

The Emergence of Risk Communication Problems

The undelivered health advisory bulletin

The first sign of difficulty in communicating food-risk information to the villagers, although not fully appreciated at the time, surfaced at the 24 May meeting of the OSHTF. The Epidemiology Section of the Alaska Division of Public Health had scrambled to obtain as much information as possible for a public health advisory. Their advisory was released on 5 May and included a three-paragraph statement about the potential impact of oil on the subsistence food chain (ADHSS 1989a). By prior agreement, the local nonprofit Native corporation, The North Pacific Rim, had agreed to use its villagers' mailing list to get this information in the hands of village subsistence users. The advisory bulletin stated:

> The best tests available at this time are the smell and taste of the fish (sensory test). If the fish smell or taste of petroleum, they should not be eaten. If they don't, they are almost certainly safe to eat. . .the same standard should be applied to clams, mussels, and shellfish. . . .We are unable to provide absolute assurances at this time and are working to have better information as our highest priority.

The USFDA not only recommended the sensory test, but they sent technical experts to Alaska to train people to use it. However, although the non-Natives on the OSHTF viewed this test as a reasonable guide, no one felt it was the final answer to food safety. In fact, as we learned, the persistence and low volatility of the heavy or high molecular weight polycyclic aromatic hydrocarbons (PAHs) rendered the sensory test alone insufficient.

The villagers were still asserting at the 24 May OSHTF meeting that "no one was telling them anything." The fact was that The North Pacific Rim had not sent out the ADHSS advisory bulletin because of the advice regarding the sensory test. They believed that if they promoted what one of their leaders described as the "scratch-and-sniff" test as a measure of food safety, they would lose all credibility. The villagers expected The North Pacific Rim to advocate rigorous testing of subsistence food. The "scratch-and-sniff" test was simply not the standard measure that the villagers would accept.

The perceived "double standard"

The Native villagers also perceived a "double standard" between the advice given to them about subsistence food safety and the so-called "zero-tolerance" standard adopted by the ADEC and ADF&G for commercial harvesting. The "zero-tolerance" standard stated that during the commercial harvesting process, no fish or gear could be potentially contaminated by oil, which meant that areas with heavy concentrations of oil or sheen were closed to commercial fishing. For example, there were concerns that the fishing gear might come in contact with oil or an oil sheen and that this contamination might not be detected until the fish were delivered to a processor. In retrospect, this standard had more to do with continued commercial marketing and confidence in the product rather than on food safety. This discrepancy, however, was not lost on the Native community, who viewed it as a double standard that cast even further doubt on the sensory test.

Conflicting paradigms

The problem that would plague the OSHTF to its end was now surfacing. Even those with a basic understanding of the Native paradigm issue did not fully appreciate its significance and implications until after the OSHTF had completed its work.

The information paradigm of the science community (including Exxon Biomedical, the health community, and the National Oceanic and Atmospheric Administration [NOAA]) includes rigorous data collection, measurement, and analysis resulting in trend lines, levels of significance, and degrees of risk. In contrast, the information paradigm of traditional Native villagers, who have a spiritual attachment to the land and the sea, is experiential and includes personal observations, oral history, and resulting patterns and dissimilarities gleaned from comparing experiences over the centuries (see Chapter 10).

The North Pacific Rim was getting information from their experts, the village elders. For example, at the end of April, the tribal chief of Tatitlek reported a die-off unlike anything they had seen before in the Narrows outside the village. The older people were seeing an unusual number of dead mussels, barnacles, starfish, and chitons. Although state biologists claimed the die-off was from an unusually hard winter kill, the elders found this unbelievable. Further, The North Pacific Rim pointed out to the OSHTF that a National Response Team report (Skinner 1989) to then-President Bush specifically mentioned the need to develop a health safety program that incorporated sensory and chemical analytic testing.

Clearly, our lack of appreciation of this paradigm difference resulted in basic misunderstandings about the value and validity of scientific sampling strategies, about our interpretation and presentation of the sampling data, and about our communication of the level of risk to the villages from consuming subsistence foods.

Lack of Food-Safety Information from Past Oil Spills

Information requests about oil contamination and food safety from various state agencies, most of whom were represented on the OSHTF, to federal agencies such as the USFDA, the Centers for Disease Control (CDC), and NIOSH were not answered to the OSHTF's satisfaction. In fact, there were no standards for hydrocarbons in food at the time and, as we eventually were to find out, no historical information on this subject existed, especially on oil contamination in subsistence foods that contribute significantly to local diets.

Through NOAA's assistance, a global literature review was conducted by toxicologist Gary Winston of Louisiana State University. He reviewed 16 international databases from as early as 1964 to 1989 and proceedings of oil spill conferences dating from 1975 to 1989. Winston found "a virtual absence of literature which investigated any human health effects, concerns, or implications as a function of oil spills other than those which were related directly to primary exposure to cleanup crews" (Winston 1990). His review concluded that there were no studies that addressed the possibility of contaminant transfer through the food chain to humans.

Of the more than 100 PAHs known to be present in food sources, 11 have been shown to be carcinogenic to test animals. However, Winston (1990) found no literature linking consumption of seafood contaminated with PAHs from petroleum sources with cancer or any other diseases in humans. He did note this caveat found in a monograph published in *Oil in the Sea* (NRC 1985): "Exceptions [to the above]. . .may arise in localized areas, as in the case of isolated fishing villages where seafood is a major portion of their diet."

Confusion as Principal Players Increase

During the summer of 1989, the OSHTF continued to meet at least every two weeks and its role and focus became clear. The membership, defined by who showed up at the meetings, expanded. In early June, the group consisted of representatives from the Alaska State Division of Public Health, the ADF&G Subsistence Division, the Alaska Native Medical Center, and the two regional native corporations, The North Pacific Rim and the Kodiak Area Native Association.

On 21 June, an important new player began attending. NOAA serves at all oil spills as the scientific advisor to the Federal On-Scene Coordinator. Although NOAA scientists had not previously been involved with health issues to any significant extent in the past oil spills, they brought experience and expertise in coordinating on-scene scientific activities and providing a link to scientific resources nationally.

Another new group to send representatives to the OSHTF meetings was Exxon's Biomedical Division. Exxon was already preparing to conduct subsistence sampling studies through their contractor, Dames & Moore, and were anxious to get food-safety information back to the villages. By 6 July, Exxon had assembled a team in Anchorage to plan and execute these studies. The team included a toxicologist, an occupational medicine specialist, an industrial hygienist, and a Native consultant from the Kodiak area (see Chapter 5). The Exxon team was invited to the 12 July OSHTF meeting, and we were informed that two separate sampling studies were occurring simultaneously: the ADF&G pilot study, and the Dames & Moore study (for Exxon), which had already sampled at four of the major Prince William Sound and Kenai Peninsula villages.

Several of the OSHTF members were unaware at the time that two other major beach sampling studies were being conducted—one by NOAA's Damage Assessment Center and the other by Exxon—and certainly none of us realized the implications of these studies for the OSHTF's credibility. Because both were collecting samples for damage assessment, their data and findings were considered "litigation sensitive" and therefore were held confidential for over two years. In fact, the data were not readily available until five years after the spill. All of our attempts to obtain timely results from their testing were unsuccessful with the exception of data from the chemical analysis of marine mammal tissues.

A lack of any central coordination further complicated this scenario. There was neither coordination of the sampling nor any single entity at the state or federal level to interpret the large volume of data that would be forthcoming. Neither was there any formalized mechanism to get this information to the villages. Even the State Epidemiologist, Dr. John Middaugh, was unsuccessful in getting any federal agency to take the lead (John Middaugh, personal communication, 1989). All the state and federal agencies involved had overlapping expertise and authority, and it was not clear to any of them who was in charge.

Attempts to Allay Confusion

A pivotal meeting of the OSHTF was held in Seattle on 30 July 1989, concurrent with the first National Forum on the Oil Spill held in Seattle, 28–30 July. It became clear that the OSHTF needed to assume the coordinating role for activities related to subsistence-food safety. The issues were straightforward. There were too many players in the food-safety testing arena. The testing was not being coordinated with the regional Native corporations, the Alaska Division of Public Health, the Alaska Native Health Service, or the ADEC. Various groups arrived at village beaches to collect samples, each of them promising (except for the damage assessment investigators) to get the results of their testing back to the villages as soon as possible.

By the third week of July, Exxon and NOAA had signed a Memorandum of Understanding (MOU) to undertake a joint study of the degree of contamination in subsistence resources (see full text in Appendix 5). The principal elements of this MOU were that 1) all chemical analysis of subsistence seafood resources would be conducted at the laboratory of NOAA's Northwest and Alaska Fisheries Center (now known as the Northwest Fisheries Science Center) in Seattle, Washington, an experienced and internationally recognized laboratory; 2) a NOAA biologist would participate in the sample collections with Exxon's Dames & Moore sampling team; and 3) all results would be immediately released to the public. By joining forces, rather than conducting separate studies, NOAA and Exxon hoped to conduct the most comprehensive and credible study possible.

All the groups now represented on the OSHTF had similar and overlapping vested interests. Thus the role of the OSHTF was becoming clearer: coordinate the testing (especially site selection), devise a mechanism to interpret the vast data that would be accumulated, and disseminate the results to the villages in an understandable way. When it became clear that no one group could accomplish its objectives by working alone, the OSHTF began to provide a focus and a structure for cooperative efforts among the various agencies and groups.

Meanwhile, the OSHTF continued to hear concerns from the villagers. Food safety remained the primary issue, even though a second Health Advisory Bulletin had been released on 14 July reporting that none of the 300 samples of subsistence food collected from the villages of Tatitlek, Chenega Bay, Port Graham, or Nanwalek (including the ADF&G samples) had measurable levels of oil contamination based on organoleptic testing (ADHSS 1989b). However, the Bulletin apparently still was not addressing the food-safety concerns of the villagers, who were reportedly angry about the lack of information on subsistence foods (other than information based on sensory testing). Villagers also wanted to know about the long-term consequences of low-dose exposure to hydrocarbons. Although their questions made sense, we could not answer them. Nonnatives eat seafood occasionally, but many coastal Natives of the Prince William Sound area eat food from the sea several times a day most days of their lives. The answer to this question is still a concern, although 10 years after the spill, no increase in cancer incidence in the villages could be attributed to the spill (Lanier 1997).

The Perceived Delay in the Return of Laboratory Test Results

The first subsistence-food safety data reported by the Epidemiology Bulletin on 14 July (except for several halibut samples) came from the qualitative sensory test conducted at the ADEC laboratory in Palmer. The OSHTF hoped that laboratory analysis of hydrocarbons in subsistence food would put the safety issue at rest and satisfy the villagers. We were anxious to get this information out as soon as possible. Although rapid turnaround of the test results was promised to the village people, the return of the results did not meet the villagers' expectations. The analytical results conducted by the USFDA (USFDA 1989; OSHTF 1989a) on the original ADF&G samples collected in May and June were not completed until the end of August 1989, after most subsistence salmon harvests were over.

The extensive sample collections from important subsistence harvest areas in Prince William Sound, Lower Cook Inlet, and Kodiak, which represented the first round of the Exxon/NOAA subsistence study, were completed in July, but the results of this testing were not available to us until 28 August (Varanasi et al. 1989). This was within the time frame for analysis and reporting agreed to by NOAA's Northwest Fisheries Science Center laboratory where the samples were sent for analysis, but unfortunately not soon enough for the timing of subsistence harvesting. Because these samples were being measured in parts per billion (ppb) using state-of-the-art techniques and extensive QA/QC review, a one- to two-week turnaround for the release of a data report was virtually impossible.

By late August, sampling results were beginning to return, but villagers wanted to know what they meant in terms of health risk. The health and science community did not have the expertise in Alaska to answer this question. At the request of the Alaska Division of Public Health (ADPH) and the OSHTF, an expert committee of nationally known toxicologists was convened by NOAA and the Alaska Division of Epidemiology to "improve the quality and reliability of health information." The Toxicological Expert Committee for Evaluating Data Relating to the Consumption of Marine Subsistence Foods was given the task of 1) reviewing all available existing information and the results of laboratory tests on Alaska subsistence foods, 2) identifying gaps in information, and 3) recommending additional studies needed to improve the quality of public-health advice about the safety of consuming subsistence foods. The Expert Committee also recommended establishing a clearinghouse of available information on oil contamination and human health relative to Alaska subsistence foods. Further, the Committee recommended a workshop to summarize the *Exxon Valdez* food-safety experience, identify continuing knowledge gaps and issues, and design strategies to respond to future oil spills. This workshop was conducted in August of 1990 in Queenstown, Maryland.

In the meantime, NOAA arranged for toxicologists from several universities, the USFDA, the National Institute of Environmental Health, the Agency for Toxic Substances and Disease Registry (ATSDR), and Exxon Biomedical to meet in Seattle on 14 September 1989 to review the hydrocarbon levels of 59 different subsistence food items from 11 villages (see Appendix 2 for the roster and summary report of the Toxicological Expert Committee for Evaluating Data Relating to the Consumption of Marine Subsistence Foods).

Based on their analysis (ADHSS 1989c), the Oil Spill Health Advisory Bulletin 16 of 22 September was able to state that "Alaskan finfish are and will continue to be safe to eat." The report went on to say that "Specimens of mollusks taken from heavily oil-contaminated beaches have shown high levels of aromatic hydrocarbons. . . .If mollusks are consumed, they should not be collected from areas that are obviously contaminated with oil."

The Village Visits

Recognizing the need for face-to-face meetings with the villagers, the OSHTF began planning village visits. The OSHTF created a subcommittee to plan village presentations in detail, including a "script" to guide what each participant would say. The team consisted of John Midthun, an Alaska Native Medical Center physician who regularly visited the villages; James Fall of the Subsistence Division of ADF&G; L. Jay Field of NOAA; Len Vining from The North Pacific Rim; and two toxicologists—NOAA consultant Gary Winston and Steve Lewis of Exxon Biomedical. The visits took place during the first week of October 1989. The discussion points for these meetings included

- the locations and kinds of subsistence foods collected;
- a description of the hazardous chemicals in crude oil and their effects;
- a description of the tests done on the samples and the results of those tests at the time of the village visits;
- the meaning of the test results relative to human health and fish and shellfish consumption; and
- the meaning of the results for those families who use subsistence food.

In addition, detailed maps showing the collection location of each sample and the analytical results were prepared for each village (see Appendix 4).

In retrospect, a fundamental flaw of the first round of village visits was including an Exxon representative on the village team as a major participant in the presentations. One week later, Alaska's Governor Steve Cowper received a complaint letter from the Tatitlek Village Council President (Kompkoff 1989):

> Why is Exxon in charge of subsistence testing? The largest subsistence study conducted so far has been done by Exxon. This makes no sense to us, and we compare it to having the fox guard the henhouse. The ADF&G Subsistence Division conducted the preliminary study, but the project was discontinued. WHY? We have confidence in the Division and their staff are very familiar with the village and our people and can work with us on our own level.

This was the village perception even though it was explained that although Exxon was paying for the study, a contractor was conducting it under strict protocols that included the participation of a NOAA representative and the analytical testing was being conducted by NOAA's Northwest Fisheries Science Center laboratory in Seattle.

Exxon Biomedical was straightforward in all of its dealings with the OSHTF. They worked as part of the team, made all of the results of their activities available, submitted their testing results to the expert toxicology committee, and consented to the committee's decision. Yet village suspicions far outweighed the realities. Exxon's participation in the OSHTF was double-edged. Although they provided the financial resources to help establish the largest database ever assembled on oil-exposed seafood, their very presence cast doubt on the veracity of the information in the minds of the people it was meant to serve. This paradox was one that was never completely resolved.

The Native Call for More Tests

Encouraged by the very low hydrocarbon levels measured in the subsistence food samples from the summer of 1989, Exxon expressed its uncertainty to the OSHTF about how many more dollars it was willing to spend until it had reviewed all the samples that it expected to see in November. When rumors of this began circulating, the villages mobilized. In a letter to Governor Cowper, the village president of Tatitlek (Kompkoff, personal communication, 1989) called for long-term studies with more samples from local areas and sampling of more species of seafood, other land animals, and their organs. A resolution passed at the annual Alaska Federation of Natives (AFN) convention in mid-October called for

> State and Federal Governments to ensure that a comprehensive, long-term subsistence-foods study be developed and implemented. The study is to evaluate short- and long-term health risks to Alaska Native people in the oil affected areas. The research is to be rigorous in its sampling design (i.e., number of samples, location, and species) and extend for a duration of at least three to five years (AFN Resolutions 1989).

The resolution further called for the "involvement of Alaska Natives during all phases of the study, from site and species selection, to sample gathering, analysis, interpretation, and finally communication of the test results. . . .Exxon's involvement should be limited to providing ongoing funding for the testing program" (AFN Resolutions 1989).

The AFN resolution was effective. The State of Alaska agreed to continue funding if it was needed in the future. Continued testing was important enough that in mid-October Dr. John Middaugh and I met with Mr. Otto Harrison, Exxon's chief of operations of oil-spill activities in Alaska, to secure a commitment for continued funding for testing. It was a brief, cordial, and positive meeting, resulting in Exxon's commitment to continued support.

Communications with the Villages

By the end of October, with the issue of continued testing resolved, the OSHTF began to focus on conveying believable information to the villages. We decided that it had to be broad-based and should include newsletters and videotapes presented at in-village, person-to-person gatherings. State resources became available, and James Fall from ADF&G explored the possibilities of hiring a publicist to work with the OSHTF. By January 1990, he had hired Andy Williams, a former newspaper reporter and publisher of a small Alaskan newspaper. In February 1990, the first of 13 issues (nine issues of the "Oil Spill Health Task Force Newsletter" followed by four issues of the "Subsistence Restoration Project Newsletter") of a professionally produced newsletter was sent to 4500 village households in 18 communities within the oil-spill area. Rita Miraglia of ADF&G took over for Williams in 1991, and the last issue was sent to the communities in April 1996. These newsletters attempted to address all of the villagers' questions in a form that would be understandable by a lay audience. They explained how the sampling was done and from where the samples were obtained, detailed how the tests were conducted, and explained the differences between the ability of fish to degrade hydrocarbons and bioaccumulation by shellfish. Most significantly, the newsletters tackled the tough issue of the short- and long-term safety of the foods based on the best available expert opinions and analyses.

Although the OSHTF newsletter was the principal communication tool, a 30-minute subsistence video, "Oil Spill: Threat to Subsistence," was produced and released in June 1990 by the Subsistence Division of the ADF&G, with assistance from the Office of the Governor. The video's release followed the first year's sample collection and laboratory testing program and came after the Expert Toxicological Committee had reviewed the 1989 results and developed its recommendations. The second year of collection and testing was underway when the video was released.

The overall goal of the video was to communicate advice about the safety of subsistence foods based upon the Expert Committee's review of the 1989 results. The primary message was that 1) finfish from the spill area were safe to eat and 2) most shellfish were also safe, although shellfish from heavily oiled areas could be contaminated and should not be eaten. The video noted the ability of fish, mammals, and birds to rid themselves of hydrocarbons, in contrast with marine invertebrates that tend to accumulate PAHs as long as they are exposed to oil. It also explained the differences between PAHs with low and high molecular weights. It was noted that light aromatics can be readily detected by sensory methods and are not likely to persist in the environment, whereas those PAHs with higher molecular weights are more persistent and cannot be discerned through smell and taste. The video recommended additional monitoring of shellfish and described the studies being conducted to answer questions about the long-term implications for human health.

The video included excerpts from interviews with personnel from the Alaska Native Medical Center, ADF&G, and NOAA. It showed scenes of village residents assisting in the subsistence foods collection program, as well as sensory testing at the ADEC Palmer laboratory, and bile-screening and gas chromatography-mass spectrometry analysis at NOAA's Northwest Fisheries Science Center in Seattle. Also included were scenes of subsistence harvesting, oiled beaches and wildlife, and cleanup activities.

The Second Toxicological Expert Committee Meeting

Based on the scant preliminary data available at the time, the Toxicological Expert committee at their first meeting in September 1989 gave very tentative recommendations. They were interested in meeting again when more sample information was available.

By February 1990, 365 analyses from 548 samples of fish and shellfish were available. Thus, on 21 February 1990 the original Toxicological Expert Committee met again in Seattle and concluded that,

> Based upon available data and cumulative scientific knowledge and consistent with the conclusions reached earlier, finfish are safe for human consumption. . . specimens of mollusks taken from heavily oil-contaminated beaches (for example, Windy Bay) showed high levels of aromatic hydrocarbons. Shellfish tested from less impacted beaches showed the presence of aromatic hydrocarbons in higher concentrations than found in uncontaminated areas but at levels that are not considered to represent a serious health hazard. If mollusks are consumed, they should not be collected from areas that are obviously contaminated with oil (Appendix 2; ADHSS 1990).

This information was quickly communicated to the villages in the Epidemiology Bulletin of 28 February 1990 and restated in the second OSHTF Newsletter in March 1990 (ADHSS 1990; OSHTF 1990).

The Expert Committee also made several other significant and far-reaching comments and recommendations (OSHTF 1990). They noted that there were no established guidelines for acceptable levels of aromatic hydrocarbons in foods and that hydrocarbons are ubiquitous and present in many foods routinely consumed, including cooked and smoked meats and fish, grains and cereal products, and fruits and vegetables (see Appendix 2). They also noted that it was impossible to provide individual recommendations for specific beaches or harvest areas because of the vast extent of the spill. Further, the Committee stated that there were no feasible tests available to measure or monitor human exposure to aromatic hydrocarbons. The Expert Committee called for

- monitoring of mollusks and fish (especially bottom fish) from heavily impacted areas to document that hydrocarbons have not increased over time;
- testing of more samples of smoked salmon;
- testing of mollusks from heavily oiled areas;

- testing of organs of seafood that were widely eaten (specifically, the hepatopancreas of crab); and
- sampling and testing of marine mammals that are part of the subsistence diet.

These tests were conducted during the following two summers (see Chapters 7 and 8).

Because of the lack of historical information on oil spills and human health, the Expert Committee recommended a "clearinghouse to be established to serve as a repository for datasets, clinical epidemiological studies, and other information on food safety related to petroleum and its impact on human health" (OSHTF 1990). Finally, they called for a workshop to summarize the experience of the oil spill, identify continuing gaps in scientific data and issues, and to design strategies to respond to future oil spills. The workshop was conducted with this agenda on 14–15 August 1990, at the Aspen Institute in Queenstown, Maryland. The draft recommendations from this meeting are incorporated in several chapters of this volume.

USFDA's Quantitative Risk Assessment Committee

Dr. Michael Bolger, a toxicologist with the USFDA who had been contacted in the early days of the oil spill, participated in the two meetings of the Toxicological Expert committee. Because the Subsistence Division of ADF&G had reliable and detailed baseline harvest data from the oil-impacted villages (see Chapter 2), he thought it would be possible to make a formal quantitative risk assessment of oil-contaminated seafood. Dr. Bolger suggested that I write to the USFDA and formally request such a study. This was done, and on 21 August 1990 the report (USFDA 1990) was received from Dr. Fred Shank, the Director of USFDA's Center for Food Safety and Applied Nutrition.

The methodology and results of the study (see Chapter 9) were based on the equivalency approach used in the relative cancer risk assessment, since carcinogenicity of aromatic hydrocarbons, especially benzene, is well established. The study conclusions were based on the amounts of subsistence foods eaten on a regular basis, the relative levels of hydrocarbons in those foods, and the relative lifetime cancer-risk estimates based on animal bioassays. Their report concluded that the lifetime upper-bound cancer risk was low for unsmoked salmon, other finfish, crustaceans, and oil-contaminated molluskan bivalves. The upper-bound risk represented a one-in-one-million chance of getting cancer. At the request of the OSHTF, two samples of smoked salmon had been sent for testing, since the Alaska Native diet relied heavily not only on seafood but also on smoked foods. The risk from traditionally smoked fish, based on two samples, was 100 times higher than anything found on the beach. One sample had a total aromatic hydrocarbon count of 22,400 ppb, far exceeding any hydrocarbon concentrations of the subsistence food that were tested for oil-spill contamination.

The Risk Communication Workshop

One of the original goals of the OSHTF—and a continued source of frustration—was effectively communicating results of the scientific analysis of subsistence food to the villages. Among other things, we wanted to communicate the concept of relative risk of eating potentially low-level contamination seafood compared with the risk of cigarette smoking, not using life vests, or even the risk of eating smoked fish.

We decided to bring together village representatives and two national experts: Dr. Bob Scheuplein, a risk communicator and Director of USFDA's Office of Toxic Science, and Dr. Gary Winston, NOAA's consultant toxicologist who had been well received in the villages. A total of 32 people met in Anchorage in September 1990, including representatives from Exxon, NOAA, and the Indian Health Service. The lessons learned from this workshop are detailed in the chapter on risk communication (see Chapter 10). Basically, the workshop concluded that "communication needs to begin early and occur frequently and that those affected should become directly involved in the process" (Usher et al. 1995). The workshop further concluded that

> The affected public should be involved directly in identifying their specific concerns, designing scientific studies, and interpreting the analytical results. They should also be given routine updates on progress and any delays in the process. A combination of written and face-to-face communication techniques should be employed to meet the needs of the various individuals' communication styles (Walker and Field 1991).

However, one point made by Dr. Winston deserves special mention. The scientific community clearly underestimated the potential importance of the subsistence food issue. Consideration of this issue and its cultural implications was unplanned and addressed too late in the scientific spill-response process. There were no historical precedents from which to build experience or provide guidance on this issue.

The OSHTF's Efforts in 1991 and 1992

Despite lingering doubts in the villages, the members of the OSHTF were increasingly confident that food not collected from obviously oil-contaminated areas was safe to eat. This conclusion was based on the results of two years of laboratory analysis of tissue samples collected from subsistence harvest areas and the concurrence of the Toxicological Expert Committee. However, there were a few unsettled issues. Mussels collected from the Windy Bay area on the outer coast of the Kenai Peninsula in 1989 had produced the highest levels of contamination observed in any of the samples analyzed in the subsistence seafood study. Although it was not a prime subsistence collection area, Windy Bay did serve as a bellwether for observing oil contamination over time. The area had been sampled multiple times in the two years following the spill, and it was important to collect some 1991 samples from this area to continue the trend analysis. Additional samples of other subsistence foods, including deer and seabirds that feed in the intertidal areas, were also collected. All additional samples from 1991 showed low to nondetectable levels of hydrocarbons. Equally important, the Windy Bay mussel samples continued to show declining concentrations of hydrocarbons.

In August 1991 we fulfilled another critical village request by preparing specific brochures by village with maps showing where each sample had been collected, the year and season of collection, and the analytical results.

One of the last full meetings of the OSHTF on 1 April 1992—three years after the spill—was devoted to preparing our last village visits that took place during the first week of June 1992. The village visitation team consisted of James Fall from ADF&G; Jay Field from NOAA; Mike Bolger from the USFDA; Judith Meidinger, the Native liaison for Exxon; a representative from the U.S. Coast Guard; and myself from the Alaska Native Medical Center. Relative to food safety, there had been a gradual return to subsistence-food use, but not with the same confidence as before the oil spill (see Chapter 4). The long-term risk to human health from eating subsistence food contaminated with oil remained the lingering question posed to the OSHTF. The villagers were polite but still angry about the spill and the cleanup. In part, this was due to the lingering food-safety questions that the sampling studies simply could not answer. For example, they wanted to know about the safety of a specific food at a specific area on a particular beach, yet this kind of specificity was not feasible in the sampling studies in which villagers helped select subsistence-use areas for sampling. One villager from Chenega Bay brought in a bucket of oil that he had recently obtained from an oil pool under a large beach rock, making it clear that concerns about seafood safety would continue to exist as long as oil could still be found on the beaches.

In essence, the world's largest sample of food potentially exposed to crude oil had been tested, including over 1000 fish and shellfish, 28 deer, 19 ducks, and 144 tissue samples from 43 individual seals and sea lions. The concentrations of hydrocarbons in the edible flesh were very low, approaching nondetectable concentrations with the exception of shellfish from a few areas and the blubber of seals from heavily oiled areas. Shellfish from clean beaches represented no risk to human health resulting from oil contamination. The more heavily contaminated beaches were becoming free of hydrocarbons as time passed, making official work of the OSHTF much easier. Yet skepticism remained.

The Subsistence Restoration Project: Food Testing in 1993

Working with NOAA and funded by the *Exxon Valdez* Oil Spill Trustee Council, ADF&G continued to attempt to restore confidence in subsistence foods. With the same protocols used in the original studies, ADF&G conducted additional collections at sites selected consensually by village representatives. An additional 51 samples demonstrated hydrocarbon levels that were very low to nondetectable and similar to levels found in reference, non-oiled spill areas.

In an attempt to increase confidence in the laboratory analysis, groups of village representatives were invited to travel to Seattle in August 1993 and September 1994 to tour the National Marine Fisheries Service Laboratory. Demonstrating their continued skepticism and mistrust of Exxon, they asked if the lab had received any money from Exxon now or in the past. The answer was no.

Just before their first Seattle trip in August of 1993, the last meeting of the OSHTF was held with village representatives. Had the OSHTF succeeded? Mr. Gary Kompkoff, President of the Tatitlek Village Council, wrote in a letter (Kompkoff, personal communication, 1993) that "it has been more than four years since the oil was spilled and the residents are still concerned and their concerns are growing with each failed commercial or subsistence fishing season." Another villager reported that "the beaches around Chenega Bay continue to ooze oil, and no one even tries to harvest clams from near their community, because they are afraid to." When I asked what could be done to convince them that their subsistence foods were safe to eat, the representative from Chenega Bay said it all: "Get the oil off the beaches."

It continued to appear that the analytical testing done in a nationally respected laboratory, under rigorous protocols by knowledgeable scientists, and presented to the villagers through written word, videos, and in face-to-face conversations simply could not completely convince all villagers of the safety of their food. Perhaps most importantly, the scientific conclusions simply were not consistent with the villagers' perceptions about the health of their environment. Larry Merculieff, the former Mayor of the Aleut community of St. Paul, Alaska, succinctly describes the native scientific paradigm:

> Native science does not divide the environment into separate components and disparate events, nor does it use numerical data systems for gathering information. It relies on information gathered by visual and physical observations of numerous natural events. This information is analyzed in the context of historical knowledge and the experience of others through many generations. Native science sees the interdependence of all life connections and constantly changing interactions (Merculieff 1993).

For state and federal agencies, nonprofit groups, and private industry with vested interests in the safety of the subsistence food and the commercial values of seafood in general, the favorable food analyses were a relief. This information was also reassuring to many villagers. But for the outspoken few and the many with lingering doubts, only time will tell. Perhaps only when the environment looks safe to them, and the beaches, birds, and fish appear as they did before the spill, will they conclude that their food is safe to eat.

References

[ADHSS] Alaska Department of Health and Social Services. 1989a. Oil spill public health advice. Anchorage AK: Division of Public Health, Epidemiology Section. State of Alaska Epidemiology Bulletin No. 6. May 5, 1989.

[ADHSS] Alaska Department of Health and Social Services. 1989b. Oil spill public health advice - Report No. 2. Anchorage AK: Division of Public Health, Epidemiology Section. State of Alaska Epidemiology Bulletin No. 8. July 14, 1989.

[ADHSS] Alaska Department of Health and Social Services. 1989c. Oil spill public health advice - Report No. 3. Anchorage AK: Division of Public Health, Epidemiology Section. State of Alaska Epidemiology Bulletin No. 16. Sept. 22, 1989.

[ADHSS] Alaska Department of Health and Social Services. 1990. Summary of findings of toxicological expert committee for evaluating data related to the consumption of marine subsistence foods (*Exxon Valdez* oil spill), Seattle, Washington—21–22 February 1990. Anchorage AK: Division of Public Health, Section of Epidemiology. State of Alaska Epidemiology Bulletin No. 6. Feb. 28, 1990.

[AFN] Alaska Federation of Natives Resolution. Alaska Federation of Natives Annual Convention; October 1989; Anchorage, AK.

Kompkoff G. 1989. Letter to Steve Cowper, Governor of the State of Alaska. Oct. 12, 1995. In the files of the Division of Subsistence, Alaska Department of Fish and Game, Anchorage, AK.

Merculieff L. 1993. Presentation: Establishing rapport between indigenous coastal cultures and the western scientific community. Fourth International Symposium of the Conference of Asian and Pan-Pacific University Presidents.

[NRC] National Research Council. 1985. Oil in the sea: inputs, fates, and effects. Washington DC: National Academy Press.

[OSHTF] Oil Spill Health Task Force. 1989a. Results of ADF&G pilot study of subsistence foods testing released by USFDA. Report dated Aug. 25, 1989. Anchorage AK: Division of Subsistence, Alaska Department of Fish and Game.

[OSHTF] Oil Spill Health Task Force. 1989b. Interim findings of Toxicological Expert Committee for evaluating data related to the consumption of marine subsistence foods (*Exxon Valdez* oil spill). Report dated Sept. 14, 1989, Seattle WA. Anchorage AK: Division of Subsistence, Alaska Department of Fish and Game.

[OSHTF] Oil Spill Health Task Force. 1990. Findings of Toxicological Expert Committee for evaluating data related to the consumption of marine subsistence foods (*Exxon Valdez* oil spill). Report dated Feb. 21-22, 1990, Seattle WA. Anchorage AK: Division of Subsistence, Alaska Department of Fish and Game.

Skinner S. 1989. The *Exxon Valdez* oil spill: a report to the President. Prepared by the National Response Team.

[USFDA] U.S. Food and Drug Administration. 1989. Summary of analyses of subsistence seafood from pilot study. Washington DC: Center for Food Safety and Applied Nutrition, Food and Drug Administration.

[USFDA] U.S. Food and Drug Administration. 1990. Advisory opinion on the safety of aromatic hydrocarbon residues found in subsistence foods that were affected by the *Exxon Valdez* oil spill. Washington DC: Center for Food Safety and Applied Nutrition, Food and Drug Administration.

[USFWS] U.S. Fish and Wildlife Service. 1991. Summary of effects of the *Exxon Valdez* oil spill on natural resources and archaeological sites. Anchorage AK: Division of Subsistence, Alaska Department of Fish and Game.

Usher PJ, Baikie M, Demmer M, Nakashima D, Stevenson MG, Stiles M. 1995. Communicating about contaminants in country food: the experience in aboriginal communities. Ottawa, Ontario, Canada: Inuit Tapirisat of Canada.

Varanasi U, Chan S-L, MacLeod WD Jr, Stein JE, Brown DW, Burrows DG, Tilbury KL, Wigren CA, Hom T, Pierce SM. 1989. Survey of subsistence fish and shellfish for exposure to oil spilled for the *Exxon Valdez.* Interim Report (Cycle I). Seattle WA: Environmental Conservation Division, Northwest & Alaska Fisheries Center, National Marine Fisheries Service, NOAA. Aug. 28, 1989.

Walker AH, Field LJ. 1991. Subsistence fisheries and the *Exxon Valdez*: human health concerns. 1991 International Oil Spill Conference. Washington DC: American Petroleum Institute. API Publication 4529. p 441–446.

Winston GW. 1990. Survey of health-related activities on previous petroleum spills: human, fish and fisheries and ecosystems. Baton Rouge LA: Institute for Environmental Studies and Department of Biochemistry, Louisiana State University.

CHAPTER 4

Changes in Subsistence Uses of Fish and Wildlife Resources Following the *Exxon Valdez* Oil Spill

James A. Fall

Soon after the *Exxon Valdez* oil spill of March 1989, images of dead and dying wildlife and miles of ravaged coastlines filled television screens and newspapers around the world. The degree of oiling and effects of the spilled oil on the natural environment and wildlife varied by subregion. The greatest impacts were in Prince William Sound but diminished to the west and the south (USCG 1993:123–129). The people of the spill-area communities witnessed these injuries to wildlife and habitat firsthand. Their observations raised deep and persistent uncertainties and apprehension. Although some of the spill's effects were obvious, they were discontinuous. Some beaches were heavily oiled, others were not. Some animals, such as sea otters and marine birds, were very vulnerable to oiling; others, such as fish and deer, showed no visible evidence of exposure to oil. Further, people observed signs in the natural environment, such as a dead starfish that washed up near Tatitlek and a dead whale near Karluk, that they interpreted as warnings of unseen dangers throughout the ecosystem.

Consequently, the following questions became very important for the people of the villages: Are our subsistence foods still safe to eat? If some beaches, waters, and animals were oiled and other, seemingly unoiled animals are inexplicably dying, are any resources safe to use? Accordingly, in the first few months after the spill when state health officials advised villagers that if resources did not smell or taste oily, they were "almost certainly safe to eat" (ADHSS 1989), villagers responded with skepticism and disbelief. As a resident of the western Prince William Sound community of Chenega Bay explained in early 1990, "We saw too much oil, and we didn't want nothing to do with [the fish]. . . .We don't want to eat them until we find out what's really going on."

Additionally, hunters and fishermen wondered whether it was advisable to harvest resources whose populations had been depleted by the spill. They were concerned about the future availability of these resources. As a hunter from Tatitlek, in eastern Prince William Sound, said in 1990 regarding waterfowl, "When you hear thou-

Evaluating and Communicating Subsistence Seafood Safety in a Cross-Cultural Context: Lessons Learned from the Exxon Valdez Oil Spill
L. Jay Field et al., editors. © 1999 Society of Environmental Toxicology and Chemistry (SETAC). ISBN 1-880611-29-5

sands of them are dying everyday, it's tough to harvest them. We didn't know what the number would be coming back."

As a consequence of these concerns about subsistence food safety and about the future of the resource populations, subsistence harvests in many villages virtually ceased soon after the spill. After the first post-spill year (1989), there was a gradual return to harvesting and use of subsistence foods, although this recovery varied by community, subregion, and resource category and was not complete five years after the spill. This chapter discusses the changes in subsistence harvest and use during the first five years after the spill and the reasons for these changes. Although this chapter draws in part on earlier preliminary reports and conference presentations (Fall 1991, 1992a, 1992b, 1993, 1996; Fall and Field 1996), the data have been updated and supplemented with the most recent study findings.

Research Methods

Community sampling

Following the 1989 spill, the Subsistence Division of the Alaska Department of Fish and Game (ADF&G) began a research program to document post-spill patterns of subsistence use. Research included 15 villages in four subregions: Tatitlek and Chenega Bay in Prince William Sound; Nanwalek and Port Graham on Lower Cook Inlet; Akhiok, Karluk, Larsen Bay, Old Harbor, Ouzinkie, and Port Lions in the Kodiak Island Borough; and Chignik Bay, Chignik Lagoon, Chignik Lake, Ivanof Bay, and Perryville along the Alaska Peninsula.

Systematic household interviews, using the methods developed before the spill (see Chapter 2; Fall 1990), were conducted in a sample of communities in each of five post-spill years. For most years, the study period extended from 1 April of one calendar year through 31 March of the following year. This 12-month period was selected to best reflect the seasonal cycle of subsistence harvests. An exception is the 1989 reporting period, which extended from 1 April 1989 through 31 March 1990 for Chenega Bay and Tatitlek, and from January through December 1989 for the remaining 12 study communities. For each study year, respondents estimated, through retrospective recall, their households' harvests of each specific type of fish, marine invertebrate, mammal, and bird used in their community. Harvests of the more general categories "berries" and "other wild plants" were also estimated. Respondents also reported whether their households attempted to harvest, used, received, or gave away specific types of subsistence resources during the study year. Additionally, respondents were asked to assess their households' use of subsistence resources during the study year and provide reasons for any changes they experienced. These evaluative comments are the source of most of the quoted statements in this chapter. These responses also were numerically coded for further analysis.

For the most part, researchers attempted to interview members of all permanent households in the smaller communities, and a 50% random sample of all permanent households in the larger villages was performed (see Table 2-1 for the 1990 population of each study community as reported by the Alaska Department of Labor). A 50% random sample was used in Ouzinkie (population 209 in 1990), Port Lions (population 222), and Old Harbor (population 284) in 1990, in Ouzinkie and Old Harbor in 1992, and in Port Lions in 1994. Complete samples were attempted in Ouzinkie in 1991, 1993, and 1994. Sample results for each round of interviews are reported in Table 4-1.

In the last three study years (1991, 1992, and 1993), an additional questionnaire was used in the interviews. This "social effects questionnaire" (SEQ) (Fall and Utermohle 1995, Volulme 6, Appendix II) contained a set of questions to assist in evaluating the long-term sociocultural consequences of the oil spill. Among other topics, respondents provided assessments of the safety of subsistence food resources and the adequacy of the food-safety advice they received after the spill (see Chapter 11). For those communities in which the SEQ was administered more than once (Chenega Bay, Tatitlek, Nanwalek, Port Graham, Ouzinkie, and Larsen Bay), the data reported in this volume pertain to the 1993 study year. For communities interviewed only once using the SEQ (Karluk, Old Harbor, Chignik Bay, and Chignik Lake), the data pertain to the 1991 study year.

Data analysis

For data analysis (see Table 4-2), harvest estimates in numbers of animals or other reporting units (such as gallons) were converted to pounds usable weight using standard factors developed by the ADF&G Division of Subsistence (Scott et al. 1998). Community harvest estimates are reported in lbs/person to facilitate comparisons among communities and across study years. As noted above, not all 15 communities were studied after the first post-spill year. To compute subregional and regional averages for years with missing data for particular communities, values for those communities not surveyed were estimated based on the data for subsequent and prior study years. These interpolated values are indicated in italics in Tables 4-2 through 4-5.

In all subregions except Lower Cook Inlet, the lists of resources used by interviewers on the household survey form were less detailed in the pre-spill study years than were the lists used to collect post-spill data. Therefore, for comparative purposes, post-spill estimates of the average number of kinds of resources used, attempted to harvest, and received per household (Tables 4-3 through 4-5; Figures 4-2 through 4-4, 4-8 through 4-10) have been adjusted using the less-detailed resource lists for the 13 study communities of Prince William Sound, the Kodiak Island Borough, and the Alaska Peninsula. For example, data were collected only for the generic term "ducks" in pre-spill research at Chenega Bay, but the data were broken down by species (goldeneye, mallard, etc.) for each post-spill year. If a household used two or

Table 4-1 Sample sizes, number of households interviewed, Division of Subsistence surveys

Community	Study Year 1989 # of Households			Study Year 1990 # of Households			Study Year 1991 # of Households			Study Year 1992 # of Households			Study Year 1993 # of Households		
	Total	Surveyed	Percent	Total	Surveyed	Percent	Total	Surveyed	Percent	Total	Surveyed	Percent	Total	Surveyed	Percent
Chenega Bay	21	18	85.7%	21	18	85.7%	22	18	81.8%	26	23	88.5%	28	23	82.1%
Tatitlek	28	22	78.6%	28	17	60.7%	27	19	70.4%				28	20	71.4%
Subtotal, Prince William Sound	49	40	81.6%	49	35	71.4%	49	37	75.5%	26	23	88.5%	56	43	76.8%
Nanwalek	41	33	80.5%	41	35	85.4%	41	29	70.7%	41	32	78.0%	37	33	89.2%
Port Graham	61	48	78.7%	55	46	83.6%	58	49	84.5%	58	48	82.8%	61	51	83.6%
Subtotal, Lower Cook Inlet	102	81	79.4%	96	81	84.4%	99	78	78.8%	99	80	80.8%	98	84	85.7%
Akhiok	13	10	76.9%							24	24	100.0%			
Karluk	17	14	82.4%	19	17	89.5%	15	13	86.7%						
Larsen Bay	39	34	87.2%	40	35	87.5%	43	38	88.4%	42	37	88.1%	49	40	81.6%
Old Harbor*	93	48	51.6%				66	42	63.6%						
Ouzinkie**	69	35	50.7%	59	53	89.8%	55	32	58.2%	59	52	88.1%	71	61	85.9%
Port Lions*	67	36	53.7%										80	45	56.3%
Subtotal, Kodiak Island	298	177	59.4%	118	105	89.0%	179	125	69.8%	125	113	90.4%	200	146	73.0%
Chignik Bay	39	35	89.7%				44	30	68.2%						
Chignik Lagoon	15	15	100.0%												
Chignik Lake	28	21	75.0%				33	24	72.7%						
Ivanof Bay	7	7	100.0%												
Perryville	31	27	87.1%												
Subtotal, Alaska Peninsula	120	105	87.5%				77	54	70.1%						
Grand Total	569	403	70.8%	263	221	84.0%	404	294	72.8%	250	216	86.4%	354	273	77.1%

* Randomly selected samples
** Randomly selected sample in 1989 and 1991.

Table 4-2 Estimated subsistence harvests in 15 Alaska Native villages in the *Exxon Valdez* oil-spill area for all study years

Location	Study period	Sample		Community		Sampling events (n)	Per capita (lbs/person)		
		# Households	# Individuals	# Households	# Individuals		Range	Mean	SE
Chenega Bay	1984/85	16	57	16	57.0	1	0–984.9	316.4	0.0
	1985/86	16	57	17	60.0	1	6.6–3605.0	375.1	27.1
	Pre-Spill Avg.	32			117.0	2	0–3605.0	346.6	13.9
	1989/90	18	63	21	73.5	1	0–549.4	148.3	14.3
	1990/91	18	66	21	77.0	1	0–460.6	139.2	12.8
	1991/92	18	66	22	80.7	1	0–1976.7	343.9	51.3
	1992/93	23	80	26	89.3	1	0–1737.2	412.5	37.5
	1993/94	23	83	28	101.0	1	0–1143.3	274.8	29.3
Tatitlek	1987/88	19	76	31	124.0	1	0–1373.4	352.5	70.9
	1988/89	21	76	28	101.3	1	2.6–3236.5	643.5	92.9
	Pre-Spill Avg.	40			225.3	2	0–3236.5	483.4	57.2
	1989/90	22	87	28	110.7	1	0–1323.4	214.8	33.7
	1990/91	17	75	28	123.5	1	2.9–1050.1	152.7	36.4
	1991/92	19	76	27	108.0	1	8.7–1255.7	346.0	47.0
	1992/93*	39			204.6	2	8.7–1513.0	308.0	29.8
	1993/94	20	69	28	96.6	1	13.3–1513.0	270.1	35.0
Prince William Sound	Pre-Spill Year 1	35			181.0	2	0–1373.4	341.2	43.5
	Pre-Spill Year 2	37			161.3	2	2.6–3605.0	543.1	41.6
	Pre-Spill Avg.	72			342.3	4	0–3605.0	436.5	38.3
	1989/90	40			184.2	2	0–1323.4	188.3	18.7
	1990/91	35			200.5	2	0–1050.1	147.5	21.3
	1991/92	37			188.7	2	0–1976.7	345.1	26.9
	1992/93	62			293.9	3	0–1737.2	357.1	23.4
	1993/94	43			197.6	2	0–1513.0	272.5	32.5

Table 4-2 continued

Location	Study period	Sample		Community		Sampling events (n)	Per capita (lbs/person)		
		# Households	# Individuals	# Households	# Individuals		Range	Mean	SE
Nanwalek	1987	33	125	40	151.5	1	0–2537.1	284.7	17.0
	1989/90	33	126	41	156.6	1	0–1364.6	140.9	11.1
	1990/91	35	157	41	183.9	1	0.4–680.7	181.3	8.9
	1991/92	29	114	41	161.2	1	8.0–1604.0	258.8	20.2
	1992/93	32	133	41	170.4	1	18.8–880.3	279.0	15.3
	1993/94	33	126	37	141.3	1	24.7–1763.0	304.9	17.8
Port Graham	1987	54	155	63	180.8	1	12.0–1661.8	228.8	15.0
	1989/90	48	127	61	161.4	1	0–1171.4	122.2	17.5
	1990/91	46	137	55	163.8	1	0.2–795.9	214.0	12.8
	1991/92	49	136	58	161.0	1	0–2573.5	280.4	15.7
	1992/93	48	138	58	166.7	1	4.0–2395.7	272.8	15.4
	1993/94	51	146	61	174.6	1	0–2313.5	212.1	19.6
Lower Cook Inlet	1987	87			332.4	2	0–2537.1	254.3	11.2
	1989/90	81			318.0	2	0–1171.4	131.4	10.4
	1990/91	81			347.7	2	0.2–795.9	196.7	7.7
	1991/92	78			322.2	2	0–2573.5	269.6	12.8
	1992/93	80			337.1	2	4.0–2395.7	275.9	10.9
	1993/94	84			315.9	2	0–2313.5	253.6	13.5
Akhiok	1983	21	80	27	102.9	1	126.7–3238.7	519.5	44.8
	1986	12	43	34	121.8	1	0–1158.9	162.4	28.4
	Pre-Spill Avg.	33			224.7	2	0–3238.7	325.9	25.6
	1989	10	43	13	55.9	1	13.9–1323.9	297.7	41.7
	1990/91*	34			135.9	2	6.0–3329.7	305.5	17.1
	1991/92*	34			135.9	2	6.0–3329.7	313.3	17.1
	1992/93	24	80	24	80.0	1	6.0–3329.7	321.1	0.0
	1993/94**	24	80	24	80.0	1	6.0–3329.7	321.1	0.0

Table 4-2 continued

Location	Study period	Sample		Community		Sampling events (n)	Per capita (lbs/person)		
		# Households	# Individuals	# Households	# Individuals		Range	Mean	SE
Karluk	1983	20	79	26	102.7	1	0–3124.0	863.1	62.3
	1986	19	76	27	108.0	1	6.2–990.5	385.2	39.3
	Pre-Spill Avg.	39			210.7	2	0–3124.0	618.1	36.4
	1989	14	60	17	72.9	1	0–1061.8	254.9	24.1
	1990/91	17	74	19	82.7	1	0–1976.8	401.5	49.7
	1991/92	13	60	15	69.2	1	24.3–856.1	268.7	24.3
	1992/93**	13	60	15	69.2	1	24.3–856.1	268.7	24.3
	1993/94**	13	60	15	69.2	1	24.3–856.1	268.7	24.3
Larsen Bay	1983	32	126	43	169.3	1	0–3076.6	403.5	51.9
	1986	37	121	52	170.1	1	0–1093.5	210.7	26.1
	Pre-Spill Avg.	69			339.4	2	0–3076.6	309.5	29.0
	1989	34	114	39	130.8	1	0–1990.5	212.0	21.0
	1990/91	35	127	40	145.1	1	0–1780.1	344.5	21.5
	1991/92	38	138	43	156.2	1	0–1641.0	294.6	19.0
	1992/93	37	120	42	136.2	1	0–2376.4	353.2	23.7
	1993/94	40	106	49	129.9	1	0–2040.3	451.0	37.5
Old Harbor	1983	77	289	94	352.8	1	0–9107.3	489.4	21.8
	1986	44	140	119	378.6	1	0–2545.3	425.4	60.2
	Pre-Spill Avg.	121			731.4	2	0–9107.3	456.3	32.9
	1989	48	144	93	279.0	1	0–1386.7	272.3	24.7
	1990/91*	90			495.9	2	0–4962.9	331.6	26.8
	1991/92	42	138	66	216.9	1	3.0–4962.9	390.9	52.3
	1992/93**	42	138	66	216.9	1	3.0–4962.9	390.9	52.3
	1993/94**	42	138	66	216.9	1	3.0–4962.9	390.9	52.3

Table 4-2 continued

Location	Study period	Sample		Community		Sampling events (n)	Per capita (lbs/person)		
		# Households	# Individuals	# Households	# Individuals		Range	Mean	SE
Ouzinkie	1983	32	105	70	229.7	1	0–2117.7	376.1	59.5
	1986	34	107	62	195.1	1	0–3774.5	404.8	45.5
	Pre-Spill Avg.	66			424.8	2	0–3774.5	389.3	38.4
	1989	35	111	69	218.8	1	0–772.9	88.9	11.6
	1990/91	53	182	59	202.6	1	0–1816.5	205.2	10.4
	1991/92	32	114	55	195.9	1	7.5–915.0	209.4	24.4
	1992/93	52	164	59	186.1	1	0–2089.9	347.1	15.3
	1993/94	61	201	71	234.0	1	0–2275.0	218.2	10.2
Port Lions	1983	55	179	89	289.7	1	0–1713.8	279.8	23.8
	1986	65	214	90	296.3	1	0–2973.4	333.9	28.2
	Pre-Spill Avg.	120			586.0	2	0–2973.4	307.2	18.5
	1989	36	105	67	195.4	1	0–753.2	146.7	19.6
	1990/91*	81			431.9	2	0–1801.0	192.9	23.4
	1991/92*	81			431.9	2	0–1801.0	239.1	23.4
	1992/93*	81			431.9	2	0–1801.0	285.3	23.4
	1993/94	45	133	80	236.4	1	8.0–1801.0	331.5	39.5
Kodiak Island Borough	1983	237			1247.0	6	0–9107.3	441.2	16.7
	1986	211			1269.9	6	0–3774.5	343.5	21.1
	Pre-Spill Avg.	448			2517.0	12	0–9107.3	392.1	13.5
	1989	177			952.8	6	0–1990.5	196.3	9.7
	1990/91	310			1494.1	9	0–4962.9	280.8	11.9
	1991/92	240			1206.0	8	0–4962.9	285.7	13.6
	1992/93	249			1120.3	7	0–4962.9	334.9	14.2
	1993/94	225			966.3	6	0–4962.9	328.1	16.3

Table 4-2 continued

Location	Study period	Sample		Community		Sampling events (n)	Per capita (lbs/person)		
		# Households	# Individuals	# Households	# Individuals		Range	Mean	SE
Chignik Bay	1984	19	82	28	120.8	1	0–728.5	187.9	22.5
	1989	35	108	39	120.3	1	0–2282.3	208.9	12.7
	1990/91*	65			241.2	2	0–2282.3	281.1	27.3
	1991/92	30	87	44	129.1	1	0–1910.0	353.4	51.4
Chignik Lagoon	1984	17	57	22	73.8	1	0–1305.1	220.3	31.4
	1989	15	41	15	41.0	1	0–990.3	211.4	0.0
	1990/91**	15	41	15	41.0	1	0–990.3	211.4	0.0
	1991/92**	15	41	15	41.0	1	0–990.3	211.4	0.0
Chignik Lake	1984	23	116	31	156.3	1	8.3–1075.2	279.0	21.6
	1989	21	84	28	112.0	1	0.5–2207.3	453.0	65.9
	1990/91*	45			268.3	2	0.5–2207.3	447.6	36.7
	1991/92	24	95	33	130.6	1	4.5–1368.8	442.3	38.3
Ivanof Bay	1984	6	22	10	36.7	1	13.1–659.1	455.7	32.7
	1989	7	32	7	32.0	1	158.3–1273.2	489.9	0.0
	1990/91**	7	32	7	32.0	1	158.3–1273.2	489.9	0.0
	1991/92**	7	32	7	32.0	1	158.3–1273.2	489.9	0.0
Perryville	1984	20	85	27	114.8	1	44.3–3977.7	391.1	34.0
	1989	27	101	31	116.0	1	10.2–7358.4	394.4	37.7
	1990/91**	27	101	31	116.0	1	10.2–7358.4	394.4	37.7
	1991/92**	27	101	31	116.0	1	10.2–7358.4	394.4	37.7
Alaska Peninsula	1984	85			502.4	5	0–3977.7	287.0	12.7
	1989	105			421.3	5	0–7358.4	346.4	20.7
	1990/91	159			698.5	7	0–7358.4	366.5	18.1
	1991/92	103			448.7	5	0–7358.4	386.6	20.9

Table 4-2 continued

Location	Study period	Sample		Community		Sampling events (n)	Per capita (lbs/person)		
		# Households	# Individuals	# Households	# Individuals		Range	Mean	SE
All communities	Pre-Spill Year 1	444			2262.7	15	0–9107.3	371.8	10.4
	Pre-Spill Year 2	420			2266.0	23	0–3977.7	332.1	12.6
	Pre-Spill Avg.	692			3694.0	23	0–9107.3	352.0	10.0
	1989	403			1876.3	15	0–7358.4	218.2	7.2
	1990/91	585			2740.8	20	0–7358.4	271.1	8.2
	1991/92	458			2165.4	17	0–7358.4	312.9	9.3
All communities (excluding Alaska Peninsula)	Pre-Spill Year 1	359			1760.4	10	0–9107.3	395.9	12.8
	Pre-Spill Year 2	335			1763.6	10	0–3774.5	345.0	15.8
	Pre-Spill Avg.	607			3191.6	18	0–9107.3	370.5	11.5
	1989	298			1455.0	10	0–1990.5	181.1	7.1
	1990/91	426			2042.3	13	0–4962.9	243.4	9.0
	1991/92	355			1716.8	12	0–4962.9	289.9	10.3
	1992/93	391			1751.2	12	0–4962.9	324.1	10.1
	1993/94	352			1479.9	10	0–4962.9	304.8	11.8

* Interviews not conducted in study year. Value based on pre- and post-study year estimates

** Interviews not conducted in study year. Value based on last previous estimate.

Table 4-3 Average number of resources used per household in oil-spill region study communities[1]

	Pre-spill average # of resources used per household			Post-spill: Average # of resources used per household				
Community	Year One[2]	Year Two[3]	Prespill value[4]	1989 (spill year)	1990	1991	1992	1993
Chenega Bay	16.9	20.6	18.8	7.2	9.8	13.2	17.7	15.0
Tatitlek	17.9	20.5	19.1	10.3	12.5	17.3	*17.2*	17.1
Prince Wm. Sound	17.6	20.5	19.0	9.0	11.3	15.5	*17.4*	16.0
Nanwalek	25.0	*25.0*	25.0	13.7	22.4	21.2	22.9	22.7
Port Graham	21.5	*21.5*	21.5	11.2	17.4	22.0	22.1	19.4
Lower Cook Inlet	22.9	*22.9*	22.9	12.2	19.5	21.6	22.4	20.6
Akhiok	18.5	7.9	12.6	18.0	*17.3*	*16.7*	16.0	*16.0*
Karluk	20.9	13.2	17.0	10.9	13.2	13.5	*13.5*	*13.5*
Larsen Bay	18.1	13.2	15.4	12.7	16.5	15.4	14.1	14.7
Old Harbor	18.3	12.8	15.2	13.6	*15.2*	16.7	*16.7*	*16.7*
Ouzinkie	20.4	16.0	18.3	7.6	13.9	15.2	15.8	12.7
Port Lions	15.7	12.3	14.0	9.4	*11.0*	*12.5*	*14.1*	15.6
Kodiak Island Borough	18.2	12.8	15.4	11.2	*14.1*	*14.9*	*15.2*	*14.9*
Chignik Bay	12.5	*12.5*	12.5	14.6	*14.7*	14.7		
Chignik Lagoon	10.7	*10.7*	10.7	13.6	*13.6*	*13.6*		
Chignik Lake	16.0	*16.0*	16.0	19.0	*20.2*	21.4		
Ivanof Bay	18.8	*18.8*	18.8	26.9	*26.9*	*26.9*		
Perryville	21.6	*21.6*	21.6	19.9	*19.9*	*19.9*		
Alaska Peninsula	15.7	*15.7*	15.7	17.6	*17.9*	*18.2*		
All communities	18.5	*15.5*	16.9	12.5	*15.6*	*16.9*		
All communities, excluding Alaska Peninsula[5]	19.1	*15.4*	17.2	11.2	*15.0*	*16.5*	*17.1*	*16.3*

[1]Because not all communities were surveyed in every study year, missing values were interpolated based upon the trend for known values and held constant for years subsequent to the final study year. Interpolated values are indicated by italics. [2]Equals 1984/85 for Chenega Bay, 1987/88 for Tatitlek, 1982/83 for Kodiak Island Borough, and 1984 for Alaska Peninsula. [3]Equals 1985/86 for Chenega Bay, 1988/89 for Tatitlek, and 1986 for Kodiak Island Borough. Otherwise, Year One values used to calculate regional average. [4]Equals average of previous estimates if two pre-spill study years available; otherwise, equals single pre-spill estimate. [5]Because post-spill changes were small in Alaska Peninsula villages and no surveys were done there after 1991, this row may best depict spill effects.

more kinds of ducks in the post-spill study years, these were counted as a single resource ("ducks") to calculate community averages for comparison with pre-spill years. Also, different resource lists were used for interviewing different communities, based on the specific resources available in each area. (For examples of the survey instruments, see Fall et al. 1995, 1996.)

An emergency food relief program was organized in May 1989 to provide communities in the spill area with wild resources and other food to replace subsistence resources lost from the spill. Wild resources received through these programs are not included in the estimates of the average number of kinds of resources used or received per household. For a discussion of these programs, see Fall et al. (1996:119–127).

Subsistence Use in the First Post-Spill Year

"No one's eating anything out of the ocean anymore."
— Ouzinkie, June 1989

Harvest quantities and variety of resources harvested, used, and shared

This section presents data on patterns of subsistence uses in the 15 study communities during the year immediately following the oil spill (1989). As shown in Table 4-2 and Figure 4-1, subsistence harvests in 1989 to 1990 declined in all eight study communities of Prince William Sound and the Kodiak Island Borough compared with pre-spill averages. Subsistence harvests also declined in both Lower Cook Inlet communities compared to the one pre-spill estimate.

Generally, subsistence harvests declined in relation to distance from the source of the spill and the degree of oiling of subsistence harvest areas. At the Prince William Sound community of Tatitlek, subsistence harvests declined 56%. At Chenega Bay, subsistence harvests declined 57% from the pre-spill average. Subsistence harvests in the Lower Cook Inlet communities dropped substantially, but less than in Prince William Sound. Nanwalek's harvests were down 51% and those of Port Graham fell 47%. For the Kodiak Island Borough, post-spill subsistence harvests in 1989 to 1990 represented a wide range of declines compared with pre-spill averages, which generally reflects the path of the spilled oil to the north and west of Kodiak Island. The greatest decline was at Ouzinkie, at 77%, and the lowest was a 9% drop at Akhiok.

These data may underestimate the extent of the decline in subsistence harvests in some communities for the first post-spill year. For example, the only pre-spill estimates for Chenega Bay are for 1984 to 1985 and 1985 to 1986, which coincide with the village's resettlement in western Prince William Sound after a 20-year absence brought on by the destruction caused by the Good Friday earthquake of 1964. As the residents of Chenega Bay gradually regained knowledge about harvest

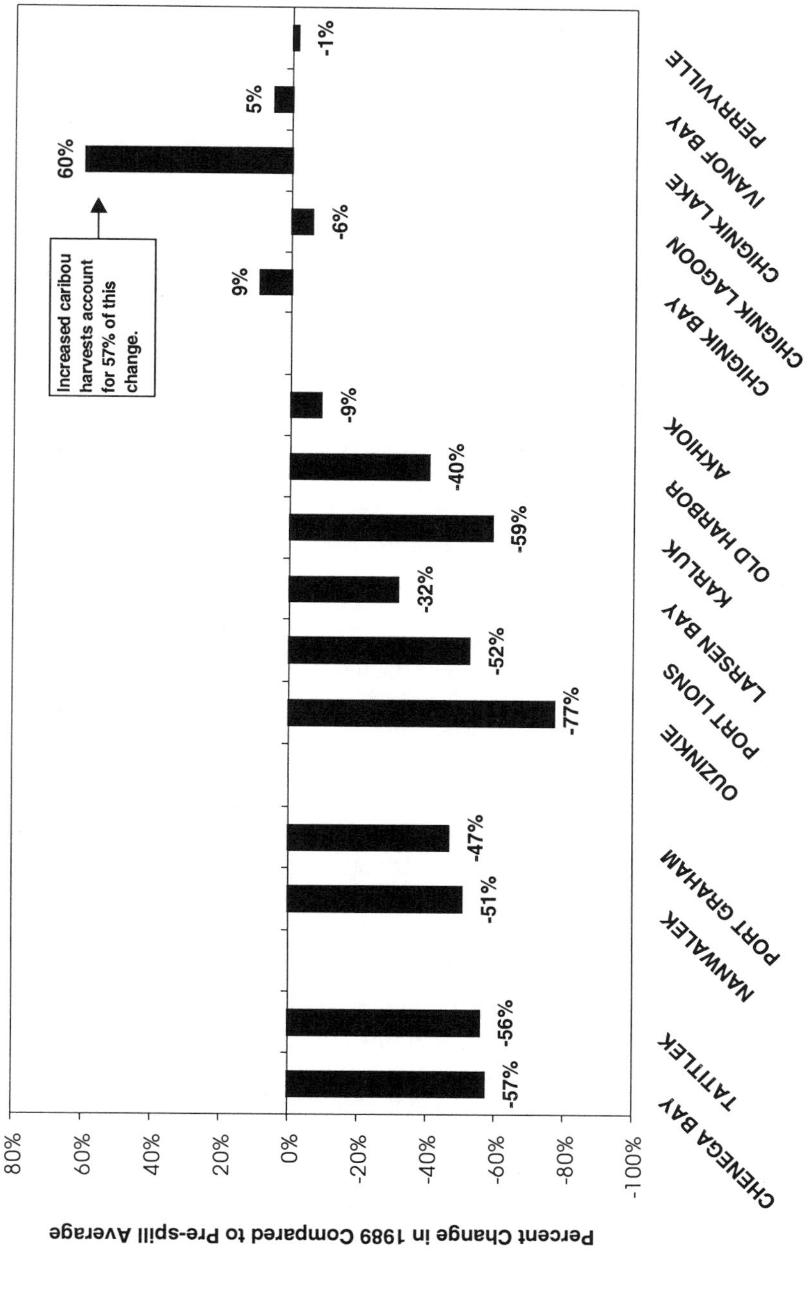

Figure 4-1 Changes in subsistence harvests after the *Exxon Valdez* oil spill in 15 study communities of the oil-spill area

areas, it is likely that harvest levels increased after the last study period of 1985 to 1986 (Stratton and Chisum 1986:113). Furthermore, an important liberalization of subsistence salmon fishing regulations took place in 1988 that eliminated seasonal limits and gear restrictions and provided more fishing time for Chenega Bay. Thus, subsistence salmon harvests in Chenega Bay for 1988 (just prior to the oil spill) were likely higher than those reported by survey respondents for 1984 to 1985 and 1985 to 1986 (see also Stratton 1990:128–131).

For Nanwalek and Port Graham, the "first post-spill study year" covers the period from January to December 1989, which includes almost three months of harvests prior to the 24 March spill. (This is also the case for the Kodiak and Alaska Peninsula study communities.) When people in Nanwalek and Port Graham learned that oil from the spill was likely to reach their subsistence harvest areas, they intensified their efforts to harvest certain resources, such as marine invertebrates, for fear that they would not again be available for many months or even years. This "stocking up" probably results in an underestimate of the drop in subsistence harvests in the "first post-spill year" for these two villages.

In contrast to the communities of Prince William Sound, Lower Cook Inlet, and Kodiak Island, the five study communities of the Alaska Peninsula—where the overall level of oiling was low compared with regions to the north and east—show no evidence of major post-spill declines in overall annual subsistence harvests (Figure 4-1, Table 4-2). (Note: The pre-spill estimate of subsistence harvests for the Alaska Peninsula communities does not include wild plants. Therefore, the following comparison, and the data in Figure 4-1, exclude the 1989 wild plant harvest estimates, whereas Table 4-2 harvest data are based on the full range of resources for which information was collected.) For four of the five Alaska Peninsula communities, subsistence harvest estimates were virtually the same as the single pre-spill estimate. These changes ranged from a post-spill increase of 9% for Chignik Bay to a 6% decrease in Chignik Lagoon. The exception is Chignik Lake, where the 1989 estimate represents a 60% increase over the 1984 estimate. However, it is important to note that Chignik Lake is the most inland village of the 15 study communities and is highly dependent on caribou as well as marine resources. The 1989 harvest estimate for caribou at Chignik Lake more than doubled the 1984 estimate, accounting for 57% of the overall 60% increase in subsistence harvests for 1989.

Although this research did not document large declines in overall subsistence activity on the Alaska Peninsula in 1989, the study did find evidence of many spill-related disruptions to subsistence activities in this subregion. As in the other subregions, the presence of oil contaminants in the water and on the beaches and the substantial documentation of dead and dying wildlife throughout the entire spill region cast doubt on the general safety of using subsistence foods. Many Alaska Peninsula households reported that they curtailed or reduced their harvests of certain resources (Figure 4-5). As in other subregions, households discarded subsistence resources they suspected to be contaminated and expressed concerns about unknown damages to fish and wildlife. Also, because of the presence of oil contaminants, the Chignik Management Area commercial salmon fishery was severely restricted; thus, overall commercial harvests were down, and local fishers removed less of their catch for home use. In combination, these factors disrupted subsistence uses on the Alaska Peninsula, although these disruptions were of shorter duration and less magnitude than in other subregions where the effects of the spilled oil were more visible and more persistent (Fall et al. 1995:205).

In addition to harvest quantities, the variety of resources used (an index of diet breadth), attempted to harvest (an index of harvest effort), and resources received (an index of sharing) declined after the spill in the communities of Prince William Sound, Lower Cook Inlet, and the Kodiak Island Borough. For example, the average number of kinds of resources used per household at Tatitlek decreased by 46% after the spill. Similarly, declines in diet breadth were reported at Chenega Bay (62%), Nanwalek (45%), and Port Graham (48%). Diet breadth also dropped in every Kodiak Island Borough community (with the exception of Akhiok, the Kodiak Island community least affected by the spill) with the most notable decline of 59% at Ouzinkie (Table 4-3, Figure 4-2).

The drop in the variety of resources that households attempted to harvest shows that, in most communities, subsistence harvest effort declined during the spill year (Table 4-4, Figure 4-3). For example, on average, households in Tatitlek attempted to harvest 47% fewer kinds of wild resources in 1989 to 1990 compared with pre-spill averages. The decline at Chenega Bay was 64%. The average number of kinds of resources that households attempted to harvest also dropped in the first post-spill year at Nanwalek (45%), Port Graham (49%), Ouzinkie (59%), Port Lions (35%), Larsen Bay (16%), Old Harbor (25%), and Karluk (21%).

Patterns of subsistence resource sharing also changed during the first post-spill year (Table 4-5, Figure 4-4), with households receiving fewer kinds of resources than in pre-spill years. For example, on average, households in Tatitlek received 53% fewer kinds of resources in 1989 and 1990 than they had in the pre-spill study years. The average number of kinds of resources received in 1989 and 1990 in Chenega Bay dropped even more (64%). Reductions in the range of resources received were reported for Nanwalek (down 54%), Port Graham (down 40%), Ouzinkie (down 60%), Port Lions (down 32%), Larsen Bay (down 21%), and Karluk (down 18%).

Respondents' explanations for changes in subsistence uses

When households were interviewed about their subsistence uses in the first post-spill year, they were asked how their resource use levels compared with those of previous years. Those who said they thought a change had occurred were asked to provide a reason for the change. As shown in Figure 4-5, almost all the households in the subregions of Prince William Sound (87%) and Lower Cook Inlet (93%) said that their overall subsistence uses had declined in the first post-spill year, and 84% of the households in both subregions gave a spill-related reason for this change. About

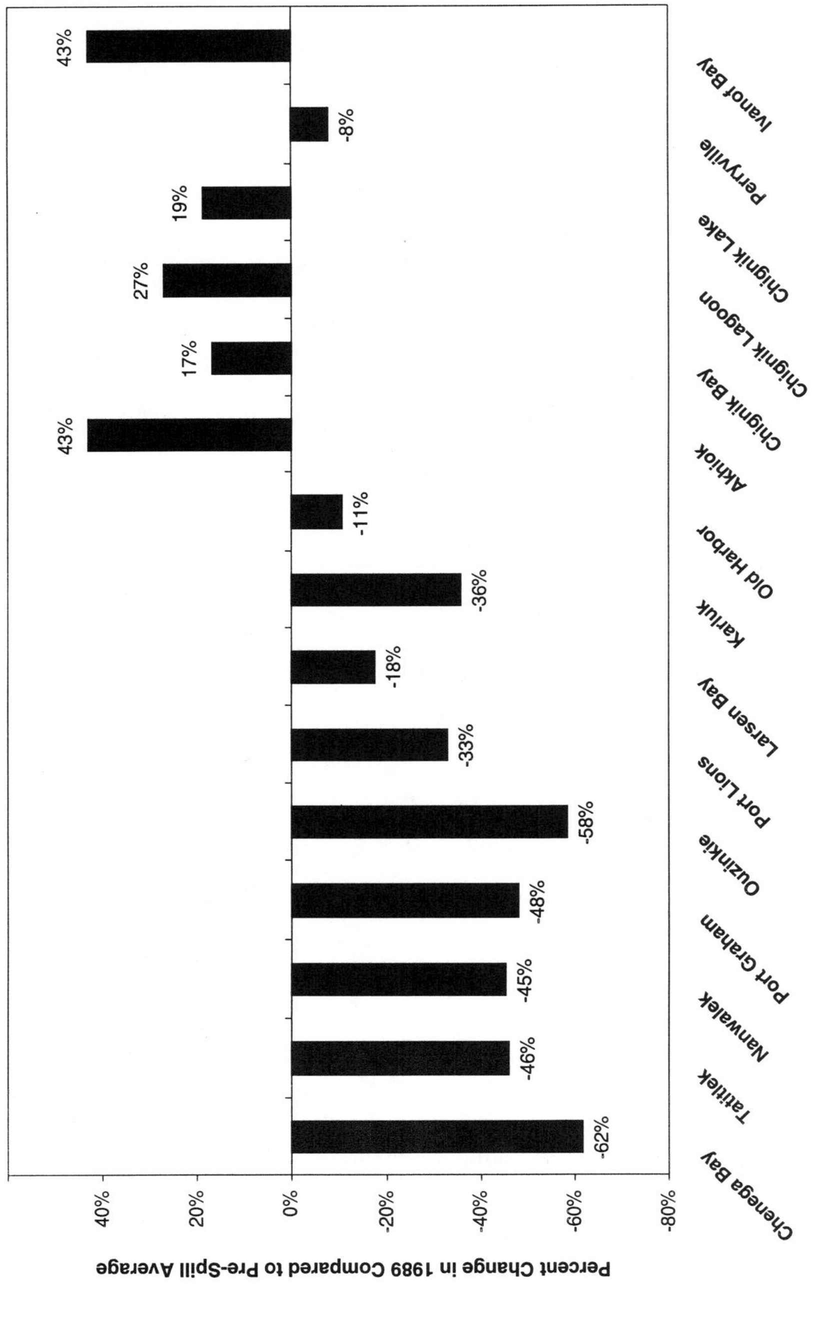

Figure 4-2 Changes in average number of resources used per household, post-spill year (1989) compared to pre-spill averages

Table 4-4 Average number of resources attempted to harvest per household in oil spill region communities[1]

Community	Pre-spill average # of resources attempted per household			Post-spill average # of resources attempted per household				
	Year One[2]	Year Two[3]	Prespill value[4]	1989 (spill year)	1990	1991	1992	1993
Chenega Bay	12.6	15.4	14.1	5.1	6.2	9.6	10.4	10.2
Tatitlek	11.1	12.3	11.7	6.2	8.4	13.1	*12.6*	12.2
Prince William Sound	11.6	13.5	12.5	5.7	7.5	11.5	*11.5*	11.2
Nanwalek	18.0	*18.0*	18.0	10.5	15.4	14.9	17.7	16.8
Port Graham	14.9	*14.9*	14.9	8.3	12.1	14.7	14.8	11.6
Lower Cook Inlet	16.1	*16.1*	16.1	9.2	13.5	14.8	15.6	13.5
Akhiok	18.0	6.8	11.8	14.2	*13.4*	*12.6*	11.8	*11.8*
Karluk	15.3	8.0	11.6	8.3	9.2	10.5	*10.5*	*10.5*
Larsen Bay	11.9	7.3	9.4	7.9	10.4	9.8	10.1	9.4
Old Harbor	16.3	9.8	12.7	9.5	*10.0*	10.6	*10.6*	*10.6*
Ouzinkie	15.3	12.7	14.0	5.7	9.5	11.1	11.1	8.8
Port Lions	11.4	9.6	10.5	6.8	*7.6*	*8.3*	*8.9*	9.6
Kodiak Island Borough	14.3	9.5	11.8	7.9	*9.5*	*10.1*	*10.3*	*9.8*
Chignik Bay	8.4	*8.4*	8.4	10.9	*10.1*	9.4		
Chignik Lagoon	6.9	*6.9*	6.9	7.8	*7.8*	*7.8*		
Chignik Lake	9.4	*9.4*	9.4	13.1	*12.8*	12.7		
Ivanof Bay	15.2	*15.2*	15.2	22.3	*22.3*	*22.3*		
Perryville	14.1	*14.1*	14.1	13.4	*13.4*	*13.4*		
Alaska Peninsula	10.3	*10.3*	10.3	12.3	*12.0*	*11.7*		
All communities	13.7	*11.0*	12.3	8.9	*10.6*	*11.4*		
All communities excluding Alaska Peninsula[5]	14.5	*11.1*	12.7	8.0	*10.2*	*11.4*	*11.7*	*10.8*

[1]Because not all communities were surveyed in every study year, missing values were interpolated based upon the trend for known values and held constant for years subsequent to the final study year. Interpolated values are indicated by italics. [2]Equals 1984/85 for Chenega Bay, 1987/88 for Tatitlek, 1982/83 for Kodiak Island Borough, and 1984 for Alaska Peninsula. [3]Equals 1985/86 for Chenega Bay, 1988/89 for Tatitlek, and 1986 for Kodiak Island Borough. Otherwise, Year One values used to calculate regional average. [4]Equals average of previous estimates if two pre-spill study years available; otherwise, equals single pre-spill estimate. [5]Because post-spill changes were small in Alaska Peninsula villages and no surveys were done there after 1991, this row may best depict spill effects.

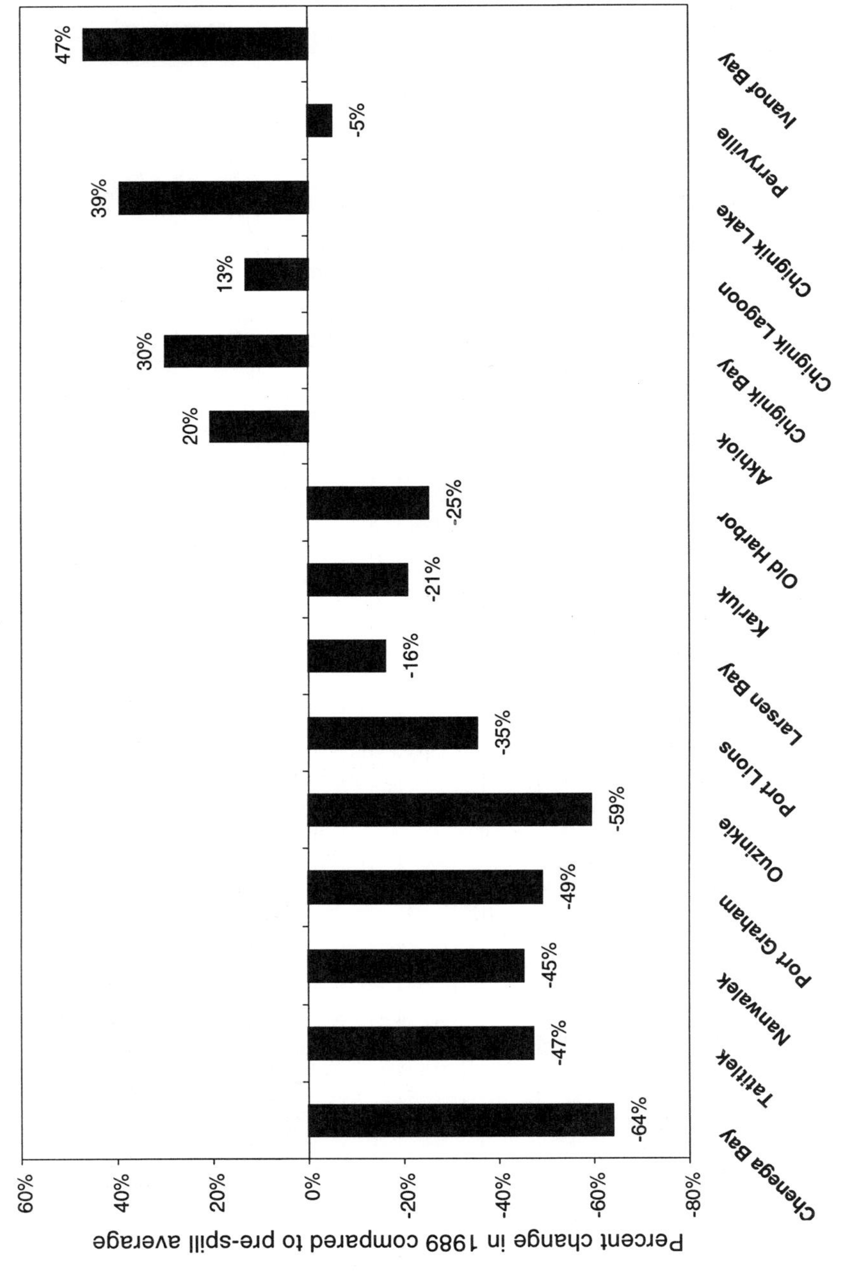

Figure 4-3 Changes in average number of resources attempted to harvest per household, post-spill year (1989) compared to pre-spill averages

Table 4-5 Average number of resources received per household in oil spill region study communities[1]

Community	Pre-spill average # of resources received per household			Post-spill: Average # of resources received per household				
	Year One[2]	Year Two[3]	Prespill value[4]	1989 (spill year)	1990	1991	1992	1993
Chenega Bay	10.4	9.2	9.8	3.5	5.4	8.0	13.0	10.3
Tatitlek	11.7	12.7	12.2	5.8	7.1	11.9	*12.0*	12.1
Prince William Sound	11.2	11.4	11.3	4.8	6.4	10.1	12.5	11.2
Nanwalek	15.1	*15.1*	15.1	6.9	13.1	12.8	14.1	13.5
Port Graham	10.6	*10.6*	10.6	6.4	9.3	13.4	14.0	13.0
Lower Cook Inlet	12.3	*12.3*	12.3	6.6	10.9	13.1	14.0	13.2
Akhiok	*1.7*	1.7	1.7	8.6	*8.3*	*8.0*	7.8	*7.8*
Karluk	*6.6*	6.6	6.6	5.4	8.4	8.7	*8.7*	*8.7*
Larsen Bay	*8.4*	8.4	8.4	6.6	10.5	8.8	7.0	8.9
Old Harbor	*7.3*	7.3	7.3	7.4	*9.1*	10.7	*10.7*	*10.7*
Ouzinkie	*7.9*	7.9	7.9	3.2	6.7	7.4	7.9	6.8
Port Lions	*5.6*	5.6	5.6	3.8	*4.2*	*4.5*	*4.8*	5.1
Kodiak Island Borough	*6.6*	6.6	6.6	5.5	*7.5*	*7.8*	*7.6*	*7.7*
Chignik Bay	7.1	*7.1*	7.1	6.8	*7.8*	8.7		
Chignik Lagoon	5.2	*5.2*	5.2	8.2	*8.2*	*8.2*		
Chignik Lake	10.1	*10.1*	10.1	10.6	*12.3*	14.1		
Ivanof Bay	9.0	*9.0*	9.0	16.0	*16.0*	*16.0*		
Perryville	13.4	*13.4*	13.4	12.1	*12.1*	*12.1*		
Alaska Peninsula	9.1	*9.1*	9.1	9.8	*10.5*	*11.2*		
All communities	*8.3*	*8.3*	*8.3*	6.5	*8.7*	*9.8*		
All communities excluding Alaska Peninsula[5]	*8.1*	*8.1*	*8.1*	5.6	*8.1*	*9.3*	*9.7*	*9.3*

[1]Because not all communities were surveyed in every study year, missing values were interpolated based upon the trend for known values and held constant for years subsequent to the final study year. Interpolated values are indicated by italics. [2]Equals 1984/85 for Chenega Bay, 1987/88 for Tatitlek, and 1984 for Alaska Peninsula. Data not collected for Kodiak Island Borough for Year One (1982/83). [3]Equals 1985/86 for Chenega Bay, 1988/89 for Tatitlek, and 1986 for Kodiak Island Borough. Otherwise, Year One values used to calculate regional average. [4]Equals average of previous estimates if two pre-spill study years available; otherwise, equals single pre-spill estimate. [5]Because post-spill changes were small in Alaska Peninsula villages and no surveys were done there after 1991, this row may best depict spill effects.

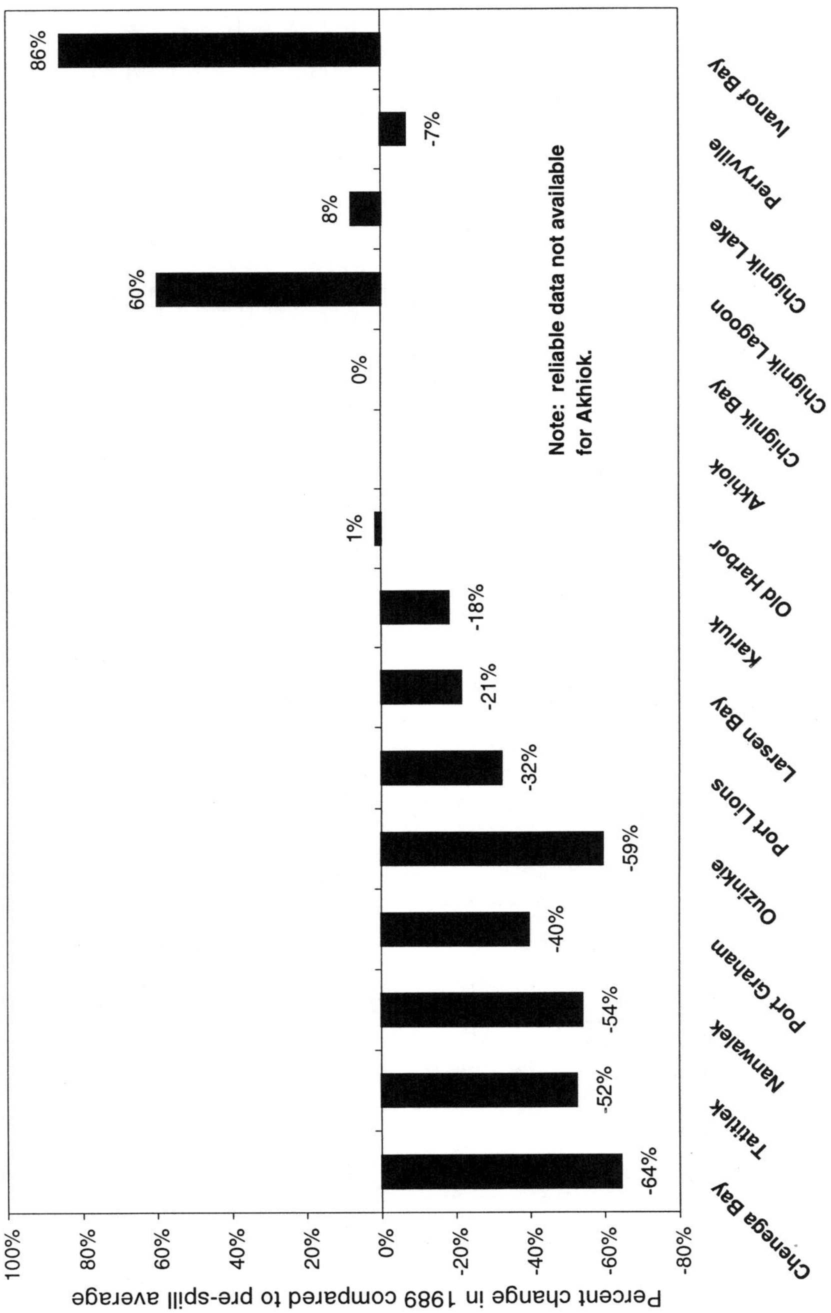

Figure 4-4 Changes in average number of resources received per household, post-spill year (1989) compared to pre-spill averages

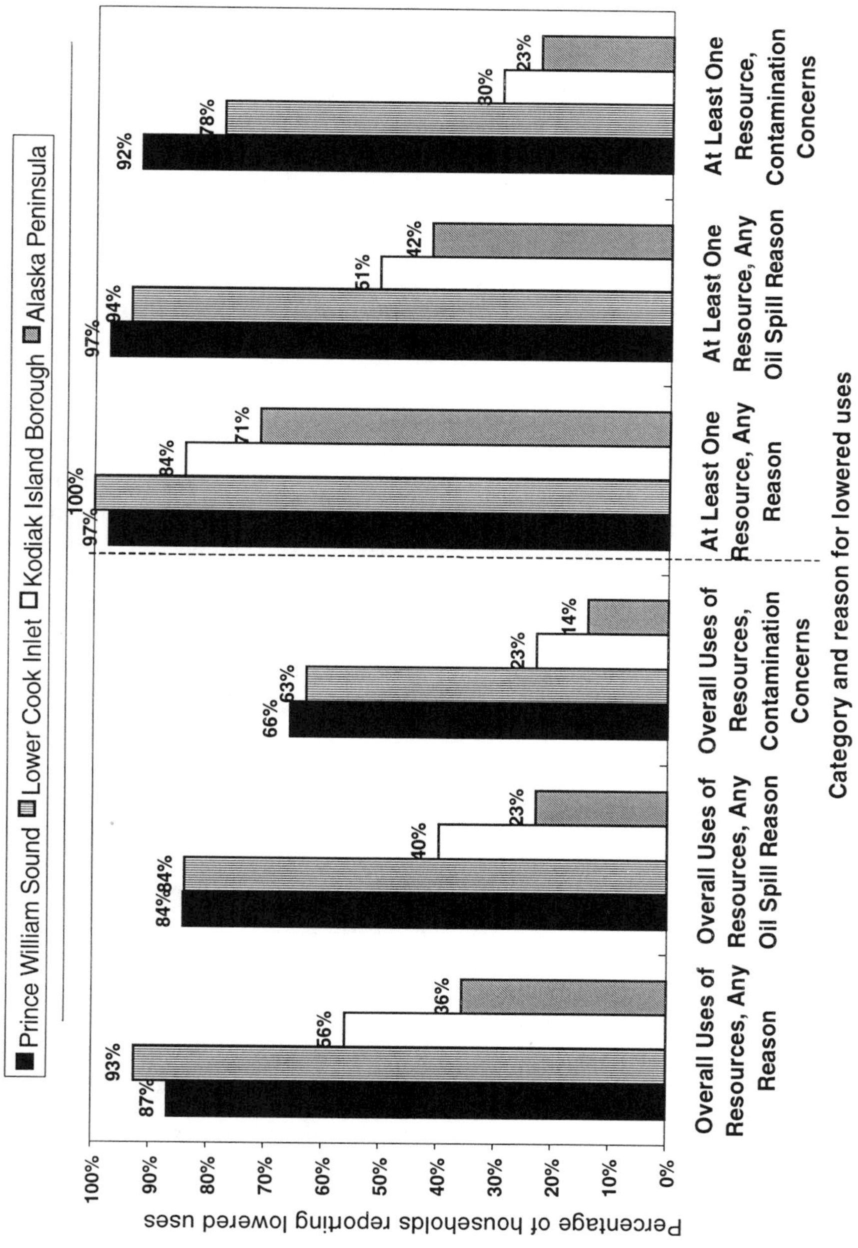

Figure 4-5 Household evaluations of subsistence uses in 1989

two-thirds of the households in these two subregions cited fear of oil-contaminated resources as the cause of this decline in overall subsistence use. This was by far the prevailing explanation throughout the entire spill region for the decline in subsistence uses. Other reasons included lower populations of species and oil spill cleanup work that reduced or eliminated the time available to engage in subsistence activities.

Percentages of households in the other two subregions reporting an overall decline in subsistence uses because of the spill and because of oil contamination were lower than those in Prince William Sound or Lower Cook Inlet, but were still notable: 40% of households in the Kodiak Borough communities and 23% of those in the five Alaska Peninsula communities experienced lowered overall subsistence uses because of the spill; 23% of the Kodiak Borough households and 14% on the Alaska Peninsula said their overall uses of subsistence foods dropped because of concerns about oil contamination (Figure 4-5). As with harvest quantities, diet breadth, harvest effort, and sharing, the geographic pattern of the assessment of lower subsistence uses generally correlates with the path of the spilled oil and reduced severity of oiling to the south and west of Prince William Sound.

As also shown in Figure 4-5, virtually every household in the two Prince William Sound communities (97%) and in the two Lower Cook Inlet communities (100%) said that their harvests of at least one type of subsistence resource had declined in 1989; almost all of these (97% and 94%, respectively) said this decline was caused by the oil spill. As with the overall decline in subsistence uses, most households in these two subregions cited concerns about oil contamination as the reason for these changes in particular resources (92% in Prince William Sound villages, 78% in Lower Cook Inlet villages). Oil contamination also was cited frequently in the other two regions as the reason that uses of particular resources declined after the spill (30% of households in the Kodiak Island Borough communities, and 23% of Alaska Peninsula households).

Comments from interviewed households demonstrate that concerns about oil contamination applied to most resource categories in the first post-spill year. For example, regarding fish, the following remarks were typical:

> This winter there was a lot of fish we caught that we were leery of, mainly because of oil contamination. The fish were looking different. Sometimes we threw them away or didn't eat them. Some red rockfish looked like they had oil on them. Some smelled like oil. Others looked odd inside. [Chenega Bay, April 1990]

> Normally at Ivanof Bay I would put up silvers for smoked fish and pinks for dried fish. [It was] a depressing year! People seemed scared of the ocean and people had a way below normal interest in seafood. My kids were deprived of their local seafood diet because [we had a] lack of trust in the ocean. [Ivanof Bay, February 1990]

Some village residents continued to use fish in 1989 because of cultural and traditional needs, despite their misgivings about the safety of these foods. For example, a Prince William Sound family reported that their salmon harvest levels had not gone down in 1989 even though they "were uncertain about using fish." They said that "even though we feared it being contaminated, we still used the fish." Another family in Tatitlek explained that

> We usually put up more fish than this year [but] we were afraid that if the fish hadn't been tested, we could be harmed by the fish. . . .We were totally against people eating stuff that hadn't been tested. We told people that it was ludicrous to eat food that hadn't been tested. Eventually the craving for those foods took over. And they ate them anyway. I never started getting over the oil spill until I first started smoking the fish in my smokehouse. It was total therapy to split and put them in my smokehouse. It was the only thing that helped me to recover from the bad feelings I had. [April 1990]

There were also concerns in Prince William Sound villages about oil contamination of deer, as the following comment from Tatitlek in April 1990 illustrates: "I didn't go to the same places [as usual] to hunt because of oil on the beach. I've seen deer eating kelp. I don't want to shoot [a] deer and find out it has been eating oil."

In communities throughout the entire oil spill region, concern was particularly high about oil contamination of shellfish resources. Following are some representative comments.

> I usually get butter clams but I stopped after the spill. They say shellfish are the most dangerous because of the spill. [Chenega Bay, April 1990]

> We won't touch clams after that oil was floating around. Not our family anyway. [Chignik Lake, January 1990]

> I can't go out and get what I want off my beach just to eat without worrying if it is contaminated or I'll get poisoned. . . .That's why I don't eat nothing off the beach. I don't eat clams no more. [Ouzinkie, February 1990]

The lost opportunities to use such traditional resources such as shellfish had cultural as well as nutritional and economic implications, as the following statements illustrate:

> We're hungry for Native food. I never thought I would be craving for octopus. But I got a liking for it and now when I want it there isn't any. [Chenega Bay, April 1990]

> If everything went dead as a result of this oil spill or others, it would greatly affect the way we live here since we primarily live off the land. The worst part about the spill is it makes me uncertain as to how it will affect the resources in the next few years, like whether the salmon that were fry [in 1989] will return as adults either diseased, in fewer numbers, or if they'll come back at all. [Ivanof Bay, February 1990]

Migratory waterfowl were another resource category about which subsistence users in the spill area expressed concerns about contamination.

> I didn't eat no ducks this year. I didn't want to take a chance on the oil, until they find if it is safe to eat. Then I'll go duck hunting. [Chenega Bay, April 1990]

There was also a great deal of concern about the effects of the oil on marine mammals. A hunter from Tatitlek said,

> It was bad. From my personal experience on the oil-spill cleanup, I saw so many marine mammals swimming in the oil, with their noses and eyes sticking out of the oil. Their eyes didn't look right. . . .I saw a sea lion trapped in oil. It made me so sad to see that. And out here, the sea lions crowded on the Bligh Reef buoy. I saw too much of oiled marine mammals to hunt them.

And a respondent from Chenega Bay said, "I was offered sea lion, but I didn't accept it because I was leery of the place it was taken from. I just didn't feel comfortable eating it because of the high impact of oil in the harvest area."

Other reasons given by surveyed households for lowered subsistence uses in 1989 included reduced resource populations resulting from oil-induced mortality and time harvesters had spent on the oil spill cleanup, which prevented them from engaging in subsistence harvests. For example, a resident of Chenega Bay offered this comment about waterfowl hunting in 1989:

> People thought there were fewer birds, so we shouldn't harvest to protect the population. We saw lots of birds wiped out by the spill. . . .There are areas around here like that. People know they are around, but not in great numbers, so they are left alone.

Another hunter from this village expressed a similar view about deer:

> I didn't hunt this year as much as last year. I was worried about contamination. Many deer died last summer. Deer not as plentiful as before. Fishermen saw deer swimming from island to island. My heart wasn't in hunting them. I didn't want to hunt them out.

Likewise, village residents began to wonder about the long-term implications of the spill on resource populations. As noted below, this became more of a concern in subsequent years. An elder in Perryville said in early 1990, "Baby salmon fry that will soon leave the rivers will be the ones most affected. The true test will be when they return to the rivers in a few years to spawn. I fear for the future of my people."

Nevertheless, fears of contamination of subsistence resources and the immediate and long-term human health implications were clearly the primary concern expressed by interviewed households for the first post-spill year. This concern transcended individual resources, or categories, to encompass the entire ecosystem. "It feels like the environment is unclean right now," a Chenega Bay resident said. In commenting on subsistence uses in 1989, a Nanwalek resident said in January 1990 that

> The other years at least we had no worries about contamination from oil spills and such. We were able to rely on our seafoods and other resources. How are our seafoods [now]? I've only heard rumors that they may be OK, and yet our monitors are still finding oil tarballs on our beaches.

Why was this concern about oil contamination of traditional foods so pervasive and widespread? As hunters and fishers, the residents of the oil spill area had lifetimes of experience in understanding and interpreting their environment. Although traditional knowledge taught them certain warning signs of danger, the oil spill had created conditions that were completely unfamiliar to them. Their skills in understanding their environment and making informed decisions had been undermined. They responded in a culturally appropriate way—with caution. Consequently, in many cases they discarded traditional foods or refrained from harvesting them entirely for fear that the resources had been poisoned.

The first specific information that addressed questions about possible oil contamination of subsistence foods in the spill area did not become available until August 1989. This was limited to findings from tests on 12 samples of fish and shellfish collected as part of a pilot study by ADF&G and the U.S. Food and Drug Administration (USFDA 1989). Although preliminary results from a more extensive study of fish and shellfish funded by Exxon were reported to villagers by representatives of the Oil Spill Health Task Force (OSHTF) in September and October 1989, the full results of that study were not made available until February 1990 (Varanasi et al. 1990). No data on marine mammals, birds, or deer were available until June 1990 or later (Walker and Field 1991).

Despite these initial efforts to inform subsistence users, many questions remained unanswered for the villages into the second post-spill year. At village meetings conducted by the OSHTF in the fall of 1989, community residents asked why more samples from more areas had not been tested. How could they be sure that resources were safe to eat based on the limited number of samples tested up to that time? They also pointed out that health bulletins and news releases often did not reach most of the families in their communities, leaving people uninformed and sometimes afraid. Also, some community representatives wondered why a subsistence foods testing project was being funded by Exxon rather than by the state, raising the question of whether there was a conflict of interest (Fall 1991:17–18). Subsequent foods testing programs were designed to address these issues.

Compounding the uncertainty about the spill's effects on subsistence resources was an embargo on the release of any findings from damage assessment studies because of ongoing litigation. Preliminary results of studies conducted by government scientists were not made available to the public until 1991 (USFWS 1991), more than two years after the spill. Full results of government and private studies (including those funded by Exxon) were not presented to the public until 1993 (Wells et al. 1995; Rice et al. 1996). Consequently, some subsistence users and community representatives wondered if they were being fully informed about potential human health risks.

Thus, the first year after the *Exxon Valdez* hit Bligh Reef ended with frustration, uncertainty, and a feeling of loss for the people whose traditional use areas had been oiled. Because of the lost subsistence opportunities, it was, as a person from Nanwalek said, "like a year of memories being erased."

Subsistence Uses after the First Post-Spill Year

"In 1989, we had nothing. In 1990, we were scared and confused. We didn't know if we should eat [subsistence foods] or not. This year, we're going to go for it. We don't care if we die or not. We live mainly on subsistence anyway."

— Nanwalek, April 1991

After the first post-spill year and through the fifth year, subsistence harvest levels gradually increased, as did the variety of resources used, harvest effort, and resource sharing, in all the communities. However, the extent of this rebound varied among communities and households. Also, distrust of resources remained, suggesting that some households resumed subsistence harvesting under a cloud of lingering uncertainty about the safety of the resources. Others observed abnormalities in the appearance or behavior of animals, reinforcing suspicions that the environment itself remained injured. Additionally, there were increasing reports that households in the Prince William Sound and Lower Cook Inlet subregions were using less subsistence foods than before the spill because key resource populations had declined and, despite their intensified efforts, they were unable to harvest these species at customary levels. Subsistence users interpreted depressed resource populations as a sign of an unhealthy natural environment, which contributed to their persistent concern about the subsistence food safety issue.

The summaries of subsistence harvests and uses of wild resources in the oil spill region should also be understood within the context of continuing efforts to inform village residents about the risks associated with using subsistence foods. The

OSHTF coordinated the collection and testing of samples of subsistence resources in 1990 and 1991; these efforts were funded by Exxon and the state. The results were communicated through a series of newsletters, a video, and in meetings held in Port Graham, Nanwalek, Chenega Bay, and Tatitlek in 1992 (see Chapter 3). The OSHTF last met in August 1993. The *Exxon Valdez* Oil Spill Trustee Council funded additional collection and testing in 1992 and 1993 and supported several newsletters and community meetings as well (Miraglia and Chartrand 1997).

The second post-spill year (April 1990 through March 1991)

Figure 4-6 illustrates estimated harvest levels for all post-spill years in all four subregions, along with pre-spill averages (see also Table 4-2). Figure 4-7 shows estimates of combined subsistence harvests for all post-spill years in three of the four subregions (excluding the Alaska Peninsula, which was not included in the research in 1990, 1992, or 1993). These study findings illustrate the temporal and geographic patterns in spill effects and recovery throughout the spill area and likely also reflect the increasing availability of food-safety information and the decreasing mistrust of villagers based on this information and their own observations.

Subsistence harvests increased over 1989 to 1990 levels in the five communities of Lower Cook Inlet and Kodiak Island that were restudied for 1990 to 1991 (Table 4-2). At the subregion level, estimated harvests increased between 1989 and 1990 to 1991 in the Lower Cook Inlet by 50% and in the Kodiak Island Borough by 43%. For the spill region communities overall (excluding those of the Alaska Peninsula), estimated subsistence harvests in the second post-spill year increased about 35% over the previous year, but they remained well below pre-spill levels (Figure 4-7).

The variety of subsistence resources used per household also increased notably in 1990 to 1991 over 1989 for the five study communities of Lower Cook Inlet and Kodiak Island. In the Lower Cook Inlet subregion, diet breadth rose 60% but was still below the 1987 pre-spill estimate; the Kodiak Island Borough subregion rose 26%, still slightly below the pre-spill average (Table 4-3, Figure 4-8).

Similar increases in the average number of kinds of resources that households attempted to harvest in these five communities suggest that in 1990 households were devoting more time and effort to subsistence activities than they did in the first post-spill year (Table 4-4, Figure 4-9). Overall, however, these averages were still below pre-spill estimates, suggesting that households had yet to return to pre-spill levels of involvement in subsistence activities.

Also, increases in the average number of kinds of resources received per household suggest that the level and frequency of sharing were up in 1990 to 1991 compared with the previous year (Table 4-5, Figure 4-10). The 1990 to 1991 average for the Lower Cook Inlet subregion was below the 1987 pre-spill estimate, while the average for the Kodiak subregion exceeded the pre-spill estimate.

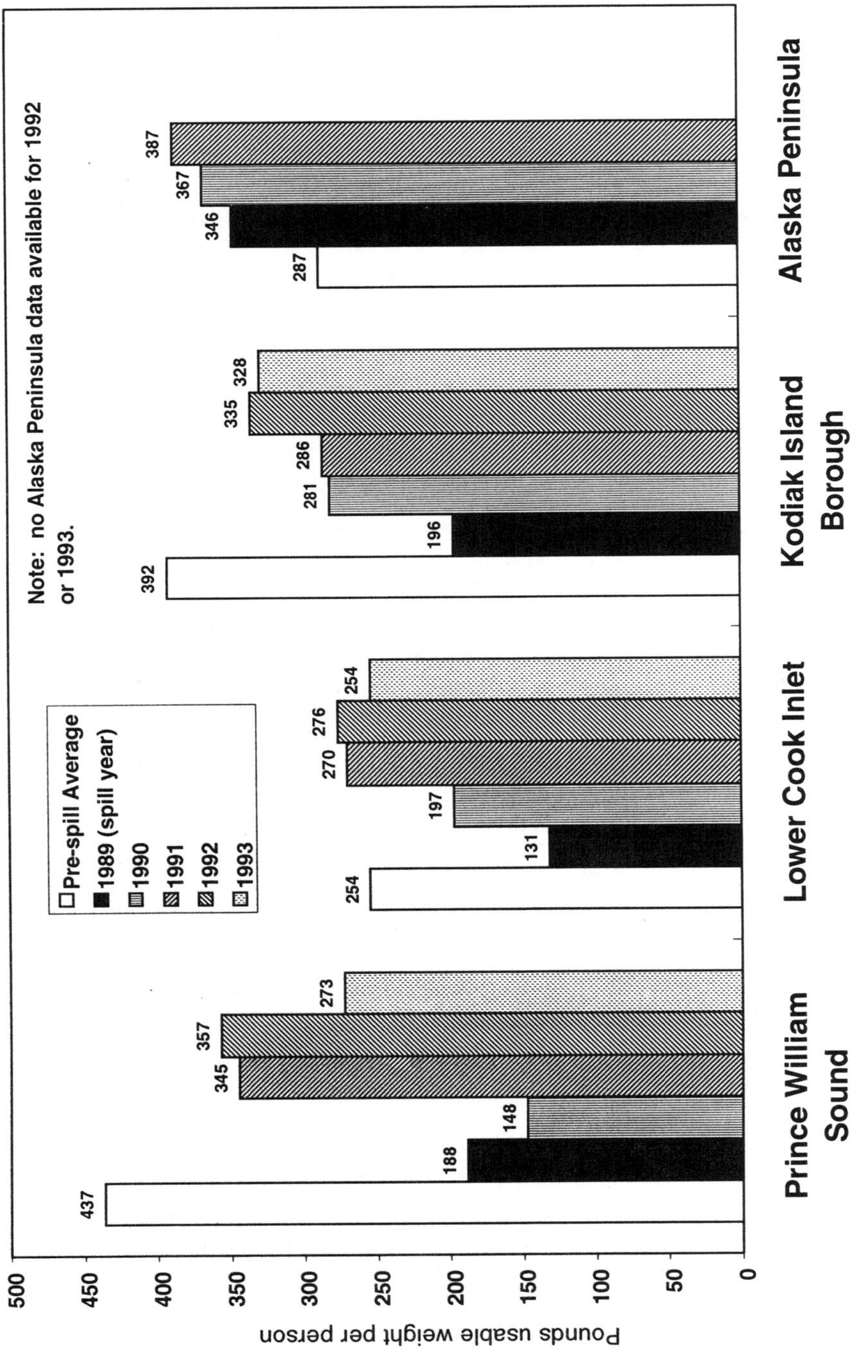

Figure 4-6 Subsistence harvests in four oil-spill subregions, pre-spill average and five post-spill years

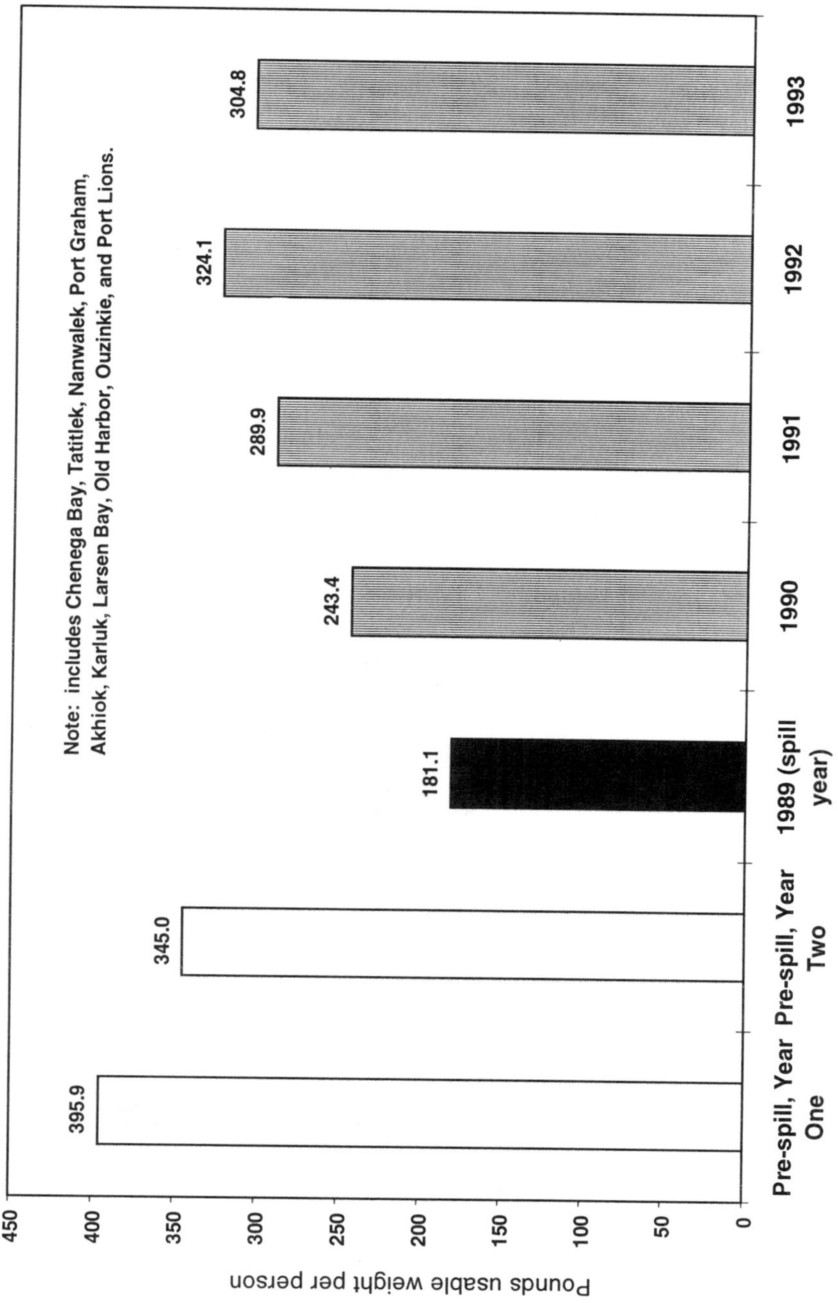

Figure 4-7 Estimated subsistence harvests in 10 oil-spill area communities, pounds per person, pre-spill study years and 1989 through 1993

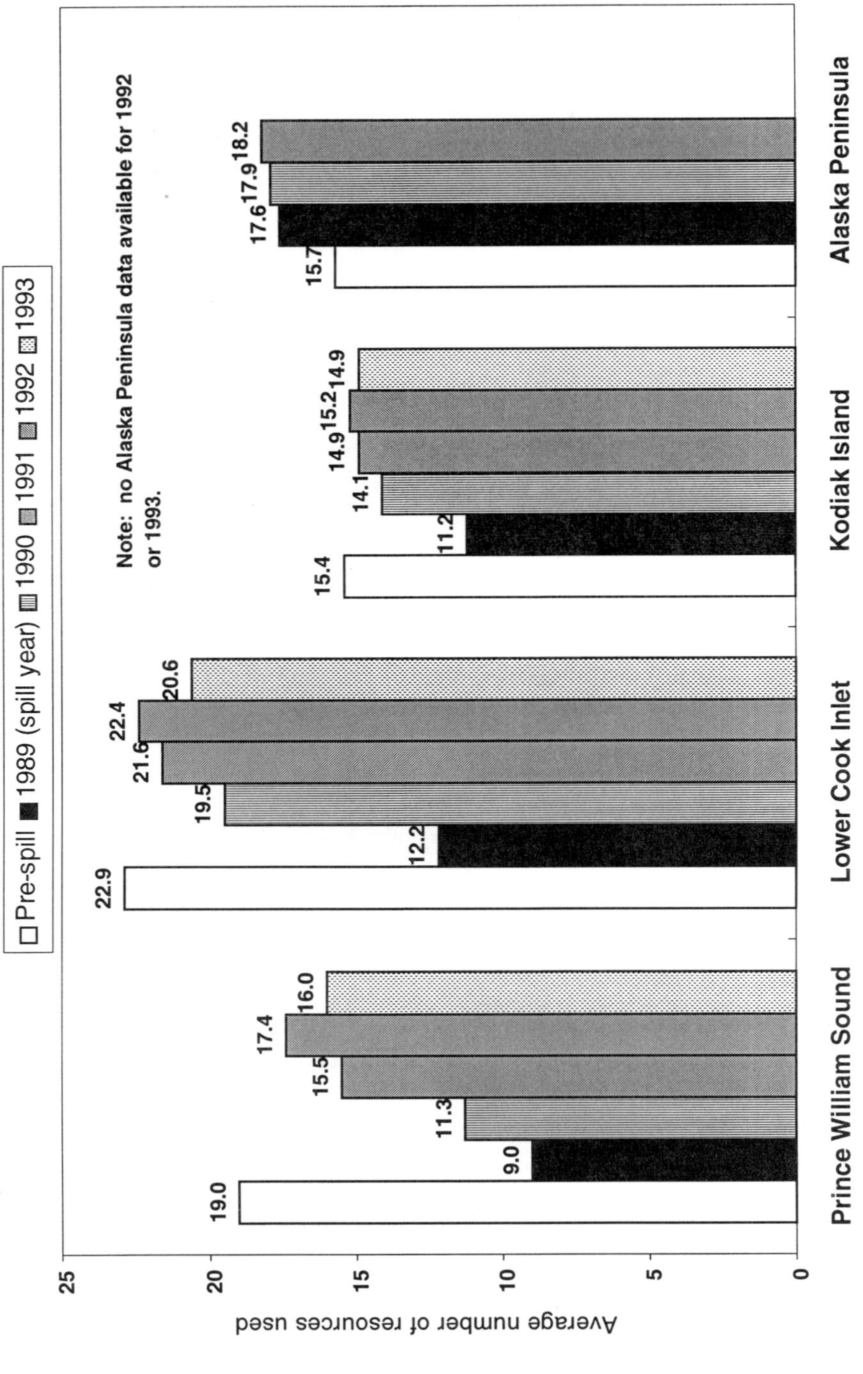

Figure 4-8 Average number of resources used per household, four oil-spill subregions, pre-spill average and five post-spill years

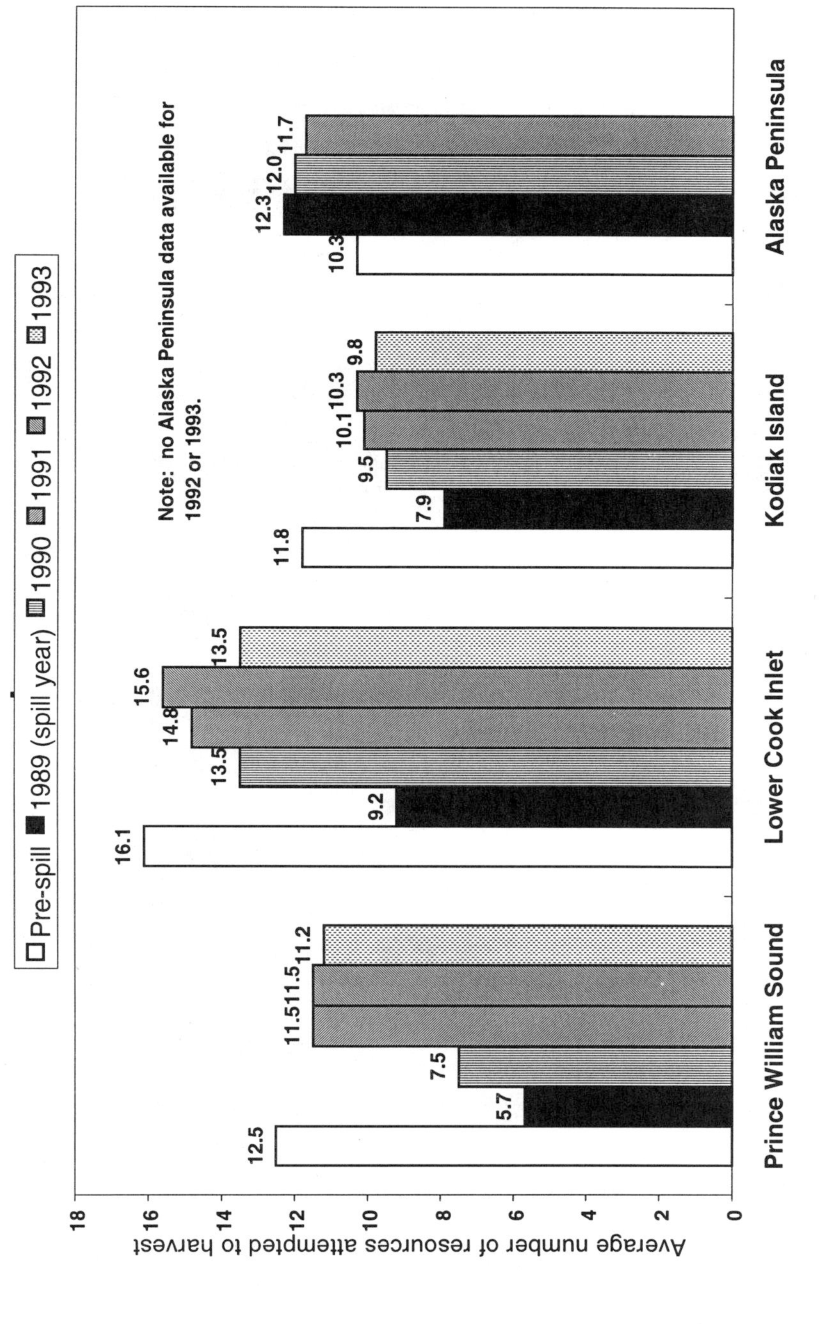

Figure 4-9 Average number of resources attempted to harvest per household, four oil-spill subregions, pre-spill average and five post-spill years

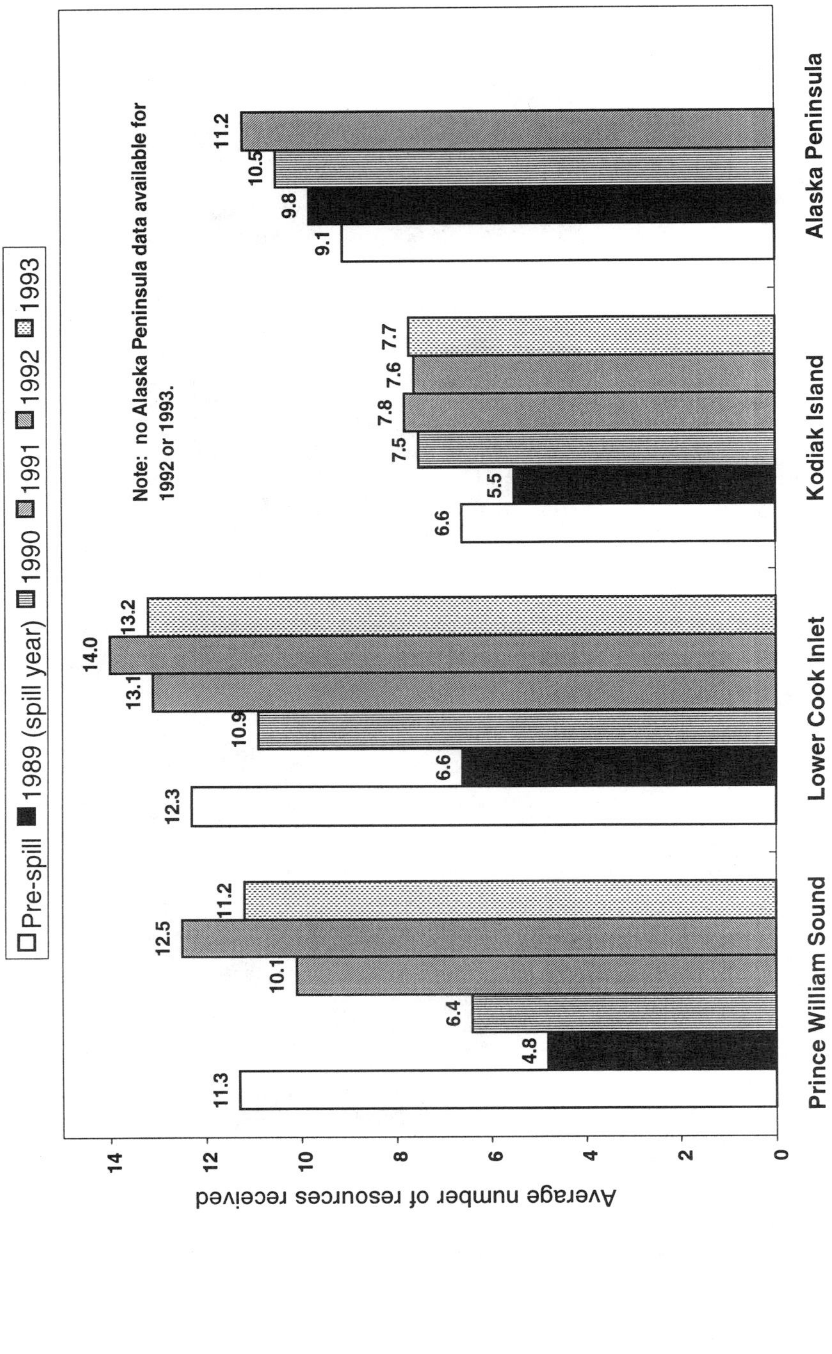

Figure 4-10 Average number of resources received per household, four oil-spill subregions, pre-spill average and five post-spill years

In sharp contrast to the findings for the Lower Cook Inlet and Kodiak Island Borough subregions, the interviews in the Prince William Sound villages of Chenega Bay and Tatitlek found no evidence of recovery in subsistence harvest levels in the second post-spill year (Table 4-2, Figure 4-6). The estimated subregional per-capita harvest remained far below pre-spill estimates (Figure 4-7).

Although the mean number of resources that households used, attempted to harvest, and received rose slightly in both Prince William Sound communities (Tables 4-3 through 4-5, Figures 4-8 through 4-10), consistent with the other subregions, the Prince William Sound means remained well below pre-spill levels and were notably lower than those of the other subregions. This demonstrates the slower recovery of subsistence activities in Prince William Sound than in the other two subregions, reflecting the greater degree oiling and the more intensive cleanup efforts in the subregion nearest the source of the spill.

These survey findings correspond well with comments from respondents and from reports from the communities themselves. A small majority of households in the Lower Cook Inlet and Kodiak Borough subregions said that their subsistence uses had increased in 1990 to 1991 compared with the first post-spill year (Figure 4-11). On the other hand, a large majority of Lower Cook Inlet households (85%) and half the Kodiak Borough households said their subsistence uses in 1990 to 1991 did not yet equal pre-spill levels (Figure 4-12). Further, virtually every household in the Prince William Sound villages said that subsistence uses were lower in 1990 and 1991 than they were before the spill and lower than in the first post-spill year (Figures 4-11 and 4-12).

Correspondingly, the following report appeared from Chenega Bay in October 1990, more than 18 months after the spill (Evanoff 1990). This comment pertains to part of the harvest period covered by the second post-spill round of surveys and comes after the second post-spill spring, summer, and fall when most of the second-year harvest should have occurred. The Chenega Bay report indicated that the people of the village

> have eaten only a small fraction of the foods they ordinarily live on daily. They reported that indications from wildlife around them make the people very uncomfortable, and they are afraid to harvest subsistence food. An abnormal seal liver, ordinarily firm, was soft and runny. The arm of a starfish fell apart when pulled from the rocks. They have reported several dead eagles and sea gulls, a dead bear and a blind sea lion found during the past month, highly unusual occurrences prior to the spill.

It was also clear from household interviews that the issue of oil contamination of subsistence foods remained a major concern during the second post-spill year, especially in Prince William Sound. As shown in Figure 4-13, 69% of Prince William Sound households, 32% of Lower Cook Inlet households, and 22% of Kodiak Island

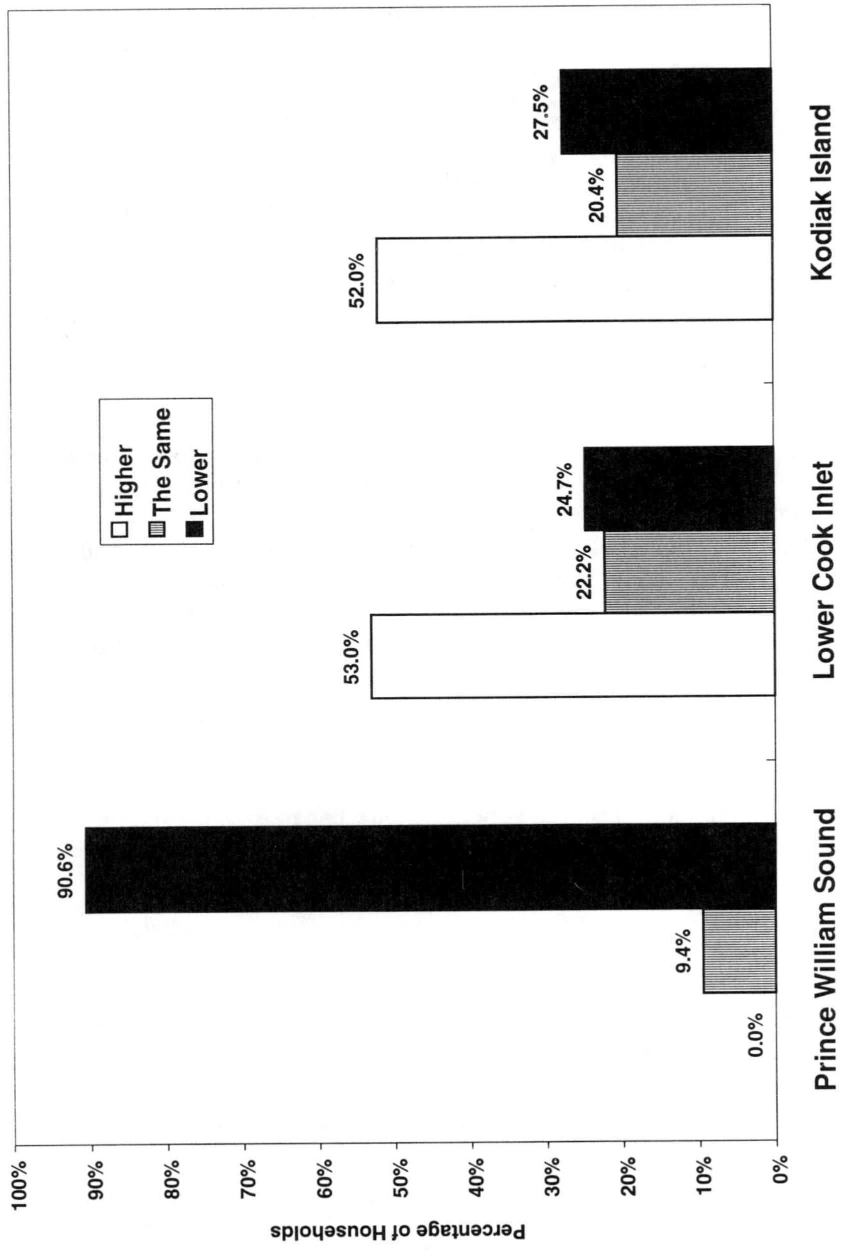

Figure 4-11 Households' assessments of overall levels of subsistence uses in 1990/1991 compared to the previous year, 1989, by subregion

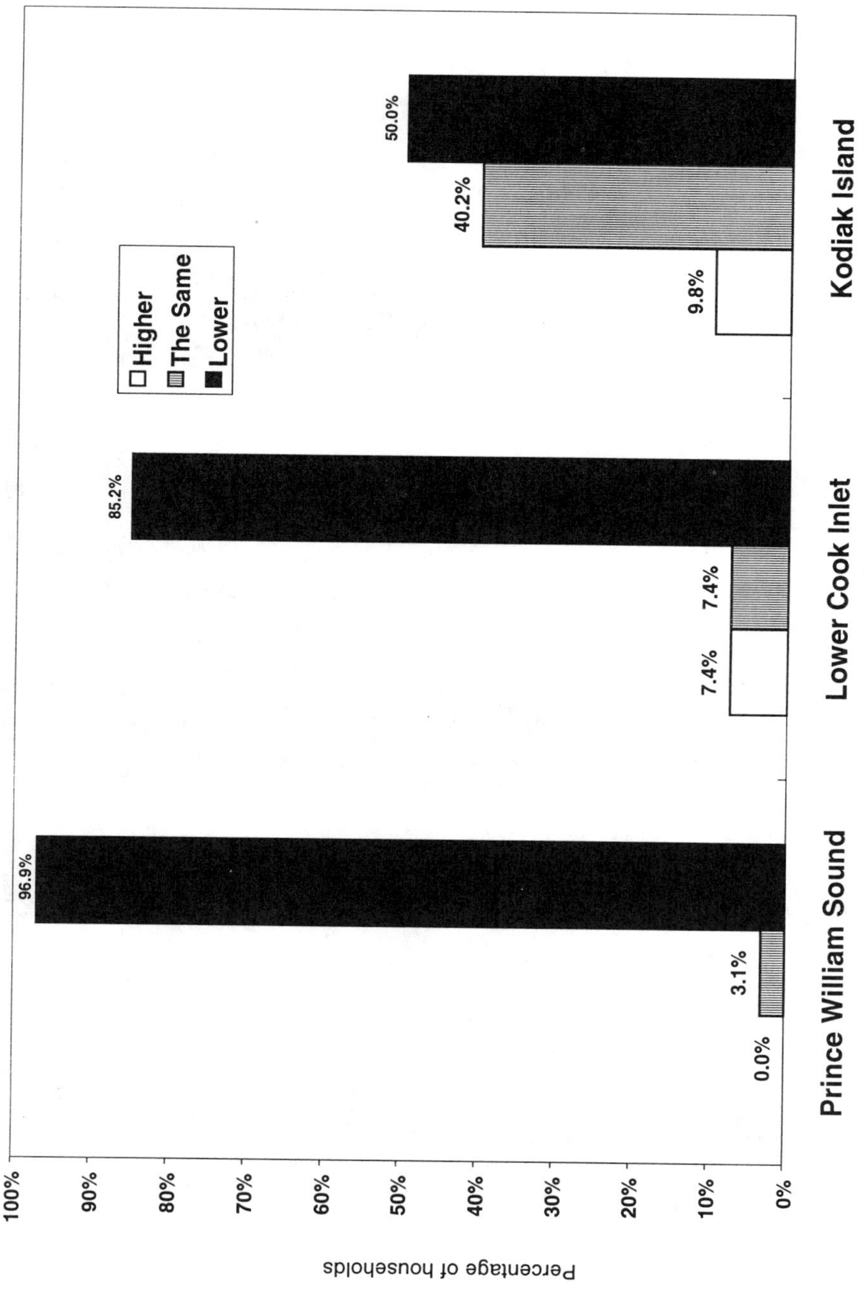

Figure 4-12 Households' assessments of overall levels of subsistence uses in 1990/1991 compared to before the *Exxon Valdez* oil spill, by subregion

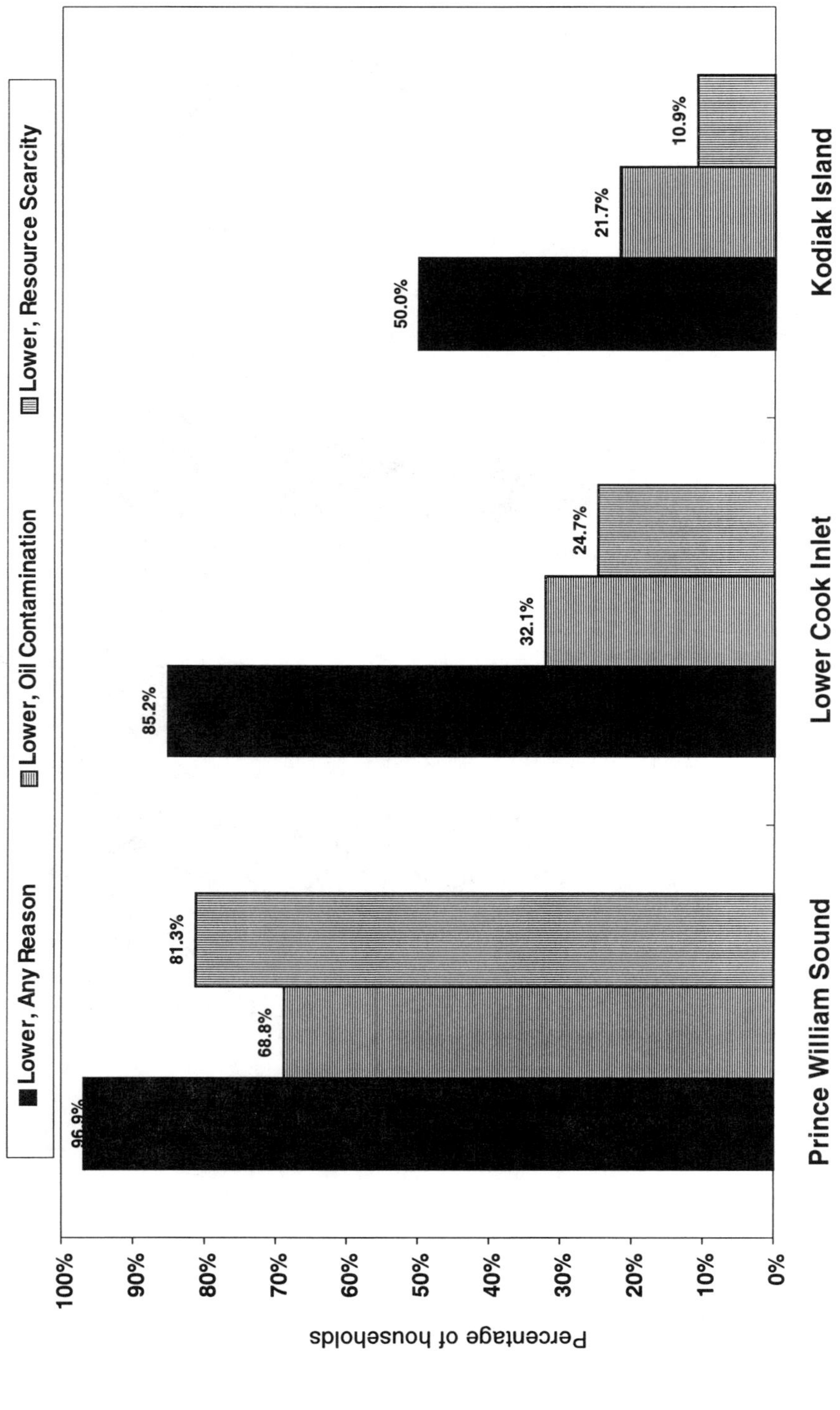

Figure 4-13 Reasons for lower overall subsistence uses in 1990/1991 compared to before the *Exxon Valdez* oil spill

Borough households stated that their overall levels of subsistence uses were lower in 1990 than they were before the spill because of oil contamination concerns. The following examples of comments are typical:

> I usually fish a lot, but I don't want to eat the fish from around here and then find out later that there was something wrong with them and I shouldn't have. [Chenega Bay, April 1991]

> I think it was worse in 1989, but last summer [1990], I was still scared to eat [salmon]. You wonder if you could get poisoned or sick. [Port Graham, April 1991]

> I'm still not sure about them [shellfish]. I used to eat a lot more. That was my upbringing. [Ouzinkie, April 1991]

On the other hand, other households reported a renewed confidence in the safety of subsistence foods and a consequent increase in their uses. This was especially the case in the Lower Cook Inlet villages, where the percentage of households with lower overall subsistence uses due to contamination concerns dropped by 50% in the second post-spill year, from 63% to 32% (Figures 4-5 and 4-13). For example, a Port Graham respondent said in April 1991 that

> We caught a lot more salmon this last year [than 1989]. We got away from the fear of oil. We were getting some information about contamination of fish, that they were not really affected, and we had a little more time for [fishing].

The following comment was offered by a Nanwalek respondent in April 1991:

> We just started going out [for shellfish] during the past few months. We did not harvest any during 1989. We are starting to trust the shellfish again. We changed our minds because there were samples tested and the results came back good, saying things were OK.

Similarly, an Ouzinkie resident in the Kodiak Island subregion reported in April 1991 that he had harvested no birds at all in the year after the spill, but that his harvests were "back to normal now because I can see what's going on with them and I got hungry for them." At Karluk, a household reported higher salmon harvests in 1990 to 1991 than in 1989 because, they said, they believed that "fish are safe to eat again." This family also said they had "more confidence [in the safety of shellfish] since the spill is over."

In interviews conducted in 1991 pertaining to the second post-spill year, many households cited perceived declines in resource populations as a cause of low subsistence harvest levels. Indeed, in the Prince William Sound villages, resource scarcity topped concern about oil contamination as a reason cited for lower overall subsistence uses in 1990 and 1991 (Figure 4-13). For example, a Tatitlek respondent said of the second year after the spill that, "It was even worse than last year. We are leery of collecting [gull] eggs. There are fewer eggs, and fewer ducks than before the oil spill. The sky is usually black with ducks during herring season, but not this year."

The following are additional examples of resource shortage concerns.

> [Harvests of shellfish] were even worse than the year before. It was very poor compared to normal. I tried to get octopus but couldn't find any. I could get three a night before the spill. I had to walk ten miles and still didn't find any. I'd still find a few last year, but this year absolutely nothing. I know it is because of the oil spill. They either died or the smell of the oil ruined their homes. That's one of our best foods in the winter. [Tatitlek, April 1991]

> There aren't as many [birds] since the oil spill. It seemed like it took months before we even seen any around. [Ouzinkie, April 1991]

> I think they [shellfish] are very scarce. You really have to look to get any shellfish or bidarkies. You can't go down the beach like we used to. [Port Graham, April 1991]

> The seals are quite a ways down [in population]. There's hardly any seal you find around here after the oil spill. We used to get them in Dogfish Bay. Now there's nothing. There's only a few sea otters. Sea lions are disappearing too. [Nanwalek, April 1991]

Also, comments in each community showed that in 1990 to 1991 some households, for economic and cultural reasons, had returned to using subsistence resources despite lingering concerns about oil contamination and long-term health risks. One probable reason is that emergency food relief programs in 1989 had supplied a variety of subsistence resources and other foods in the spill villages of Prince William Sound, Lower Cook Inlet, and the Kodiak Island Borough. However, these relief programs did not operate in 1990. Further, in 1989 many village residents obtained seasonal employment during the cleanup efforts, providing cash income to purchase food. Because fewer cleanup jobs were available in 1990 to 1991 (Piper 1993; Fall 1997), cash incomes for many families dropped and economic alternatives to subsistence harvests vanished. The following comments illustrate this point.

> Our [deer harvest] was less than usual, even less than 1989. There were less deer to hunt. We were afraid to eat them, worried about oil. We ate them anyway, because otherwise we wouldn't have anything to eat. We say, "At least if we die from it, we all die together." [Tatitlek, April 1991]

> We started craving for [seal meat]. We could only go so long without it. We get tired of eating beef and chicken. We wouldn't

> touch [seal] that first year after the spill. [Now] subsistence food is on our table at least twice a week. [Tatitlek, April 1991]
>
> There was a big increase [in harvests] in 1990 over 1989. We had a great need and were willing to take the risk of contamination because we needed the food and nutrition. [Port Graham, April 1991]

The third post-spill year (April 1991 through March 1992)

Household harvest surveys for the third post-spill year were conducted in 10 villages in all four subregions of the oil spill area (Table 4-1). The upward trend in harvest levels continued in the combined Prince William Sound, Lower Cook Inlet, and Kodiak Island Borough subregions in 1991 to 1992, with the average per capita harvest of subsistence resources at 289.7 lbs usable weight/person, 19% over the 2nd post-spill year and 60% over the first post-spill year (Figure 4-7). However, this regional average was still below pre-spill levels.

The Alaska Peninsula communities of Chignik Bay and Chignik Lake were resurveyed for the third post-spill year after a one-year hiatus (Table 4-2, Figure 4-6). Harvest levels (lbs/person) in 1991 to 1992 at Chignik Lake were very similar to 1989 levels, although there was a relative decline in caribou harvests caused by shifts in the herd's migratory pattern and a corresponding increase in harvests of salmon. Chignik Bay's subsistence harvest in 1991 to 1992 increased over that of 1989, possibly because of reduced commercial fishing incomes and increasing costs of living in the community. In 1991 to 1992, there were virtually no oil spill concerns voiced by respondents in either Chignik Bay or Chignik Lake (Hutchinson-Scarbrough 1995a, 1995b).

The most notable study finding for the third post-spill year was the large increase in subsistence harvest levels at Chenega Bay and Tatitlek (Table 4-2, Figure 4-6). Also, as in 1990 to 1991, the variety of resources that households used, that households attempted to harvest, and that households received increased in both Tatitlek and Chenega Bay, although these levels still were below pre-spill averages and were lower than those for the Lower Cook Inlet communities of Port Graham and Nanwalek (Tables 4-3 through 4-5, Figures 4-8 through 4-10).

Despite rebounding levels of harvest, use, and sharing of subsistence foods in Chenega Bay and Tatitlek in 1991 to 1992, important differences between subsistence uses before and after the spill were still evident. First, harvest levels and diversity remained depressed. The large majority of Prince William Sound households (93%) continued to report that their subsistence uses were lower than before the spill; in contrast, the percentage of households in the other subregions that reported lowered harvests declined from the two previous years (Figure 4-14). Unlike past years, few households in any subregion cited oil contamination as a cause of reduced subsistence harvests; in all subregions, reduced resource populations was

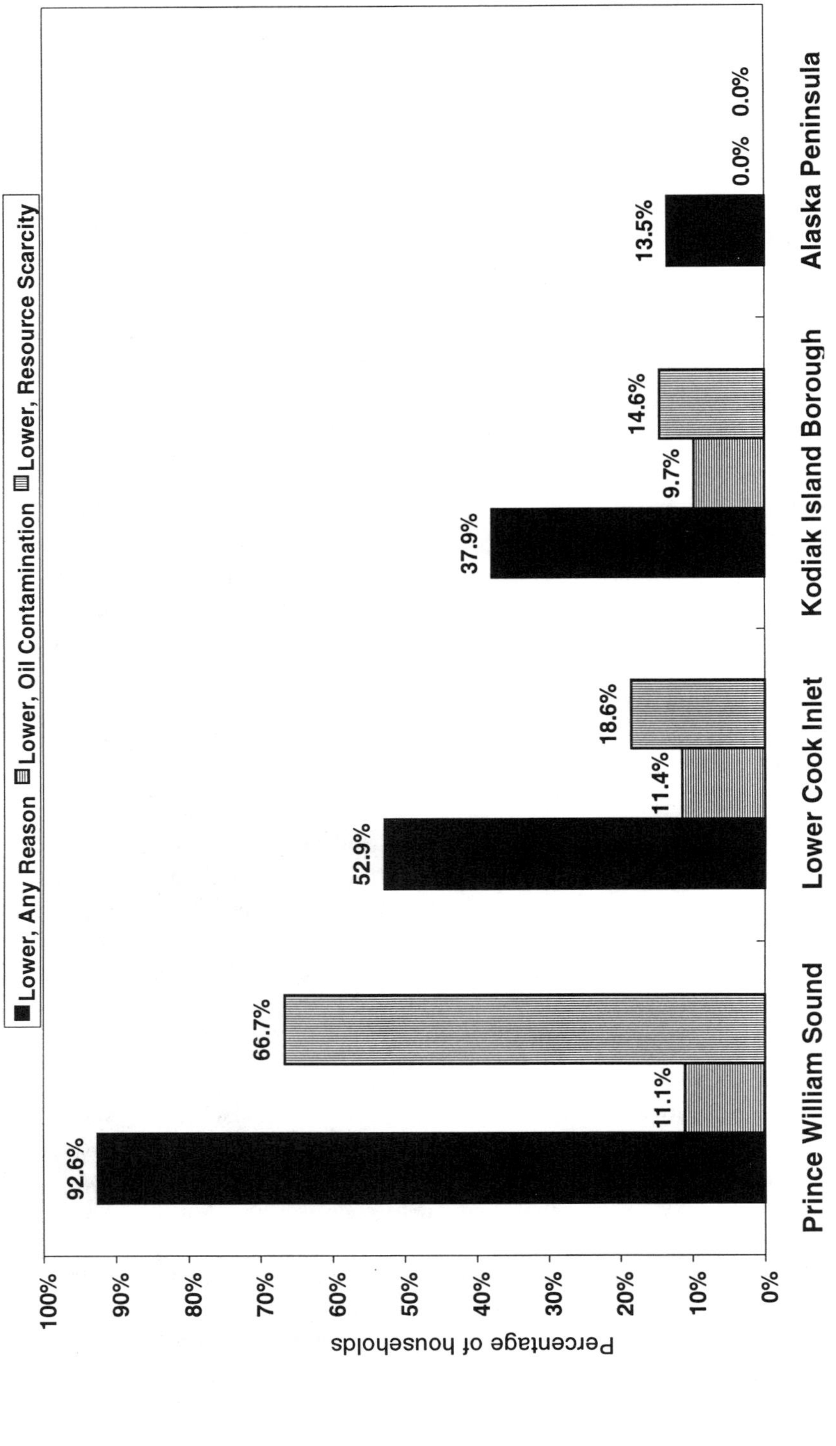

Figure 4-14 Reasons for lower overall subsistence uses in 1991/1992 compared to before the *Exxon Valdez* oil spill

the primary explanation that respondents offered for why their subsistence uses were lower than before the spill. It should be noted that this does not necessarily mean that oil contamination of subsistence resources and associated human health risks were no longer an issue. Rather, these findings suggest that such concerns were no longer preventing households from using subsistence foods, in part because some households felt they needed to use subsistence resources for economic and cultural reasons or because they had traveled to unoiled areas to harvest subsistence foods.

Another difference between pre-spill and 1991 to 1992 subsistence harvests in the Prince William Sound villages is evident in harvest composition. In 1991 to 1992, marine mammal (harbor seal and sea lion) harvests were substantially lower than before the spill, while, conversely, the relative harvest of salmon and other fish had increased (Figure 4-15). This change is related to the relative abundance of fish and the continued scarcity of marine mammals, as well more confidence in the safety of eating fish as opposed to seals and sea lions.

Residents of both villages attributed reduced availability of seals and sea lions as the major cause of this decline in subsistence harvests of marine mammals.

> Seals are very scarce. When you go out on a boat, you seldom see seals or sea lions like before. Man, the water is just dead. . . .Now we have to go thirty miles by boat to find seals. We used to get them less than two miles away from the village. [Chenega Bay, April 1992]

Marine mammal hunters blamed the oil spill for this decline, a view that is partially supported by post-spill damage assessment studies. A study of harbor seal populations in Prince William Sound found that the spill had accelerated the drop in an already declining population. Further, in 1992, molting counts found that the continuing population decline was much more rapid in oiled areas than in unoiled sites (Frost and Lowry 1993:302). In Tatitlek in 1992, two seal hunters reported that

> [Seal harvests] are a lot less because they are more scarce. There are not as many around and they're dropping yearly. We think the *Exxon Valdez* oil spill had a lot more to do with it than people believe. The pups sank. We saw it. How can a mother seal identify its pup if it's covered with crude?

> [Seals] have gotten harder to find. We think the pups died during the oil spill. The rookeries got hit hard. Seals recognize their babies by their smell. They can't smell them with oil.

In some Prince William Sound households, even if seals were harvested or received, contamination concerns lingered into the third post-spill year. "I'm real leery of eating seals. I like the liver, kidney, and intestines. That's where the toxins are." [Chenega Bay, April 1992]

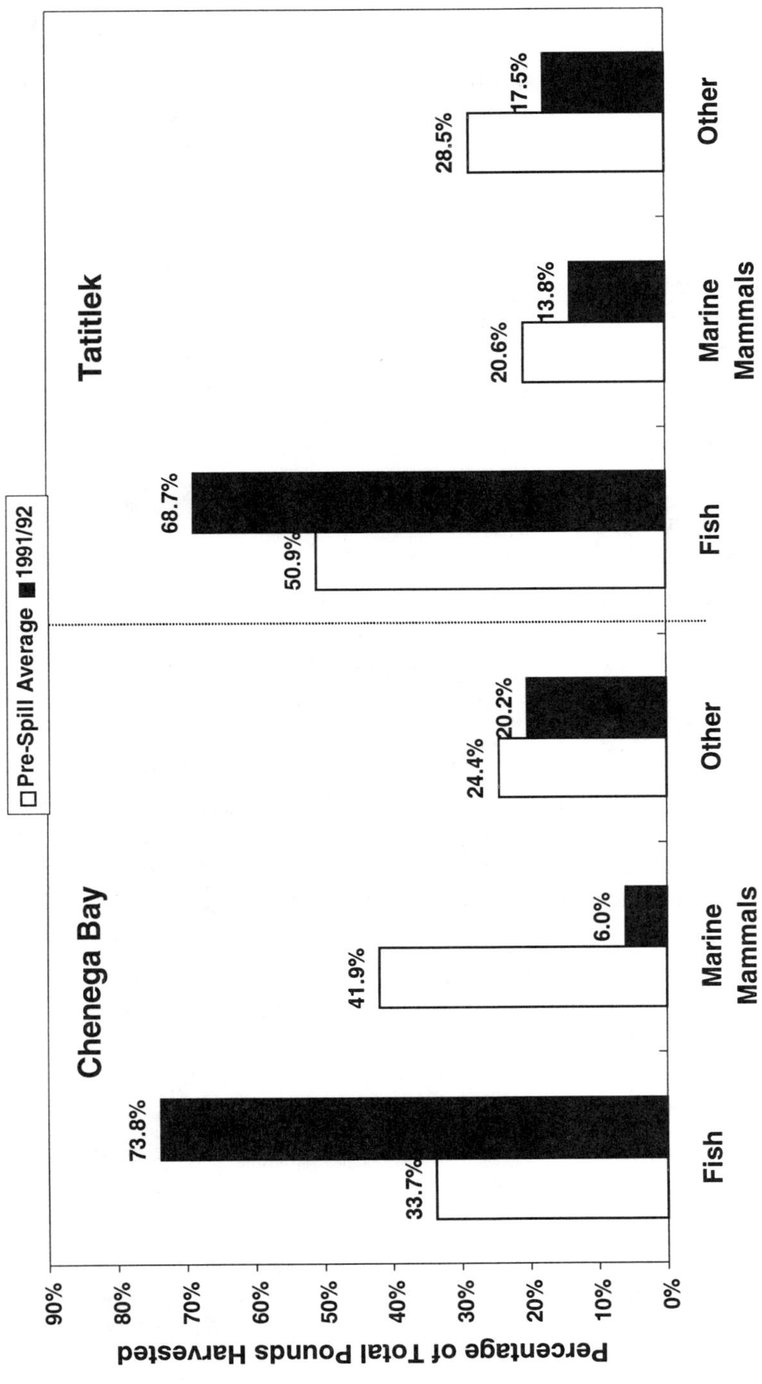

Figure 4-15 Composition of subsistence harvests in Chenega Bay and Tatitlek, pre-spill average and 1991/1992

Likewise, concerns about oil contamination of shellfish persisted in the Prince William Sound villages, as these statements from Chenega Bay in April 1992 illustrate.

> I used to go out to get shellfish all the time. There's less there now, and I'm worried about contamination.
>
> I wouldn't even dare try [to harvest shellfish]. I miss that real hard, but I'm worried about the oil.

In the 1991 to 1992 study year, some households in Chenega Bay obtained subsistence resources by traveling outside the community's traditional harvest area. One household, which was responsible for about 21% of the community's entire marine invertebrate take, harvested all its shellfish along the shores of Cook Inlet on the Kenai Peninsula to avoid areas oiled by the *Exxon Valdez* spill. The normally reliable dens along the shores near Chenega Bay were devoid of octopus. While harvests increased, this decrease in octopus was the result of octopus being taken further offshore; these are larger than those normally hunted, and are less prized for subsistence use (Seitz and Miraglia 1995:9).

The fourth post-spill year (April 1992 through March 1993)

In 1992 to 1993, the fourth post-spill year, the Subsistence Division conducted systematic household harvest surveys in six of the 15 oil spill area villages (Table 4-1). The estimated harvest for the combined subregions increased again, to 324 lbs/person (Figure 4-7).

At Chenega Bay in Prince William Sound, subsistence harvests in the fourth post-spill year increased to 412.5 lbs/person, the highest estimate for that community since its founding in 1984 (Table 4-2). Increases in salmon harvests accounted for most of this growth, while harvests of marine mammals and birds remained well below pre-spill levels. The pattern of subsistence harvesting outside the local area continued, with one hunting party traveling, at great expense, to the Copper River basin to harvest caribou. The variety of resources used per household at Chenega Bay in 1992 to 1993 approached, but not quite equaled, the diet breadth at Chenega Bay and Tatitlek before the spill (Table 4-3). Correspondingly, the variety of resources that households attempted to harvest increased but was still below the pre-spill average (Table 4-4). This fact shows that while harvest levels had increased by 1992 to 1993, a relatively small number of households in Chenega Bay accounted for most of this growth. These active households shared their takes widely in the village, illustrated further by the increase in the variety of resources received per household at Chenega Bay compared to other post-spill years (Table 4-5).

Oil-contamination concerns persisted in Chenega Bay into 1993. These concerns focused primarily on marine invertebrates, reflecting OSHTF advice that these resources should not be used from beaches with oil on the surface or subsurface (e.g., ADF&G 1995). Mixed with this contamination issue was the continuing perception of the reduced populations of these resources since the spill. A Chenega Bay respondent in April 1993 said,

> You don't just pick clams anyplace anymore. The clams in the area, I'm afraid to use. We went to Port Ashton, to get as far away from oil as possible, and not go too far away. We're not gonna eat clams from the oiled areas. They have the highest level of hydrocarbons of all of them. I still hunger for clams, shrimp, crab, octopus, gumboots. Nothing in this world will replace them. To finally be living in my ancestors' area and be able to teach my kids, but now it's all gone. We still try, but you can't replace them.

The theme of declining subsistence resources and suspicion of the oil spill as the cause was evident in many comments by Chenega Bay households interviewed in 1993.

> We don't see the animals. We used to have eagles perched out here [on Evans Island], and grouse and porcupine. [Elrington Passage] is dead. You don't see the little brown ducks. . . .They're gone. [There are] few seagulls and seals.
>
> I keep watching for seals. I don't see them anymore. . . .I traveled from Esther Island to Chenega Bay and saw one seal. I also went around Knight Island and never saw any.

The fifth post-spill year (April 1993 through March 1994)

Interviews were conducted in eight of the 15 villages of the oil spill region regarding subsistence harvest levels in the fifth post-spill year (Table 4-1). Generally, there was a leveling off of the recovery of subsistence harvests and uses that had been taking place in the Lower Cook Inlet and Kodiak communities since 1990 and in the Prince William Sound communities since 1991. In the three subregions combined, the estimated subsistence harvest was 304.8 lbs/person, slightly lower than that of the previous year (Table 4-2, Figure 4-7). At the subregion level, there was a 21% decrease in subsistence harvests in the two Prince William Sound communities compared with 1991 to 1992, the most recent year in which both villages were surveyed (Table 4-2, Figure 4-6).

One factor that may account for these harvest and use declines in Prince William Sound in 1993 to 1994 is the continuing low levels of key resource populations (Figure 4-16). Even in this fifth year after the spill, 88% of households in Tatitlek and 75% in Chenega Bay said their overall subsistence uses were below pre-spill levels because of depressed resource populations. A second factor was the renewed issue of the health of subsistence resources and the consequent implications for humans. This issue focused on concerns about particular animals as well as a broader suspicion that the spill had damaged resources in ways that scientific studies had failed to detect. One incident in April 1993 involved a sea lion killed by two young

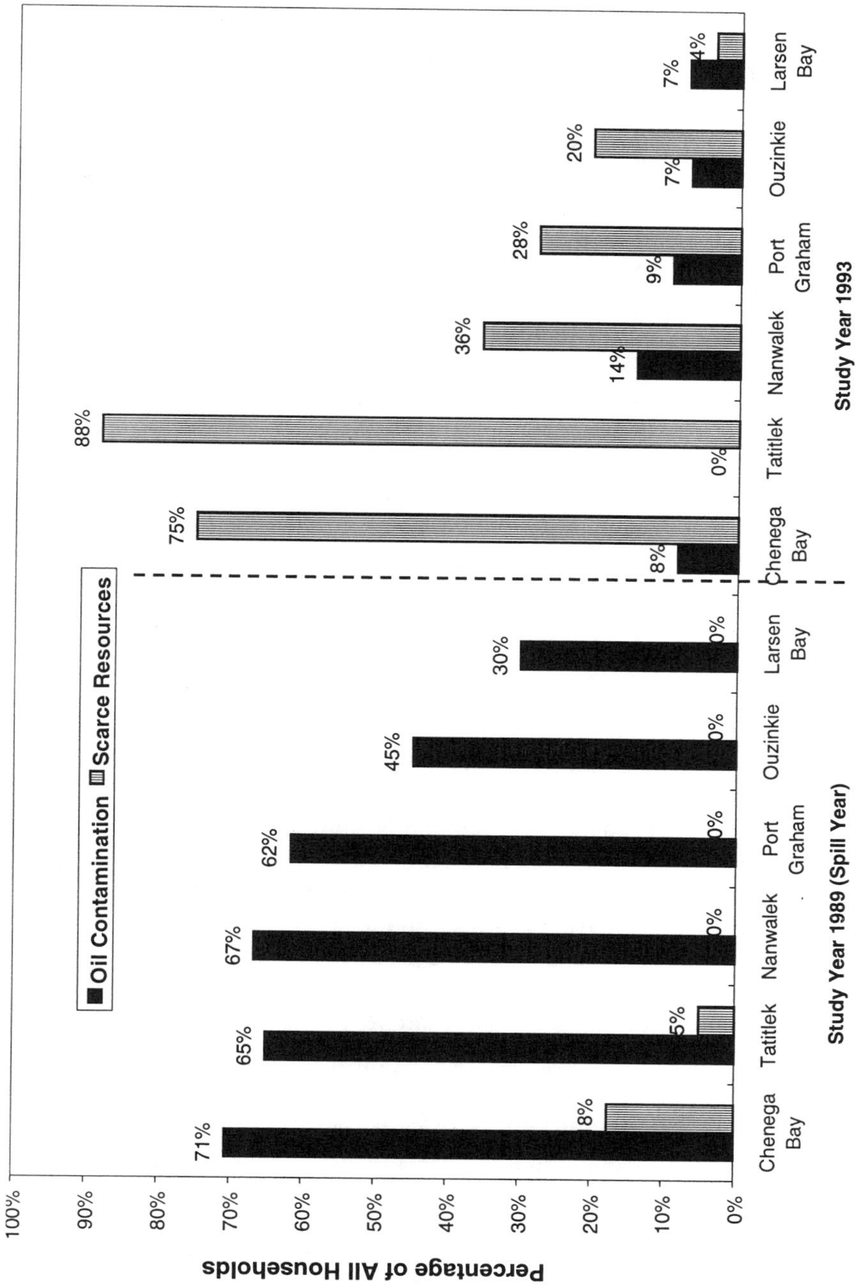

Figure 4-16 Reasons cited for reduced overall subsistence uses, 1989 and 1993, selected communities of the oil-spill region

Tatitlek hunters that "had spots all over it." With the hunters' aid, ADF&G obtained photographs of this animal and diagnosed the problem as an unusually large number of target lesions, which are caused by a skin fungus. ADF&G advised that such lesions would not affect the health of the animal or render it unsafe to eat. However, when members of 11 households in Tatitlek were shown photographs of this animal, they said they had never observed these lesions before. One elder shook his head and vehemently stated that he had never seen anything like this on a sea lion (Seitz and Fall 1995:19). News of the condition of this sea lion soon reached Chenega Bay, where lingering doubts about the safety of using marine mammals consequently were reinforced.

Another incident involving herring in Prince William Sound also illustrates this persistent concern about the safety of subsistence food and the health of all resources of the Sound following the spill (Seitz and Fall 1995:20–22). The 1993 herring run in Prince William Sound was about half the size that was forecast. During sampling at Montague Island in April, commercial fishermen reported abnormal behavior and surface hemorrhages on the herring. Although the cause of the hemorrhages was unknown at the time, ADF&G believed that no human-health risk was involved, and commercial fisheries for sac roe and spawn on kelp took place (Donaldson et al. 1994:21). In early May 1993, before results of tests on the herring were available, the OSHTF received a letter from the President of the Tatitlek Indian Reorganization Act (IRA) Council (G. Kompkoff, personal communication, 4 May 1993). The letter announced that the council was recommending to community residents that they not use subsistence resources from Prince William Sound:

> The residents of the Native Village of Tatitlek, most of whom are very dependent on subsistence resources for their lifestyles have become extremely concerned (probably more concerned than we have been since the first days of the *Exxon Valdez* Oil Spill) with the safety of consuming any of the marine subsistence resources. Our concerns relate primarily to the condition of the herring, which is not only a staple subsistence resource in our village, but also a main food source of many of the other resources that we enjoy. The effect that the herring may have on the safety of consuming any of the resources has necessitated the discontinuance of harvests of any of the subsistence resources until we are certain that they are safe for human consumption.

Subsequently, later in May, the results of tests on the herring indicated a viral infection called viral hemorrhagic septicemia (VHS), a condition that posed no human-health threat (Meyers 1993). In response to the letter from the IRA Council, the ADF&G provided the community with background on the VHS virus from the chief fisheries pathologist for ADF&G, who attended a meeting of the OSHTF in August 1993 to provide community representatives with further information about the virus. An account of this overview also appeared in a February 1994 subsistence restoration newsletter distributed by the Subsistence Division (ADF&G 1994).

In June 1993, personnel from the Division of Subsistence, ADF&G, traveled to Tatitlek to discuss findings regarding the VHS virus with the community. (The following account of this visit is from Seitz and Fall 1995.) Village residents remained concerned, despite the assurances from ADF&G and the commercial fishery openings, about impacts of the disease on other animals in the food chain and on humans. These concerns were exacerbated by several factors: the poor returns of herring and pink salmon; the harvest of a sea lion with target lesions (described above); and the extended presence of a school of herring near the Tatitlek dock from mid-April until late June that showed obvious signs of the disease. People reported that these herring were lethargic and moved erratically. In contrast, large schools such as this usually move in synchronized patterns and pass by the village quickly. The presence of herring was particularly significant because everyone in the community, not just hunters in the field, could observe this phenomenon. These observations supported the widely held view in the village that oil contamination was creating long-term effects on the environment, some of which only would be detected years after the spill. One elder, in commenting on damage assessment studies, said that they had ended too early: "Where it was heavily oiled, they'd start noticing the effects right away. Here [near Tatitlek, which was not directly oiled] it was too early to tell." This elder had predicted in 1991 that oil-spill effects would appear in a few years. When the herring failed to return and exhibited effects of the VHS virus, people remembered this prediction: "[The elders] said [the spill's impacts] would show up this year, and they're right on time."

When the herring near the Tatitlek dock were observed with "white patches and spots" along with hemorrhaging under the scales, village residents concluded that they were unsafe to eat because they were clearly sick. Villagers expressed frustration and outrage that they had been told that such fish could be safe to eat. "A virus is a virus. You don't feed something sick to humans," one person said. Another said, "We're not going to test these fish around here. [That is, people refused to "test" the fish themselves by eating them and then seeing if they got ill.] Everything is not okay, no matter what Exxon said." This remark also illustrates the continuing and troubling association, for at least some people, of health advice with Exxon, the party responsible for spilling the oil. And an elder expressed the shared cultural norm concerning the healthfulness of resources as follows "We never ate anything strange. We hardly had occasion to throw away things. We want to know why we are seeing so many strange things."

It was thus clear from this incident that the people of Tatitlek had a fundamental problem with the idea that an animal can have something wrong with it and still be safe to eat. The view is that if an animal has an abnormal appearance or behaves oddly, it is sick, and if it is sick, it is not good for food.

A further problem was that the ADF&G had opened the commercial herring fishery based on assurances that the herring were safe to use without knowing what the cause of the aberrant behavior and hemorrhages might be. In a letter addressed to the OSHTF, the village council president stated the crux of the issue for Tatitlek (G. Kompkoff, personal communication, 24 August 1993):

> Residents of the Native Village of Tatitlek were concerned with the safety of consuming *any* of the subsistence resources in 1989; it has been more than four years since the oil was spilled and the residents are still concerned and their concerns are growing with each failed commercial or subsistence fishing season. Prior to the oil spill, our people never had to worry about their resources, for generations we have been able to harvest whatever we wanted without worrying about the safety of consuming anything. The total failures of the herring and salmon seasons this year have made residents of Prince William Sound wonder what the *true* impact of the oil spill has been on the Sound. The herring are an integral part of the food chain, almost all of the subsistence resources that we rely on depend largely on herring for their sustenance. When the herring returned to the sound with sores and lesions on them, we became extremely concerned about the safety of harvesting any and contacted the Alaska Department of Fish and Game and the Department of Environmental Conservation about their condition; we were told that while both agencies were not sure what was affecting the herring, they were safe for human consumption. This made absolutely no sense at all to us. Suppose there were meats in the American Super Markets that had sores and lesions on them, do you think that either agency would have told the consumers that the meats were safe, even before they had determined what was affecting the meats? We very seriously doubt that. Why is this so?

Thus, as in the first several years after the spill, the community of Tatitlek raised questions about the quality of the information being used to reassure them about food safety, casting doubt on the trustworthiness of any advice about this critical issue.

Nevertheless, as shown in Figure 4-16, by 1993 and 1994, few households in any of the subregions reported that their overall subsistence uses were lower than before the oil spill because of oil-contamination concerns. In Prince William Sound and Lower Cook Inlet villages, from 1989 to 1990 (the first post-spill year) to 1993 to 1994 (the fifth post-spill year) there was a large decline in the percentage of households citing oil contamination as the reason for lower overall subsistence uses and lower uses of any particular resource; this decline occurred in every resource category (Figure 4-17). As was increasingly the case with each passing year, far more

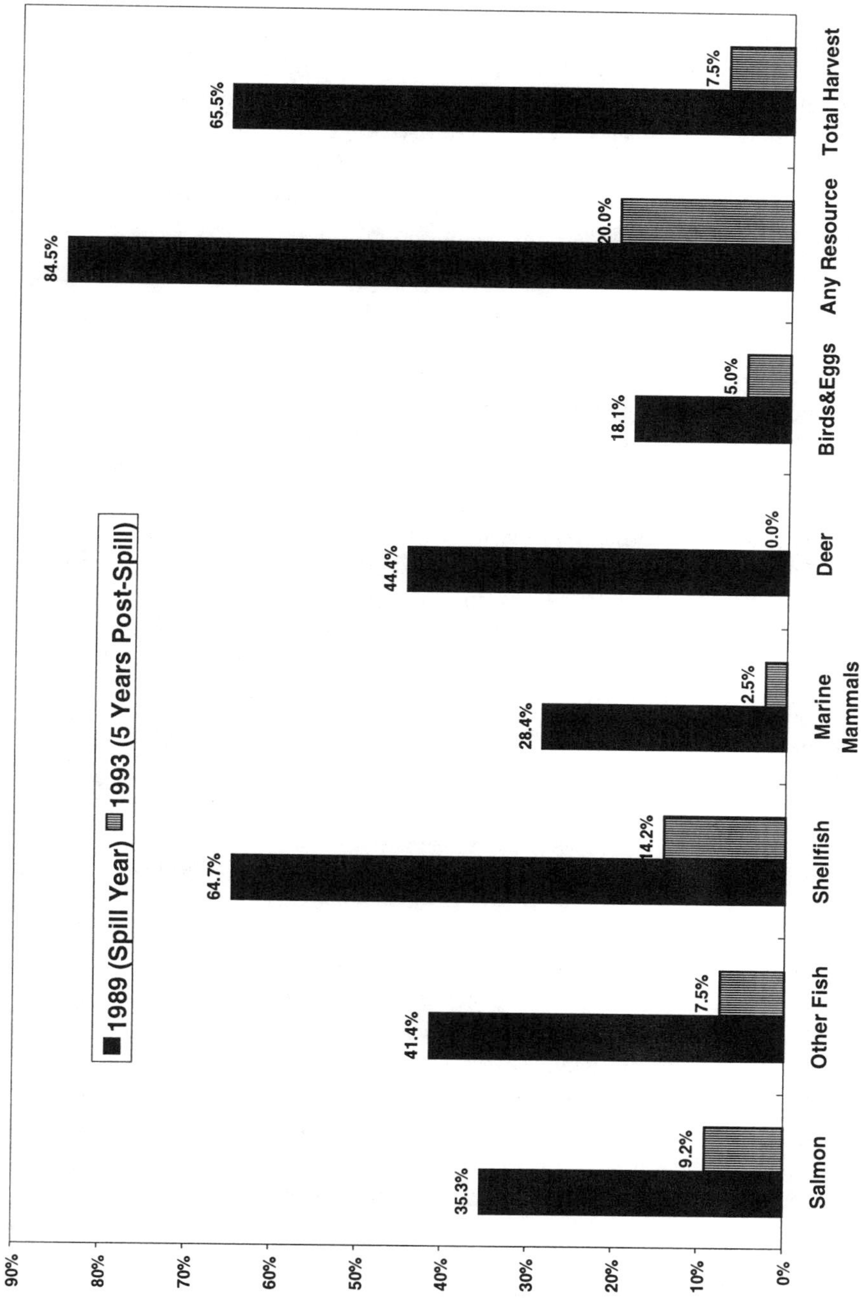

Figure 4-17 Percentage of households citing oil contamination as the cause of reduced subsistence uses, Prince William Sound and Lower Cook Inlet Villages, 1989 and 1993

households pointed to resource shortages as the cause of continued below-normal levels of subsistence uses (Figure 4-16). As illustrated in the two examples just reviewed, however, the condition of natural resource populations, including the condition of particular animals and the scarcity of key resources such as herring, were evidence to subsistence users that the natural environment of Prince William Sound was not healthy. Their assessment that subsistence uses remained low because of scarcity may indeed subsume an underlying suspicion that resources could be unsafe to eat. With few alternatives and the strong cultural values associated with wild foods, people used them anyway and gradually invested more effort to secure subsistence harvests.

Summary and Conclusions

Subsistence uses of fish, marine invertebrates, birds, and mammals are of fundamental economic, social, and cultural importance to the communities of the area affected by the *Exxon Valdez* oil spill of March 1989. The oil spill severely disrupted patterns of subsistence use (see also Palinkas et al. 1993; Jorgensen 1995). In the 12 months after the spill, subsistence harvest quantities dropped, the variety of wild resources used for food was much reduced, people directed far less time than normal to subsistence activities, and traditional sharing was curtailed. Although many households in all 15 Alaska Native communities in the spill area suffered reduced subsistence uses in the first post-spill year, the greatest effects were in Prince William Sound, Lower Cook Inlet, and in some Kodiak Island Borough communities.

The large majority of households whose subsistence uses declined in 1989 pointed to oil-contamination concerns as the reason for their unusually low use levels. Little specific information was available to subsistence users until most subsistence harvest opportunities in the spring, summer, and early fall of 1989 had passed. Advice from health officials that sight, smell, and taste were reliable indicators of subsistence food safety was rejected by many subsistence users in these villages because it contradicted their own observations of dead and dying wildlife. Further, despite generations of traditional knowledge about the natural environment, the potential unseen effects of the spilled oil on subsistence resources could not be interpreted without assistance from health officials and scientists. The experience of the oil spill cast doubt on subsistence users' own abilities to understand their environment and make informed decisions about subsistence resources. In addition, no final results of tests of resources for oil contamination were available until more than nine months after the spill. The health advice offered at that time was based on a limited number of samples of fish and marine invertebrates from relatively few sites. No specific information was available about birds, deer, and marine mammals until a year or more after the spill.

After the first post-spill year, levels of subsistence harvests, the variety of resources used, effort invested in harvesting, and the level of sharing of resources gradually increased in all of the spill region communities. Generally, subsistence uses rebounded first in communities of the Kodiak area and Lower Cook Inlet, but they lagged behind by a year or more in the Prince William Sound villages. Reasons for increases in subsistence uses after the first post-spill year are varied and difficult to pinpoint. Some households had renewed confidence in traditional foods after receiving information and health advice from the OSHTF. Others returned to using subsistence foods despite their misgivings because of economic and cultural reasons. Still others traveled to unoiled areas, sometimes outside their traditional use areas, to harvest subsistence resources.

Also, while the number of households citing oil-contamination concerns as the cause of their unusually low use of subsistence resources had declined substantially by the fifth post-spill year (1993 to 1994), many households, especially in Prince William Sound and Lower Cook Inlet, continued to believe that populations of key resources such as marine mammals, birds, deer, and marine invertebrates had declined since 1989. Many suspected the spill as a cause of these declines. Others pointed to the spill when unusual conditions were observed in resource populations or on individual animals. Examples from 1993 include a proliferation of lesions on a sea lion taken by Tatitlek hunters, an unexpectedly poor return of pink salmon to Prince William Sound, and an outbreak of a virus in the Sound's herring stocks. (As of 1998, investigations funded by the EVOS Trustee Council were still underway to determine the causes of this poor return of herring and of the virus, as well as possible connections to the spill.)

As these examples show, even in 1993 and 1994, more than five years after the *Exxon Valdez* oil spill, some subsistence users of the spill area were still raising questions and still looking for answers, as they had since the first post-spill year. Although subsistence harvest and use had bounced back to pre-spill levels for most people and communities, a view persisted in the Prince William Sound communities, and to a lesser extent in the other subregions, that the natural environment had changed in ways that still posed a potential threat to their health and their way of life. Correspondingly, as of 1999, the *Exxon Valdez* Oil Spill Trustee Council—the agency charged with administering the program to restore the environment damaged by the spill—continued to list subsistence as a natural resource service for which recovery was still not complete.

References

[ADF&G] Alaska Department of Fish and Game. 1994. Subsistence restoration project: February 1994 report. Anchorage AK: Division of Subsistence.

[ADF&G] Alaska Department of Fish and Game. 1995. Subsistence restoration project: August 1995 report. Anchorage AK: Division of Subsistence.

[ADHSS] Alaska Department of Health and Social Services. 1989. Oil spill public health advice. State of Alaska Epidemiology Bulletin 6. May 5, 1989. Anchorage AK:

Donaldson W, Morstad S, Shar D, Wilcock J, Sharr S. 1994. Prince William Sound management area 1993 annual finfish management report. Anchorage: Alaska Department of Fish and Game, Division of Commercial Fisheries. Regional Information Rep. 2A94-XX. Division of Public Health, Section of Epidemiology.

Evanoff G. 1990. News from Chenega Bay. Around the rim: A newsletter serving the people of the Chugach Region. 12(3):6.

Fall JA. 1990. The Division of Subsistence of the Alaska Department of Fish and Game: An overview of its research program and findings, 1980–1990. *Arctic Anthropology* 27(2):68–92.

Fall JA. 1991. Subsistence uses of fish and wildlife and the *Exxon Valdez* oil spill. Arctic Issues Digest. Anchorage AK: Cooperative Extension Service, University of Alaska. p 12–25.

Fall JA. 1992a. Changes in subsistence uses of fish and wildlife resources in 15 Alaska Native villages following the *Exxon Valdez* oil spill. Alaska OCS Region Fourth Information Transfer Meeting. Anchorage AK: U.S. Department of the Interior, Minerals Management Service. p 261–270.

Fall JA, editor. 1992b. Subsistence harvests and uses in seven Gulf of Alaska communities in the second year following the *Exxon Valdez* oil spill. Report to the U.S. Fish and Wildlife Service. Juneau AK: Alaska Department of Fish and Game, Division of Subsistence. Technical Paper 218.

Fall JA. 1993. Subsistence uses of fish and wildlife. *Alaska's Wildlife* 25(1):4–6.

Fall JA. 1996. Overview of research by the Division of Subsistence, Alaska Department of Fish and Game, on the sociocultural consequences of the *Exxon Valdez* oil spill. Peer Review Workshop, Social Indicators Monitoring Study. Anchorage AK: U.S. Department of the Interior, Minerals Management Service. OCS Study MMS96-0053. p 35–54.

Fall JA, editor. 1997. Subsistence harvests and uses in seven Gulf of Alaska communities in the second year following the *Exxon Valdez* oil spill. Report to the U.S. Fish and Wildlife Service. Juneau AK: Alaska Department of Fish and Game, Division of Subsistence. Technical Paper 218.

Fall JA, Field LJ. 1996. Subsistence uses of fish and wildlife before and after the *Exxon Valdez* oil spill. In: Rice SD, Spies RB, Wolfe DA, Wright BA, editors. Exxon Valdez oil spill symposium. Bethesda MD: American Fisheries Society Symposium 18. p 819–836.

Fall JA, Hutchinson-Scarbrough LB, Coiley PA. 1995. Fish and wildlife harvest and use in five Alaska Peninsula communities, 1989. Juneau AK: Alaska Department of Fish and Game, Division of Subsistence. Technical Paper 202.

Fall JA, Stratton L, Coiley P, Brown L, Utermohle CJ, Jennings G. 1996. Subsistence harvests and uses in Chenega Bay and Tatitlek in the year following the *Exxon Valdez* oil spill. Juneau AK: Alaska Department of Fish and Game, Division of Subsistence. Technical Paper 199.

Fall JA, Utermohle CJ, editors. 1995. An investigation of the sociocultural consequences of outer continental shelf development in Alaska. Six volumes. Prepared for U.S. Department of the Interior, Minerals Management Service, Alaska OCS Region. OCS Study MMS-95-010. Anchorage AK: Alaska Department of Fish and Game, Division of Subsistence.

Frost KJ, Lowry LF. 1993. Assessment of damages to harbor seals caused by the *Exxon Valdez* oil spill. *Exxon Valdez* oil spill symposium abstracts book. Anchorage AK: *Exxon Valdez* Oil Spill Trustee Council. p 300–302.

Hutchinson-Scarbrough L. 1995a. Chignik Bay. In: Fall JA, Utermohle CJ, editors. Volume 5: Chapter 17, An investigation of the sociocultural consequences of outer continental shelf development in Alaska. Prepared for U.S. Department of the Interior, Minerals Management Service, Alaska OCS Region. OCS Study MMS-95-010. Anchorage AK: Alaska Department of Fish and Game, Division of Subsistence.

Hutchinson-Scarbrough L. 1995b. Chignik Lake. In: Fall JA, Utermohle CJ, editors. Volume 5: Chapter 18, An investigation of the sociocultural consequences of outer continental shelf development in Alaska. Prepared for U.S. Department of the Interior, Minerals Management Service, Alaska OCS Region. OCS Study MMS-95-010. Anchorage AK: Alaska Department of Fish and Game, Division of Subsistence.

Jorgensen JG. 1995. Ethnicity, not culture? Obfuscating social science in the *Exxon Valdez* oil spill case. *American Indian Culture and Research Journal* 19(4):1–124.

Meyers T. 1993. North American viral hemorrhagic septicemia virus isolated from Pacific herring in Prince William Sound. Juneau AK: Alaska Department of Fish and Game, Division of Commercial Fisheries Management and Development. Memorandum.

Miraglia RA, Chartrand AW. 1997. Subsistence restoration project: food safety testing. *Exxon Valdez* oil spill restoration project 94279. Juneau AK: Alaska Department of Fish and Game, Division of Subsistence. Final Report.

Palinkas LA, Downs MA, Petterson JS, Russell J. 1993. Social, cultural, and psychological impacts of the *Exxon Valdez* oil spill. *Human Organization* 52:1–13.

Piper E. 1993. The *Exxon Valdez* oil spill: Final report, State of Alaska response. Anchorage AK: Alaska Department of Environmental Conservation.

Rice SD, Spies RB, Wolfe DA, Wright BA, editors. 1996. Proceedings of the *Exxon Valdez* Oil Spill Symposium; Anchorage, Alaska; 2–5 February 1993. Bethesda MD: *Am Fish Soc Symp* 18.

Scott CL, Paige AW, Jennings GB, Brown L. 1998. Community profile database catalog, 6 volumes. Juneau AK: Alaska Department of Fish and Game, Division of Subsistence.

Seitz J, Fall JA. 1995. Tatitlek. In: Fall JA, Utermohle CJ, editors. Volume 2: Chapter 5, An investigation of the sociocultural consequences of outer continental shelf development in Alaska. Prepared for U.S. Department of the Interior, Minerals Management Service, Alaska OCS Region. OCS Study MMS-95-010. Anchorage AK: Alaska Department of Fish and Game, Division of Subsistence.

Seitz J, Miraglia R. 1995. Chenega Bay. In: Fall JA, Utermohle CJ, editors. Volume 2: Chapter 4, An investigation of the sociocultural consequences of outer continental shelf development in Alaska. Prepared for U.S. Department of the Interior, Minerals Management Service, Alaska OCS Region. OCS Study MMS-95-010. Anchorage AK: Alaska Department of Fish and Game, Division of Subsistence.

Stratton L. 1990. Resource harvests and use in Tatitlek, Alaska. Juneau AK: Alaska Department of Fish and Game, Division of Subsistence. Technical Paper 181.

Stratton L, Chisum EB. 1986. Resource use patterns in Chenega, Western Prince William Sound: Chenega in the 1960s and Chenega Bay 1984-1986. Juneau AK: Alaska Department of Fish and Game, Division of Subsistence. Technical Paper 139.

[USCG] U.S. Coast Guard. 1993. Federal On Scene Coordinator's Report: T/V *Exxon Valdez* Oil Spill. Washington DC: U.S. Department of Transportation.

[USFDA] U.S. Food and Drug Administration. 1989. Summary of analyses of subsistence seafood from pilot study. Washington DC: Center for Food Safety and Applied Nutrition, Food and Drug Administration..

[USFWS] U.S. Fish and Wildlife Service. 1991. Summary of effects of the *Exxon Valdez* oil spill on natural resources and archaeological sites. Anchorage AK: Division of Subsistence, Alaska Department of Fish and Game.

Varanasi U, Chan S-L, MacLeod Jr WD, Stein JE, Brown DW, Burrows DG, Tilbury KL, Wigren CA, Hom T, Pierce SM. 1990. Survey of subsistence fish and shellfish for exposure to oil spilled from the *Exxon Valdez*, Summary (Cycles I-III). Seattle WA: Environmental Conservation Division, Northwest Fisheries Science Center, National Marine Fisheries Service, NOAA.

Walker AH, Field LJ. 1991. Subsistence fisheries and the *Exxon Valdez*: human health concerns. 1991 International Oil Spill Conference. Washington DC: American Petroleum Institute. API Publication 4529. p 441–446.

Wells PG, Butler JN, Hughes JS. 1995. *Exxon Valdez* oil spill: Fate and effects in Alaska waters. Philadelphia PA: American Society for Testing and Materials.

Chapter 5

Response Mobilization Following the *Exxon Valdez* Oil Spill and Its Effects on Subsistence Villages

*Judith Meidinger**

My first view of the *Exxon Valdez* hard aground on Bligh Reef was from 27,000 feet aboard an Alaska Airlines jet on my way south on a business trip three days after the initial grounding on 24 March 1989. The vessel could be clearly seen, surrounded by a slowly spreading slick of crude oil. Dozens of small fishing boats and other vessels were close at hand, and what looked like miles of boom had been deployed to try to contain the oil that had poured from its punctured tanks.

I was away from Alaska for eight days. During my absence, a serious storm had spread the oil into the Western Prince William Sound. The oil would continue to move to the Lower Cook Inlet, the Barren Islands, and through Shelikof Strait, affecting shorelines along both the Alaska Peninsula and Kodiak Island. All of the populated areas within its path would be affected by the spill and by the efforts to clean it up. The oiled shorelines within the spill path included areas used for subsistence activities by Alaska Natives.

Upon my return, I had several messages from our Koniag, Inc., secretary to call Milt Alberstadt, the public affairs specialist with whom I worked out of the Anchorage office during program implementation. I had worked as a private consultant to Exxon USA from 1981 to 1986, developing and implementing an information and public relations plan for their offshore leasing program for the Bering Sea.

Alberstadt had been called to Valdez in the first days following the spill to assist Exxon Shipping with media and other external affairs issues. He was one of more than a dozen employees called in from the "lower 48" to work for Exxon Shipping before the parent company, Exxon USA, came in to manage the spill response. He remained with the community liaison group for two summer cleanup seasons. I arrived two days later. Exxon was concerned about food supplies in Tatitlek and Chenega, having quickly realized that this was the beginning of spring hunting,

*Judith Meidinger is a senior planner for emergency and crisis management with Alyeska Pipeline Service Company in Anchorage, Alaska. An Alaska Native originally from Kodiak Island, she served as a Native liaison for Exxon during the spill response, including participation in the Oil Spill Health Task Force.

fishing, and other subsistence activities, all of which had been seriously interrupted by the oil spill. There was a need to begin shipping food and other supplies to these villages to alleviate this immediate problem. Investigating, I discovered that other problems were also surfacing. Fuel supplies were getting low. Expected shipments had been disrupted because boats were being placed under contract to work on the spill response. Planned village projects, such as school building and other village construction work, also were to be disrupted in much the same manner.

The Post-Spill Situation

Prince William Sound

On 10 April I began making calls to Tatitlek and Chenega to assess their situation and find out their immediate needs. Both villages were running low on supplies and were unprepared to deal with an interrupted effort and prolonged delay in gathering spring subsistence foods. Also, many of the adults from both villages were signing up to work on the cleanup. Tatitlek food supplies were low, subsistence activities were at a standstill, homes were running out of fuel, and people were anxious. Gary Kompkoff, Tatitlek's Village Chief, was trying to take care of village needs and spent time patrolling and surveying the spill area in his fishing boat. Anxiety levels were high and nobody knew quite what to do; working to clean up the oil spill seemed the most productive way to focus their efforts. Calls to Chenega Bay resulted in the same response: low food and fuel supplies, no subsistence activities, lots of anxiety, and people trying to figure out who to contact and what to do next. Both villages had literally been inundated with outsiders responding to the spill. Meanwhile, the residents seemed to have been overlooked.

Early in April, Exxon began a regular series of commercial food and fuel shipments to Tatitlek and Chenega. These shipments were supplemented by fish and subsistence foods from areas outside the Prince William Sound. Many organizations either initiated or supported efforts to provide subsistence foods to these two villages and some of the villages located on the lower Kenai Peninsula. Fish and subsistence foods from outside areas included shellfish, seals, and clams from tribal groups in southeast Alaska; herring roe from Togiak; king salmon from Tyonek through the combined efforts of a Russian Orthodox priest, the Alaska Division of Emergency Services, and Exxon; and fresh red salmon from Chugach Alaska Corporation's cannery in Cordova were sent to villages in Prince William Sound and Lower Cook Inlet. In all of these cases, the food came from the community or a community organization; Exxon assisted with packaging, storage, and distribution. In the fall, the Alaska Department of Fish and Game (ADF&G) issued a special permit to harvest fish in Olga Bay for freezing and canning to supply Kodiak Island residents. Exxon made arrangements with Chugach Alaska Corporation for supplies of canned and frozen fish to go to Prince William Sound and Lower Cook Inlet villages. In total, Exxon provided over 114,000 pounds of commercial food to Chenega and Tatitlek and distributed about 115,000 pounds of subsistence foods to all of the villages affected by the spill. None of the villages went without food during the response.

Lower Cook Inlet

As the oil spread to the Kenai Peninsula—affecting the communities of Seward, Nanwalek, Port Graham, Seldovia, and Homer—it was important to assess needs and problems in these areas as well. A command post had been set up in Homer to conduct cleanup operations in this region, and a community liaison team was in place. The anxiety from these small communities manifested itself in several ways. Nanwalek and Port Graham had assembled crews to construct log booms to protect their lagoon and were working round the clock to get these anchored in place. Both of these villages had shifts of women going out to collect chitons and other shellfish before the oil came. Some went to areas in Kachemak Bay to dig clams. There was a deep sense of urgency to gather as much food as they could. Everyone feared for the salmon that were due to arrive in early May and would mark the beginning, in earnest, of their summer subsistence activities. What was going to happen? What could they do? They, too, began to sign up to work on the oil-spill cleanup. Most seemed to feel that it was the most practical thing they could do.

In Homer and Seldovia, volunteer groups formed to build and anchor log booms to try to prevent the spread of oil into their sensitive lagoons and bays. The City of Seward quickly formed an incident command team, made up of the mayor, fire chief, police chief, and harbor master along with council members and other citizens, to deal with their emergency situation. Multi-agency committees made up of federal, state, and local government representatives began meeting in Seward and Homer to begin assessing the situation. Local governments formed incident command groups to manage spill impacts and response. Exxon established command centers in these cities to provide on-site operations, community liaison, and claims teams to work with the local communities and respond to their needs.

Kodiak Island

As the oil spill advanced through the Barren Islands and to the Shelikof Strait, Kodiak village teams had been mobilized by their tribal organizations and village corporations to protect their bays, beaches, and salmon streams. The Ouzinkie and Afognak (Port Lions) Village Corporations had village crews cutting trees and constructing log booms that were anchored to protect their most sensitive areas. Knowing that they couldn't protect everything, the two villages made a priority list of their most valuable fishing and subsistence areas and anchored the log booms in these places. The villages of Larsen Bay and Karluk are treeless and had to rely on outside help. Because their subsistence fishing areas are more widely and openly exposed to the Shelikof Strait, it was virtually impossible to boom their critical subsistence areas. The villages of Akhiok and Old Harbor were expected to be less impacted, since both were somewhat less exposed. However, by the time the oil spill reached the south end of Kodiak Island, the oil was mixed with water, seaweed, sand, and other debris. There was a perception among the villages that the oil was mostly submerged and largely out of sight, which made the situation all the more ominous to them. In fact, the oil was only partially and temporarily submerged. Indeed, the villagers' persistent fear of submerged oil prompted Exxon to hire the environmental consulting firm Dames & Moore to sample subsistence food resources in all of the villages in the area. The Mayor of Old Harbor issued an executive order declaring the beaches officially off limits to all residents. Fears of contamination and being poisoned were causing high anxiety. "We can't see it or smell it, but it's there, we know it," said Sven Haakensen, the Mayor of Old Harbor. "The people need to be protected."

Mobilization

Command centers

VECO, Exxon's main spill cleanup contractor, had set up command centers in each village to hire day crews to work within a certain radius of each village, returning each night. Anxious to help with cleanup—with mixed emotions about working for Exxon, yet glad for the employment opportunity and guilty at the same time—whole villages went to work during the summer, leaving the young and elderly at home and thereby creating other sets of village problems that would have to be resolved later. Old and young alike felt abandoned, there was a need for adequate child care, and normal village activity ceased in favor of day crews who came and went seven days a week. Tribal offices were left unstaffed and mail sat unopened. Ironically, the villagers' involvement in the cleanup work may have fueled rumors about the amount and extent of oil in other areas, leading to a sense of inevitability that the oil from elsewhere would reach their own village. The village command centers, manned by local residents and led by the local Village Protection Safety Officer, were helped by the Coast Guard, occasionally the Alaska Department of Environmental Conservation (ADEC), and other agencies in guiding local cleanup operations. The village crews did outstanding cleanup work and were critical to the success of cleanup operations, working 12-hour shifts, seven days a week, until the teams were demobilized in September for safety reasons. After 1989 cleanup operations were suspended, Exxon worked with the villages to fund and activate village winter monitoring teams until cleanup operations could resume in the spring of 1990.

Exxon USA/community liaison

Exxon set up a community liaison team in early April under the direction of Monte Taylor, a former Manager of Exxon's Alaska operations from the late 1970s until 1981. An Exxon retiree, Taylor was called to Alaska at the end of March 1989 by the President of Exxon USA, Bill Stevens, to set up and manage the community liaison group and respond to community and village problems. Taylor assigned one or two liaisons to every community and hired three Native consultants to respond to subsistence and commercial fishing issues. We also were to work with Native organizations and villages and help Exxon grapple with Native issues by responding to the growing concerns in communities and advising Exxon on what solutions might work. This proved very practical.

The Exxon Command team was concerned and anxious to make the appropriate responses and commitments to everyone who was affected by the oil spill. Based on recommendations from the liaisons, regular meetings were held with community and village leaders and Native organizations. Arrangements for financial assistance were quickly made. Subsistence-food safety was made a priority, and a testing program was designed. Many others had made food safety a priority as well. In conjunction with several State of Alaska departments (i.e., ADF&G, ADEC, Office of Emergency Services, Health and Human Services), the Indian Health Service, and regional and village tribal organizations, food safety was made a top priority. The environmental consulting firm Dames & Moore was hired to design and manage the program. Sampling was to be conducted in all spill areas over a period of several weeks. Four rounds of sampling were initially scheduled, although only three took place because of weather constraints and tidal changes as autumn approached. There was simply not enough time to complete sampling in all areas before winter set in.

During the planning phase of the sampling program, the U.S. Secretary of Transportation and a U.S. Coast Guard (USCG) Admiral visited the oil-spill region. As they listened to villagers' and others' concerns about subsistence, both officials expressed the critical need to have a program in place to deal with the issue of food safety and to keep Alaska Natives informed of progress in this area. In July 1989, National Oceanic and Atmospheric Administration (NOAA) and Exxon signed a Memorandum of Understanding (MOU) to cooperate fully in the sampling and analysis of subsistence food resources. The four major components of the MOU were that 1) NOAA would participate in the sampling program, 2) the National Marine Fisheries Service (NMFS) would conduct the chemical analyses, 3) all information would be immediately made public, and 4) Exxon would actively support and fund the program. NOAA's Scientific Support Coordinator also expressed his intent that NOAA work with ADF&G and participate fully in the Oil Spill Health Task Force (OSHTF). Later, NOAA organized an expert committee of toxicologists to assist in interpretation of the data generated by the studies. These relationships and agreements were acknowledged by Exxon as vital to conducting the most comprehensive and credible study possible.

Subsistence was not the only issue in communities and villages: there were impacts from the influx of transients looking for work; there were local businesses on the verge of shutting down, abandoned by their work force for jobs on the oil-spill cleanup at double the wages and continuous overtime; and there were impacts to hospitals, airports, and garbage dumps. There was a serious lack of available housing and hotel space; local communities had to beef-up their police force. Harbor masters, accustomed to dealing only with a local fleet, were affected by cleanup and survey vessels and boats waiting to be hired. Fishermen unable to fish because of fishery closures were parked at the docks, restless and frustrated. Through their Community Liaison and claims organizations, Exxon attempted to deal with these issues fairly and promptly by advancing or reimbursing local governments for spill-related expenses and paying claims to individuals and businesses for spill-related economic losses. Housing facilities in Valdez, restoration of tribal operations in villages, and other programs were initiated to mitigate effects of the oil spill.

Exxon USA and The Oil Spill Health Task Force

Representatives of Exxon Biomedical Research were to take the lead in this scientific sampling and testing program for Exxon USA. An Exxon toxicologist arrived in Valdez in early June to begin coordinating this project with the different parties. Indian Health Service set up meetings with the OSHTF and the first meeting occurred in mid-June. A long relationship was about to begin. The OSHTF would take the lead oversight role for the program, including the analytical testing and developing an information program for the villages on food safety. The sampling, analytical testing, and information program was to extend to 1992. Exxon continued to provide support throughout.

One problem for Exxon during negotiation of the MOU with NOAA was the release of unedited test results to the public early in the testing phase. This caused concern for Exxon's lawyers and some in Exxon management. A class action lawsuit had been filed against Exxon on subsistence issues less than a month after the spill, and the idea of releasing test information to the public was perceived as risky by Exxon. Nevertheless, to their credit, Exxon management decided to agree to immediately release all test results, good or bad, from the NOAA laboratory. Exxon management expressed a greater concern about the villages' need for information on the safety of subsistence foods than their concern about their own liability. They reasoned that if some of the results indicated a health risk, village residents needed to know where not to hunt or gather in order to protect their health. This meant that Exxon received the results at the same time as the OSHTF.

Exxon USA and the villages

The ADEC had completed a limited amount of testing in early April, and some results were available to release to the villages. The Exxon Native Liaison team had just begun to meet with the OSHTF to begin coordinating the subsistence food-safety studies and to determine the extent of other issues with which Exxon might assist. The Exxon command team was concerned about the urgent need for information and communication on subsistence-food impacts, toxicity of oil to residents, health threats to cleanup workers, etc. Exxon Command had decided that a team led by Exxon's toxicologist and that included a medical doctor and industrial hygienist should begin a series of meetings in the villages and with concerned organizations to assess growing concerns in the communities and to provide information to the extent available. Meetings were held with the board of directors of Chugachmiut (then known as the North Pacific Rim) and the Native tribal organization for the Prince William Sound and Lower Cook Inlet villages to discuss presentations in the villages about oil impacts and health concerns. Exxon's toxicologist also wanted to present information from early testing results from the U.S. Food and Drug Administration (USFDA) and the organoleptic test results from the ADEC lab in Palmer. We also arranged with the Kodiak Island Borough and the Kodiak Area Native Association to hold a series of meetings in Kodiak and in the villages represented by Chugachmiut to present the same information. After reviewing the proposed village presentations with the State of Alaska, the Alaska Native Medical Center, and some of the Native associations, we held these meetings in early July, visiting each village in the Prince William Sound, Lower Cook Inlet, and Kodiak Island. Although the meetings were well received, skepticism and uncertainty were apparent. Everyone wanted greater assurance, more testing, and more information. It was clear that this was to be a long-term program and that ongoing sampling and testing would be necessary. This also demonstrated to us the importance of our relationship with the OSHTF and the need to have a unified communication team to provide ongoing information to villages and the public.

Smaller Exxon command centers, set up in the villages for local hiring and directing of cleanup operations, were key to maintaining contact with village leadership. Other command centers had been set up in Cordova, Seward, Homer, and Kodiak, with the main headquarters moved to Anchorage in the fall of 1989, thus allowing communities and villages easier access to the company. Claims representatives were also available in each area to respond to claims issues. Although this system was adequate for operational and most cleanup issues, for the most part it left villages devoid of leadership because they were so involved in the cleanup. This made it difficult for Exxon and the OSHTF to involve the village leadership and to provide information to those in the villages who needed it. This also meant that many ongoing village programs and basic services were unmanaged or not implemented. Day-to-day village business was not conducted; in many cases, mail was left unopened and bills were left unpaid. Uncertainty about their future and the ultimate impacts of the oil spill were uppermost in everyone's mind; concern about the future of subsistence was especially prevalent. There was not an easy way to address these concerns. Sampling and testing and getting results back to the villages in a way that was easily understood or in a framework appropriate for lay understanding were very difficult for the OSHTF. Unfortunately, although the OSHTF made extensive efforts, effective communication remained an issue throughout the program.

Exxon took a proactive approach. After negotiating with the Federal and State On-scene Command Team and consulting with the chairman of the OSHTF, Exxon committed the financial and technical resources to complete the comprehensive sampling and testing program through 1991. A final round of informational meetings was held in June of 1992. However, although Exxon had committed personnel and their Native consulting staff to these efforts, they were not well trusted. Some of the OSHTF members and many of the public gave mixed reviews to the teams' general makeup. The OSHTF needed the cooperation and support of Exxon, but at the same time needed to be free of any appearance of influence from the company in order to be credible. The trust and credibility of the ADF&G Subsistence Division among the villages were essential to the OSHTF's ongoing research programs. NOAA provided valuable support in its scientific role and guidance and advice to all parties. The Indian Health Service and Alaska Department of Health and Human Services were perceived as the most trustworthy. No one needed to be perceived as being "in cahoots" with Exxon. This wide-ranging coalition succeeded, for the most part, in accomplishing their objectives; there were results, although they came slowly at times. Unfortunately, effective communication continued to be an issue.

Difficulties in Communicating Effectively with the Villages

Adding to the difficulty in providing feedback to villages and discussing food safety were the many messages conveyed by the media and newspapers about the devastating effects of the spill and subsequent cleanup operations. News, featuring discussions about toxic waste, death and destruction, were daily occurrences. The spill cleanup was declared a "hazardous waste" cleanup, requiring special training and worker protection. "Decontamination" sites were set up for vessels engaged in cleanup. Workers were to be decontaminated after spending a day on cleanup activities. There was also the problem of the conflicting messages about the safety of commercial versus subsistence fish. On one hand, ADEC and ADF&G declared a "zero tolerance" for oil contamination of commercial fish and closed much of the salmon season; on the other hand, villagers were being told that fish were safe to eat and that shellfish showing no evidence of oil contamination were also safe to eat. As time progressed, the advice from the health experts regarding fish and shellfish was consistent with, and supported by, more and more data. Yet villagers who rely on all of their senses when fishing or hunting—and who had seen the oiled, dying birds, oiled seals and otters, and oiled contaminated beaches—could not reasonably be expected to believe toxicologists, physicians, or scientists who were sending a different message. Also, all of the above occurred after lawsuits had been filed against Exxon, and the added complexity of ongoing litigation among governments, Native Alaskans, and Exxon compounded the communication difficulties. This clearly was not the framework for realistic communication.

Conclusions

The challenges to dealing with the variety of impacts of the *Exxon Valdez* oil spill were great indeed. In retrospect, it seems wise to reflect on exactly what was done, how and by whom it was done, and the results. This can help a company or agency or village devise strategies for the future. At the time of the spill, none of the parties—Exxon, the governments, or health agencies—was adequately prepared to address concerns of Natives, i.e., to implement testing programs or effectively communicate information regarding the effect of oil on subsistence resources. The intensive efforts and cooperation among the parties eventually produced positive results, although not as rapidly as hoped. The responsible party and government agencies should examine their specific roles and the laws and regulations governing their activities to determine what, if anything, they might do differently. Should government agencies mandate how soon testing programs should occur and what constitutes "safety" in subsistence food? What happens if there is an oil spill in winter when cleanup activities cannot be safely conducted? Because the responsible party has more latitude in making decisions about certain issues than does a government agency, it should be proactive in developing response strategies. Should Exxon have taken a more neutral stance and simply provided behind-the-scenes financing for the subsistence-testing program through a government agency or through a Native corporation in order to help achieve a higher level of trust with the villages? This might be one solution to the problem of perceived conflict of interest and distrust in communication. These are examples of options or strategies that should be thought out ahead of time, not when oil is hitting the beaches.

Personal Reflections

As an Alaska Native, representing Exxon to my own Native communities was difficult at times, to say the least. To the credit of insightful managers, Exxon hired additional Native liaisons who had the authority to make decisions, develop plans, and commit resources. An understanding of social and cultural issues, of Native organizations, and of Native issues was important to ensuring that village and local needs were met. Exxon's Native liaisons also enabled the Company to quickly lend financial support to tribal and local governments, Native regional corporations, and their nonprofit counterparts. It also meant immediate communication with the company and a quick response to village and community needs. Initially, however, the long delay in setting up these programs, in some cases two or three months, resulted in the general view that Exxon was difficult to work with and not responsive to communities. And this general view persisted. The good news about what Exxon did during the spill response did not make the headlines, unlike the bad news.

The fact is that oil spills should never happen. If or when they do, citizens have a right to expect that those who are at fault will act responsibly. There are many lessons to be learned from the *Exxon Valdez* oil spill. It is unlikely that all of the problems associated with the oil spill would have gone away, even had there been extensive pre-planning. The oil industry must continue its work in developing good communication and relationships with villages and communities in Prince William Sound and other coastal areas to establish a foundation for responsible actions should another spill occur.

Acknowledgments—The author wishes to acknowledge the leadership and direction provided to the Oil Spill Health Task Force by Jim Fall, ADF&G, and Dr. Tom Nighswander, Indian Health Service; the support and integrity of the NOAA staff, especially Jay Field; all of the Village people impacted by the *Exxon Valdez* oil spill; and their leadership in being so patient with all of us while we attempted to work the impossible and failed much of the time.

CHAPTER 6

Developing a Sampling Strategy for Assessing Potential Contamination of Subsistence Seafood Resources Following the *Exxon Valdez* Oil Spill

*L. Jay Field**

Initial Response

The *Exxon Valdez* oil spill (EVOS) was unprecedented in terms of subsistence resources in the affected area. Another spill of this magnitude had yet to occur in proximity to local Native communities who depend on subsistence seafood resources for such a large percentage of their diets. State and federal resource agencies focused considerable attention on major commercial fisheries that were scheduled to open during the spring and summer. A conservative "zero-tolerance" policy was established by the State of Alaska for commercial salmon fisheries, resulting in many fishery closures that were due to the presence of oil in the fishing area. This policy was based on a need to protect the market for Alaskan salmon rather than on human-health concerns. When villagers began raising questions about the safety of consuming fish or shellfish from the spill area, the initial response from public health officials (ADHSS 1989a, 1989b) was that fish were safe to eat but shellfish from oiled areas should be avoided. This advice was based on the general knowledge that shellfish accumulate aromatic contaminants (ACs) in oil, whereas fish, because of their ability to rapidly metabolize ACs, would not be expected to accumulate more than trace amounts of ACs in edible tissue (Varanasi et al. 1989). Meanwhile, the initial oil-spill response lacked a plan for sampling subsistence resources for potential contamination.

The first attempt to address the growing concern about the safety of subsistence foods was a pilot study conducted by the Alaska Department of Fish and Game

*L. Jay Field has been a marine biologist with NOAA's Hazardous Materials Response and Assessment Division (now Office of Response and Restoration) since 1986. Most of his work has focused on the fate and effects of contaminants in coastal aquatic systems. During the EVOS, he served as NOAA's representative on the Alaska Oil Spill Health Task Force.

(ADF&G). Samples of fish and intertidal shellfish were collected in April and May of 1989 from customary subsistence harvest areas of the Prince William Sound communities of Tatitlek and Chenega Bay, and the Lower Cook Inlet communities of Nanwalek and Port Graham. Village representatives and the Alaska Department of Environmental Conservation (ADEC) laboratory in Palmer, Alaska evaluated samples for petroleum contamination using organoleptic methods (i.e., sight and smell). A U.S. Food and Drug Administration (USFDA) laboratory in Washington, DC conducted chemical analysis. However, in part because results from these chemical analyses were not available until late August (USFDA 1989), concern continued to increase in the subsistence communities.

During the same time period, the Kodiak Island Borough, which includes all the villages in the Kodiak Island archipelago, contracted with ENSR Consulting in April 1989 to conduct a baseline evaluation of the degree of petroleum contamination of intertidal shellfish from eight subsistence areas around Kodiak Island. One of the objectives of this study was to provide baseline information about the shellfish before oil from the spill reached those areas. ENSR consulted with ADF&G Subsistence Division personnel and village representatives to select important subsistence use areas. Samples were collected from three locations in each of the eight areas. Unfortunately, the results of the chemical analysis for petroleum hydrocarbons in these shellfish samples were never released because of a dispute between the Kodiak Island Borough and Exxon over funding. However, the locations identified were used in subsequent sampling.

Early in the summer of 1989, Exxon began planning a more comprehensive evaluation of the extent of petroleum contamination in subsistence resources throughout the spill area. During the same time period, the National Oceanic and Atmospheric Administration (NOAA) was asked by the Federal On-Scene Coordinator and the Oil Spill Health Task Force (OSHTF) to take an active role in addressing the subsistence food safety concerns of native villagers. In order to put together the most comprehensive and credible study possible, NOAA and Exxon signed a Memorandum of Understanding that had three principal features: 1) NOAA biologists would accompany the Exxon collection team to the villages and participate in the sample collections, 2) tissue samples from fish and shellfish subsistence resources would be analyzed for aromatic contaminants by NOAA's National Marine Fisheries Service Environmental Conservation laboratory in Seattle, and 3) all data from the study would be made public. These steps were taken to ensure the validity of the data produced by the study and to make certain that the results and their interpretation were made available to public health officials and the communities in a timely manner. The OSHTF reviewed the objectives of the study and was instrumental in determining the best methods to communicate the goals and results of the study to the villages. This chapter describes the sampling strategy that resulted from that decision.

While it was clear that the concerns of the communities about the effects of the oil spill on subsistence-food safety needed to be addressed, there was much debate about the data needed to evaluate the potential risk. To conduct a risk assessment, information was needed on exposure and toxicity. It was assumed that the toxicity assessment would be conducted using available information in the published literature and documents from governmental and international public health organizations; thus, the immediate focus of the study was to evaluate the potential exposure of subsistence users to petroleum-contaminated seafood.

An exposure assessment has two primary components: 1) what foods are consumed, in what quantity, and with what frequency? and 2) to what extent are these subsistence foods contaminated with petroleum-related compounds as a result of the oil spill? Before the oil spill, the ADF&G Division of Subsistence had compiled information on the amount of subsistence seafood resources harvested by the villagers in the spill area, and also had identified the specific locations of important subsistence harvest areas (Mishler and Cohen, unpublished data; Stanek 1982, 1985; Stratton and Chisum 1986; Stratton 1990). Consequently, the major data-collection effort was focused on determining the extent of petroleum contamination of subsistence resources. Thus, 13 subsistence harvest areas that were potentially affected by oil from the spill were identified for sample collection, including two in Prince William Sound, three in Lower Cook Inlet, and eight on Kodiak Island (Figure 6-1). In 1990, an additional four subsistence areas from the Alaska Peninsula were added to the study area. The principal criterion for selecting specific sampling locations was their importance for subsistence harvests. The degree of oiling from the spill was not a major factor in their selection.

Initial Study Design

The ADF&G pilot study provided the basis for the design of a more comprehensive food-safety study. The specifics of the study design were modified substantially throughout the first three years following the spill, based on evaluations of the data, village responses to the information provided in reports and presentations, and recommendations of other scientists (i.e., the "Expert Committee"; see Chapter 3,).

The overall objectives of the OSHTF food safety study were 1) assess the extent of petroleum contamination of subsistence resources in the area known to be affected by the oil spill and 2) to provide subsistence harvesters with reliable information to make their own decisions about the safety of subsistence seafood. To develop a study plan, several major issues had to be addressed:

- definition of the study area,
- selection of sampling locations,
- selection of target species,
- sampling frequency,

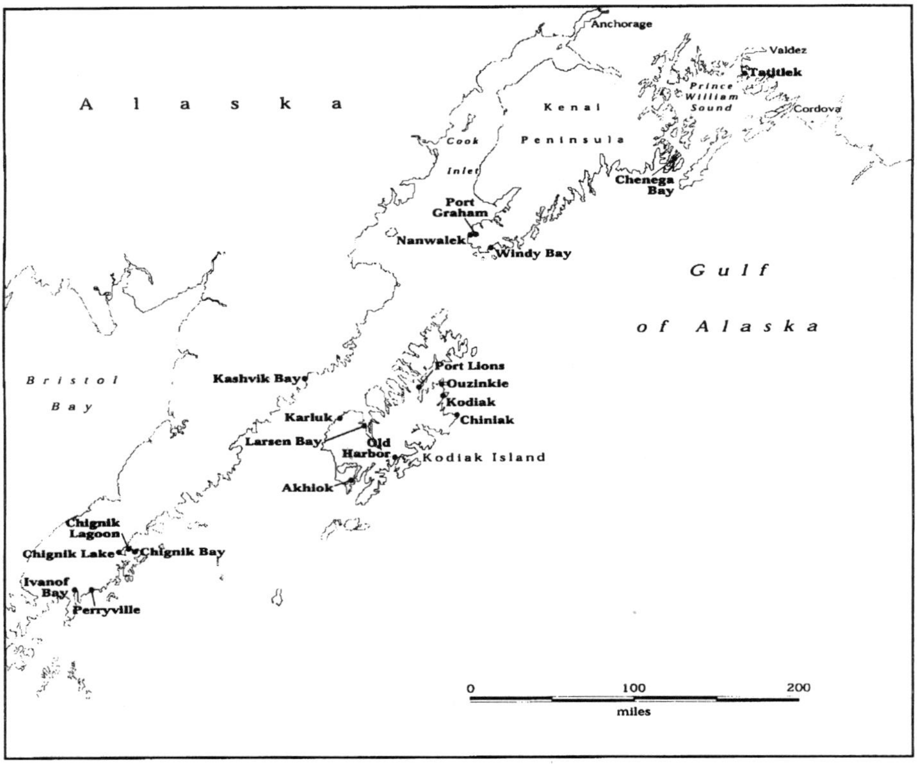

Figure 6-1 Subsistence food sampling study sampling locations, 1989–1991

- numbers of samples,
- collection methods, and
- analytical approach.

Design of the sampling plan also had to accommodate complicated logistics in collecting several different types of samples from multiple locations in a short time period. Sampling was scheduled to coincide with periods of extreme low tides, which occur for periods of three to five days in two-week intervals. Because of the remoteness of the areas, the sampling crews had a very limited window of opportunity to collect samples from each area. Problems with weather and transportation between villages (usually by chartered plane or helicopter) added further complications. The high level of activity involved with the spill response throughout the area resulted in great difficulties in finding available transportation and maintaining the necessary schedule.

Target species were not always available for sampling. The large number of sampling locations and the time limitations for sample collection (particularly for intertidal invertebrates) meant that the collection team could spend only a limited time at any one location, which sometimes resulted in incomplete collections.

In 1989, a Dames & Moore crew from Anchorage carried out the sample collection under contract with Exxon, accompanied by representatives from NOAA and ADF&G. In most cases, a village member served as a guide to the sampling areas and participated in the sample collection. In subsequent years (1990 and 1991), both ADF&G and Exxon collected samples with local assistance following the same sample-collection protocols (Figures 6-2 and 6-3).

Figure 6-2 Residents of Port Graham catch a Pacific cod for hydrocarbon testing

Figure 6-3 A resident of Perryville fishes for samples to test for hydrocarbons

Definition of the study area

All of the subsistence communities in the path of the spilled oil—including villages in Prince William Sound (Tatitlek and Chenega Bay), Lower Cook Inlet (Port Graham and Nanwalek), and Kodiak Island (Kodiak, Chiniak, Larsen Bay, Karluk, Old Harbor, Akhiok, Ouzinkie, and Port Lions)—expressed concern about the potential effects of oil contamination on the safety of subsistence food. The initial study area included 13 subsistence seafood collection areas that were near these villages or identified as important resource collection areas (Figure 6-1). Although the degree of oiling on the beaches differed considerably among areas, all areas were included and were given equivalent weight in terms of the amount of sampling effort. This approach was designed to provide each subsistence community with comparable information about the degree of contamination in subsistence resources from locations that the communities had identified as their priority subsistence harvest areas.

To provide background levels of ACs, reference-area samples of the same fish and shellfish species were collected from comparable subsistence areas outside the possible range of contamination from the *Exxon Valdez* spill and which had no known exposure to prior spills or other sources of petroleum products. In summer 1989, a limited number of samples were collected from the vicinity of Angoon in southeastern Alaska, which was selected as a reference area. Additional reference samples were collected from subsistence areas near Yakutat in southeastern Alaska in summer 1990.

Selection of sampling locations

The primary criterion used in the selection of sampling locations was the importance of the location for subsistence harvests. The locations previously identified by ADF&G for Prince William Sound and Lower Cook Inlet and by ENSR Consulting and ADF&G for Kodiak Island were used to establish the 13 sampling areas and the specific locations for intertidal shellfish and finfish collections. These locations had been selected through consultation with representatives in each village who identified important subsistence collection sites for different subsistence fish and invertebrate resources. Two beaches for the collection of intertidal shellfish and two fish-collection sites (one site each for salmon and bottomfish) were selected. Specific sampling sites were selected without consideration of the degree of oiling. Of the identified subsistence harvest areas, Windy Bay, which was designated as an important subsistence collection area by the Lower Cook Inlet villages of Port Graham and Nanwalek, was the most heavily oiled.

Selection of target species

Based on the studies conducted by ADF&G (Mishler and Cohen, unpublished data; Stanek 1982, 1985; Stratton and Chisum 1986; Stratton 1990), salmon represented the most important component (by weight) of the subsistence-seafood diet. Invertebrates, primarily clams and chitons, represented a much smaller percentage of the diet. Salmon, however, were considered some of the least likely species to accumulate petroleum compounds in their edible flesh for several reasons: salmon rapidly migrate from the open ocean to their freshwater spawning sites, limiting the amount of time they spend in the vicinity of the oiled shorelines; salmon usually stop feeding when they get close to spawning; and, like other fish species, salmon have the ability to rapidly metabolize and excrete aromatic contaminants (see Chapter 8).

The villagers within the study area consider numerous species of marine invertebrates important subsistence resources. Intertidal shellfish target species included clams (butter clams, *Saxidomus giganteus*; and littleneck clams, *Protothaca staminea*) and chitons (primarily *Katharina tunicata*) (Table 6-1). Mussels (*Mytilus edulis*), although not as highly prized by most subsistence collectors, were also included as target species because they are more readily available at a higher tidal elevation than most clam species and are easy to collect. In addition, mussels are commonly used for monitoring (e.g., National Mussel Watch Program) and were considered to be indicators of exposure for the beach area. Initially, an attempt was made to collect at least one sample of other species, such as sea urchins, snails, and octopus, brought to the attention of the study team by village representatives.

Table 6-1 List of invertebrate species sampled and number of samples analyzed for aromatic contaminants between 1989 and 1991

Common name	1989	1990	1991	Total
Chitons	33	116	34	183
Butter clams	44	147	17	208
Littleneck clams	14	128	33	175
Mussels	41	222	105	368
Soft-shelled clams		30	9	39
Bent-nosed clams		1		1
Horse clams	1	21		22
Razor clams		4		4
Other clams			3	3
Cockles	3	6	1	10
Limpets	1	5		6
Octopus		1		1
Sea urchin	2	7		9
Snails	6	1		7
Dungeness crab	5	2		7
King crab	2			2
Tanner crab	4	6		10
Spot shrimp		4	3	7
Total	156	701	205	1062

A few samples of different species of crab and shrimp were collected at a few locations but were not designated by the communities as high-priority subsistence foods for testing. Crustaceans also metabolize aromatic hydrocarbons, although not as efficiently as do most fish species (Chapter 7).

Salmon and halibut were the primary target fish species (Table 6-2). The species of salmon (*Oncorhynchus* spp.) collected varied among sampling periods and sampling areas, depending on which species were available at the time of sampling. In addition to halibut (*Hippoglossus stenolepis*), bottomfish such as Pacific cod (*Gadus macrocephalus*) and rockfish species (*Sebastes* spp.) were collected.

Table 6-2 List of fish species sampled and number of samples analyzed for aromatic contaminants between 1989 and 1991

	1989	1990	1991	Total
Salmonids				
Chinook salmon	1			1
Chum salmon	4	8		12
Coho salmon	29	4		33
Pink salmon	112	25		137
Sockeye salmon	10	9		19
Dolly varden	3	6		9
Bottomfish				
Halibut	31	10		41
Pacific cod	10	16		26
Rockfish species	7	4		11
Greenling		7		7
Irish lord	2	1		3
Ling cod		2		2
Rock sole		7		7
Starry flounder		2		2
Yellowfin sole	1	1		2
Total	210	102		312

Marine mammals, especially harbor seals and sea lions, represent an important part of the subsistence diet for a number of villages. Samples of liver, blubber, muscle, and kidney tissue were collected from 33 harbor seals and 10 sea lions in 1989 and 1990 from Prince William Sound and the Gulf of Alaska. Unlike the invertebrate and fish samples collected for the subsistence study, many of these animals were deliberately collected from heavily oiled areas with a high potential for exposure to *Exxon Valdez* oil as part of a natural resources damage assessment study (Frost et al. 1994). Samples from these highly exposed animals were analyzed to provide potential worst-case information. Since marine mammals are known to metabolize

ACs very efficiently, it was considered unlikely that these animals would accumulate aromatic hydrocarbons in their tissues. In 1990, a representative of NOAA's Alaska Marine Mammal Tissue Archival Program in Anchorage accompanied subsistence hunters from the Prince William Sound villages of Chenega Bay and Tatitlek and the Lower Cook Inlet villages of Port Graham and Nanwalek to collect tissue samples from seven harbor seals and one sea lion.

Sampling frequency

Collections during different times of the year were necessary to account for any seasonal differences in oil accumulation possibly resulting from the biology of the organisms or for any changes in the amount of oil on the beaches resulting from continued oil movement or ongoing cleanup activities. Warmer water temperatures also may affect the availability of the oil to biota. Some species, such as bottomfish, also tend to move into nearshore waters during the summer to feed, possibly increasing their exposure to oil.

Three collections of intertidal shellfish, bottomfish, and salmon were made in each village area on a monthly schedule during periods of the most extreme low tides from July to September 1989. Both Exxon and ADF&G collected additional samples of intertidal shellfish and fish from most of the same areas during winter, spring, and summer 1990.

Numbers of samples

In 1989, the study plan called for collection of approximately the same number of samples from each of the 13 sampling areas and a minimum number of samples of each target species per sampling location. Numbers of samples to be collected were three to five composite shellfish samples, four individual bottomfish samples, and 10 salmon samples. Because of various logistical problems, these target numbers often were not reached during the early sampling rounds.

In 1989, a total of 156 composite samples of intertidal shellfish, primarily mussels, two species of clams, and chitons) (Table 6-1) and 210 samples of fish, primarily pink, coho, and sockeye salmon and halibut (Table 6-2) from 13 areas were analyzed for ACs in edible tissue.

Sample collection and preservation

Samples for each target species were selected in the same manner that might be expected for a subsistence collector. The specific location on the beach was determined primarily by availability of the target species. In general, larger individuals of intertidal shellfish were collected preferentially. The amount of time available to sample multiple species on two different beaches during a single low-tide period was an important limiting factor on the approach to sample collection. Partly because of these time constraints, no transects or specific sampling locations were established, and no formal procedures for random collection of individual samples were used.

This approach limited the use of the data for statistical evaluation of temporal trends.

Collection methods emphasized the prevention of possible external contamination of samples during the sampling process. Collection gear was decontaminated by washing it in soapy water and rinsing it in clean seawater. Individuals handling the samples used latex surgical gloves. Clean gloves were used for each composite sample. Samples were rinsed in seawater to remove any superficial sediment, wrapped in aluminum foil (shiny side out) that had been baked at 350 °C for one hour, and placed inside locking freezer bags. Samples were immediately put in coolers with ice and transferred to a freezer as soon as possible (usually later the same day). Chain-of-custody sample-tracking procedures were followed.

Individual fish samples were collected using a variety of methods, including hook-and-line, longline, and gill net. Tissue samples consisted of a skin-on fillet. Bile was collected from the gall bladder of each fish, when possible. Individual samples of edible tissue (e.g., muscle, blubber, liver, and kidney) were collected from each marine mammal.

Selection of samples for analysis

Each sample of intertidal shellfish (mussels, clams, chitons, etc.) was a composite of multiple, similarly sized individuals of the same species. Compositing of samples was necessary to provide sufficient quantity of tissue for analysis. Composite samples also increase the number of individuals sampled and tend to reduce the variability among samples.

Fish tissue samples (fillets) were analyzed either as individuals or as composites of no more than three fish. Results from the bile analysis were used to composite fish that had similar levels of exposure to petroleum (see Chapter 8). All marine mammal tissue samples were analyzed as individual samples.

Analytical approach

Edible tissues from invertebrates, finfish, and marine mammals were analyzed for ACs , including alkylated PAHs and dibenzothiophenes, at NOAA's National Marine Fisheries Service laboratory in Seattle, Washington. The list of contaminants analyzed was selected to include the ACs found in Prudhoe Bay crude oil and those considered to be persistent in the environment with the potential for long-term human-health effects (see Chapter 9). Bile collected from the gall bladders of fish was also analyzed, since fish rapidly metabolize PAHs and the metabolites are concentrated in the bile before excretion (often at concentrations that are orders of magnitude greater than those in edible tissue) (Varanasi et al. 1989; Chapter 8). Analysis of fluorescent aromatic contaminants (FACs) in bile was used as a rapid screening test for indications of exposure to petroleum hydrocarbons and as a basis for compositing samples for analysis of ACs in edible tissue. The analytical protocols are described in detail in Appendix 1.

Modifications of sampling strategy in 1990 and 1991

The primary focus of the subsistence-seafood study was to provide the subsistence communities with information they could use to make their own decisions about the safety of consuming their traditional seafood resources. Following the release of the first round of data (July 1989 samples), an expert committee of toxicologists and other scientists reviewed the analytical approach and results (see Chapter 3). The results and the interpretation provided by the expert committee were presented by representatives of the OSHTF in visits to the subsistence communities in the fall of 1989. The types of questions raised during these village visits to present the preliminary findings included the following:

- You sampled beaches X and Y. What about beach Z?
- What about other species (e.g., sea urchins, tomcod, harbor seals, sea lions)?
- What can you tell from so few samples?
- Are subsistence resources safe to eat?

In response to some of these concerns and based on the analytical results from the previous years, the sampling strategy was modified in 1990 and 1991. Additional locations and additional species specifically requested by subsistence consumers were included. New sampling locations with a higher probability of exposure to the spilled oil also were included, such as southwestern Prince William Sound in the vicinity of the village of Chenega Bay and the outer Kenai Peninsula area between Windy Bay and the villages of Port Graham and Nanwalek. The emphasis in 1990 and 1991 was on specific intertidal shellfish species that were identified as primary "target" species, including two species of clams (butter clams and littleneck clams), mussels, and chitons. These species were commonly available in most locations, included species that were considered the most important subsistence shellfish species (clams and chitons), and represented different intertidal exposure regimes. The number of samples collected of each of these shellfish species was increased to provide a more reliable estimate of the degree of contamination associated with specific areas. Larger numbers of shellfish samples were collected from two small islands in Windy Bay—which represented the most heavily oiled location in the study area that was identified as a subsistence collection area—to provide data on temporal changes in AC concentrations.

All of the original intertidal sampling locations were included in the 1990 collections, with additional areas in the general use area of Chenega Bay included because of the higher probability of oil exposure. ADF&G sampled four additional subsistence areas on the Alaska Peninsula (Chignik, Perryville, Ivanof Bay, and Kashvik Bay) in 1990. The 1991 sample collections focused exclusively on Windy Bay and

Chenega Bay subsistence areas because beaches in those areas were the most likely to have been oiled during the spill.

In 1990, sample collection began in February in several areas because of a concern that winter storm activity could remove oil from beaches and make it more available to nearshore bottomfish. Sampling was conducted during several other time periods in 1990 and 1991, although not all locations were sampled during each collection period.

Finfish muscle tissue and bile samples were collected again in 1990. However, only half as many tissue samples as the 1989 analysis were analyzed because the results from 1989 demonstrated a lack of accumulation of ACs in edible flesh, despite evidence of a high concentration of metabolites in the bile of some samples, which indicated evidence of exposure. (Varanasi et al 1993; Chapter 8). In 1990, analysis of bile FACs was used to prioritize samples for tissue analysis—samples from fish showing evidence of a high degree of exposure were analyzed as well as a random selection of other fish samples (see Chapter 8). No fish tissue samples were collected in 1991.

Marine mammal samples, collected early in the spill as part of the natural resources damage assessment, were analyzed as a "worst case," since many of these animals were either visibly oiled at the time of collection or came from heavily oiled areas. Samples from harbor seals and sea lions collected from some of these same areas in 1990 were also analyzed, along with samples from animals harvested by subsistence hunters. No additional marine mammal samples were collected in 1991.

Important Issues in Sampling Strategy Development

Complicating factors in developing a sampling design

Determining whether subsistence marine resources were contaminated following the EVOS was complicated by a number of factors, including the large geographic area potentially affected by spilled oil, the irregular nature of the coastline, the patchy distribution of oil, the variety of species harvested by subsistence users, and the difficult logistics involved in carrying out the sample collections.

Because of the high degree of variability in distribution of the oil, samples from one beach within an area may not be considered representative of other beaches in the same area or even of other parts of the same beach. For example, composite samples of mussels collected at the same time from different sections of the same small beach on an island in Windy Bay, which had been heavily oiled in 1989, differed in total AC concentration by more than two orders of magnitude during the summer of 1990.

Extrapolating the results from one species to another in the same area is generally not appropriate because of physiological differences between species or because of different exposure pathways resulting from interspecies differences in diet or habitat preference. For example, chitons, which primarily inhabit rocky intertidal areas, have a different exposure pathway than do mussels on coarse-grained sediment. Also, the distribution of mussels extends higher in the intertidal zone than that of either clams or chitons. In most cases, mussels had higher AC concentrations than did either clams or chitons from the same beach (Varanasi et al. 1993; Chapter 7). Similar or slightly higher AC concentrations in clams were reported in another study in 1995 (Roberts et al. 1998) in which clams and mussels were collected from the same location on two different beaches on Block Island with residual oil. These apparent differences may have less to do with interspecies differences in uptake and accumulation than with the distribution of the oil remaining on the beaches. Interspecies differences in the ability to metabolize ACs, however, can have a significant influence on the amount of ACs accumulated, even among related taxonomic groups with comparable exposure (Meador et al. 1995).

Seasonal differences in exposure may complicate interpretation of the results for individual species. For example, the availability of the oil may change because of redistribution during storms or increased temperatures that make the oil more mobile. Beach cleanup activities also may increase temporarily the availability of oil. Biological changes associated with seasonal differences such as reproductive cycle or filtration rate also may affect accumulation (Meador et al. 1995).

Allocation of sampling effort

The degree of oiling was not factored into the initial study design and allocation of sampling effort relative to the areas sampled in order to provide each subsistence community with a similar amount of information on their selected subsistence harvest areas. In subsequent years, the study focused on subsistence areas with greater likelihood of contamination. Because an estimated 40% of oil spilled from the *Exxon Valdez* was stranded on the beaches in Prince William Sound, with much smaller amounts reaching the beaches on the Outer Kenai Peninsula (Lower Cook Inlet) and Kodiak Island (Galt et al. 1991; Wolfe et al. 1994), areas within southwestern Prince William Sound with a higher degree of oiling on the beaches and higher concentrations in intertidal shellfish samples were given much greater emphasis in the sample collections in 1990 and 1991.

Sampling effort also initially was not weighted according to importance of a subsistence resource or its likelihood of contamination in order to provide information on a range of important subsistence resources. For each village, sampling effort was distributed equally among fish and intertidal shellfish (Table 6-3). The knowledge that invertebrates were much more likely to accumulate ACs present in the spilled oil than were finfish—which have a much greater ability to metabolize and excrete ACs (Varanasi et al 1989)—was the basis for the advice that shellfish from oiled areas should be avoided and that fish were safe to eat. Measurements of edible tissue AC concentrations in fish, in addition to the bile FAC analysis that was used to

Table 6-3 Number of samples of invertebrate and fish samples analyzed between 1989 and 1991 by study area

Invertebrates	Location	1989	1990	1991	Total
Prince William Sound					
	Chenega Bay	7	81	106	194
	Tatitlek	9	36	0	45
Lower Cook Inlet					
	Windy Bay	7	81	99	187
	Pt. Graham/ Nanwalek	16	68	0	84
	Other Areas	4	73	0	77
Kodiak					
	Akhiok	7	18	0	25
	Chiniak	21	31	0	52
	Karluk	7	16	0	23
	Kodiak	8	39	0	47
	Larsen Bay	17	33	0	50
	Old Harbor	18	53	0	71
	Ouzinkie	9	52	0	61
	Port Lions	20	49	0	69
Alaska Peninsula					
	Chignik	0	19	0	19
	Ivanof Bay	0	14	0	14
	Katmai	0	4	0	4
	Perryville	0	10	0	10
Reference areas					
	Angoon	6			6
	Yakutat		24		24
Fish					
Prince William Sound					
	Chenega Bay	31	17		48
	Tatitlek	17	6		23
Lower Cook Inlet					
	Windy Bay	0	2		2
	Pt. Graham/ Nanwalek	13	17		30
	Other Areas				

Table 6-3 continued

Fish	Location	1989	1990	1991	Total
Kodiak					
	Akhiok	4	3		7
	Chiniak	19	0		19
	Karluk	6	7		13
	Kodiak	16	3		19
	Larsen Bay	27	4		31
	Old Harbor	24	9		33
	Ouzinkie	23	12		35
	Port Lions	22	5		27
Alaska Peninsula					
	Chignik				
	Ivanof Bay				
	Katmai				
	Perryville		5		5
Reference areas					
	Angoon	8			8
	Yakutat		12		12

evaluate recent exposure to oil, provided direct confirmation of the lack of AC accumulation in fish.

The first priority was to measure the degree of contamination in selected resources at locations specifically identified as important subsistence collection sites by the villages. A worst-case approach would have selected sampling locations within the study area with the greatest probability of exposure (i.e., beaches that were most heavily oiled). Emphasizing the collection of species such as mussels that may be more likely to have higher AC body burden in edible tissue because of a lack of metabolic ability or because of exposure pathway or location would increase the probability of finding evidence of contamination. It was assumed that other studies, particularly those assessing the injury to biological resources resulting from the spill, would focus on locations and organisms that would be most likely to be affected.

Selection of target species

Subsistence harvests included a long list of species, and the importance of individual species varied among communities and individuals. Although the focus of the study was to provide subsistence users with information on AC concentrations in selected species at specific locations that were important to subsistence users, extrapolation of the results to other species and locations was expected. Identification of target species that could be considered representative of the types of intertidal exposure was based primarily on habitat type and availability. Smaller numbers of other species were collected at the request of individuals or if the target species were not available at the location and time of sampling. For salmon, the species collected were primarily determined by availability at the time of sampling. The shellfish species targeted—chitons, two species of clams, and mussels—inhabited different intertidal habitats, were generally available at most locations, and, except for mussels, were consistently high on the lists of important shellfish resources for the subsistence communities. Mussels, in addition to being a moderately important subsistence resource, are often used as a sentinel species that can provide information on the general degree of contamination in an area (e.g., National Status and Trends Mussel Watch). Thus, the concentrations of ACs in mussels from subsistence beaches could be compared with the values from other parts of the country to provide a comparative frame of reference for the degree of contamination. In addition, pre-spill data on concentrations in mussels from Prince William Sound were available (Short and Babcock 1996).

Logistical problems affecting sample collection

Any sampling strategy had to take into account the collection of samples from many remote locations, using a variety of gear types with a narrow time period for intertidal sample collection. Weather conditions often affected the ability of the sampling team to arrive at the designated beaches at low tide or even to get into or out of the villages. During the first year, with all of the spill-response activity taking place, it was often difficult to find air transportation to the more remote villages and boats to charter for the sample collections. One solution to some of these types of logistical problems was to have the sampling teams spend more time in each village, although this requires additional sampling teams and training to ensure consistency of collection methods.

Trends in concentrations over time

Evaluation of temporal trends in concentrations was not one of the original objectives of the subsistence study. The lack of established, fixed transects for intertidal invertebrate sample collections made it difficult to follow trends over time in the concentrations of ACs in the commonly collected species. Also, most of the subsistence beaches included in the study, with the exception of the stations on two small islands in Windy Bay, received very little oiling, and the concentrations in shellfish were low even in 1989 (Varanasi et al 1993; Chapter 7). Although mussels collected from the islands in Windy Bay clearly showed a decline in concentration over the three years of sampling, differences in concentration appeared to be associated with the tidal elevation of the collection location (with samples collected from higher intertidal elevations generally having higher concentrations) and with seasonal variations in concentration.

A natural resources damage assessment study of heavily oiled mussel beds in Prince William Sound, which employed fixed sample transect locations and regular random sample collections, reported a very patchy distribution of oil in sediment and in mussels, even along the same tidal elevation (Babcock et al. 1996; Harris et al. 1996). Even within the same mussel bed, tissue concentrations of mussels varied by as much as two orders of magnitude, with some of the samples having concentrations comparable to background locations. This demonstrates a very high degree of variability in AC concentrations in a single species from a small, heavily oiled area.

Summary and Lessons Learned

The primary goal of the subsistence sampling program was to provide subsistence users with information to assist them in making informed decisions about the consumption of subsistence resources. Subsistence users wanted to know whether subsistence resources were safe to eat and made it clear that they would not be satisfied with assurances from public health officials that were based on sensory evaluations. They wanted samples of subsistence resources collected and tested for oil contamination using current analytical chemical procedures and instrumentation.

The first, and most immediate, question that the sampling program needed to address was whether subsistence resources were contaminated with oil following the EVOS. More specifically, were concentrations of ACs (considered to be the components of crude oil most likely to cause long-term health effects) elevated in subsistence resources? If subsistence resources were found to be contaminated, other questions became important: Are the concentrations high enough to represent a significant health concern? Are concentrations declining? Is EVOS the source of the contamination?

Determining whether subsistence resources were contaminated with oil required the identification of priority harvest areas and species for all of the subsistence communities within the spill area. Many of these areas and species already had been identified prior to the spill by ADF&G subsistence surveys. This information was supplemented by direct input from village representatives in the selection of specific sampling locations. While this approach provided information for many priority subsistence-collection areas, not all subsistence-collection locations or species could be sampled.

Because no pre-spill data on AC concentrations were available for subsistence resources from the selected sampling locations, it was necessary for comparative purposes to collect background data from the same species from subsistence areas outside of the spill area. However, the background samples were collected only during one sampling period in both 1989 and 1990, compared with at least three sampling periods from the spill area, and the numbers of samples were limited, particularly in 1989. More comprehensive sampling of key target invertebrate and fish species from a suitable background area would have improved the ability to make statistical comparisons in order to put the observed concentrations into perspective.

While equitable, the decision in 1989 to distribute the sampling effort equally among the subsistence villages within the spill area meant that each village had only two intertidal locations selected. In subsequent years, the focus of the program shifted to include additional shellfish sampling locations in the areas most likely to have been affected by the spill (i.e., southwestern Prince William Sound and Lower Cook Inlet). By collecting fewer samples from areas with the least evidence of heavy oiling, perhaps by reducing the number of sampling cycles from three to one, it would have been possible to increase the number of locations sampled in the higher-risk areas while still providing coverage of the lower-risk areas.

Few of the sampling locations selected as priority subsistence areas showed evidence of moderate to heavy oiling in shellfish (Varanasi et al. 1993; Chapter 7). For those locations, it was important to document temporal changes in concentration. Information on temporal changes would be useful for the human-health risk assessment to estimate changes in exposure concentrations over time. However, because the concentrations appeared to vary greatly in collections made from the same sampling location at the same time, quantifying the temporal changes was difficult. To measure such changes, it would have been preferable to identify several contaminated beaches as trend-monitoring stations as soon as possible, establish permanent, fixed transects for each target species, and conduct regularly scheduled random sampling for statistical comparisons. Without a statistical sampling design, qualitative observations on the temporal changes were all that was possible.

Many other studies also collected biological samples from the area of the spill (e.g., damage assessment studies conducted by both Exxon and state and federal trustees to evaluate injury to natural resources). Because none of these other studies were able to release information to the public, it was impossible for the subsistence sampling program to coordinate with these other collection efforts. Some of these studies collected information that would have complemented the subsistence study (e.g., studies using standard statistical sampling designs to evaluate temporal changes in intertidal shellfish concentrations from contaminated beaches).

The subsistence sampling program was designed to provide information to subsistence collectors that could be used to supplement their own observations. The health advice consistently recommended that subsistence users avoid collecting shellfish from obviously contaminated areas, although very few of the areas sampled were obviously contaminated. In 1991, a number of mussel beds in Prince William Sound were found to be highly contaminated with residual oil (Babcock et al. 1996; Harris et al. 1996). The dense mussel beds appeared to trap oil in the sediment beneath the beds, with the result that the concentrations of ACs declined very slowly and oil remained bioavailable for uptake by the mussels. While these beds are apparently readily identified by sight and smell (Babcock et al. 1996), which should make them relatively easy for subsistence collectors to avoid, it illustrates the potential persistence of the spilled oil in some subsistence collection areas and the importance of identifying and monitoring these areas.

Acknowledgments—The design and implementation of the subsistence study represents the efforts of many individuals. David Schmidt, formerly of Dames & Moore, was responsible for the initial design of the subsistence study and directed the field sampling effort during 1989. James Fall, Robert Wolfe, Philippa Coiley,and Rita Miraglia (Subsistence Division of the Alaska Department of Fish and Game) played a major role in the development of the study design and sampling strategy. Steven Lewis of Exxon Biomedical directed Exxon's participation in the subsistence study. Usha Varanasi, Sin-Lam Chan, Donald Brown, Thomas Hom, Margaret Krahn, and others at the Environmental Conservation Division of NOAA's Northwest Fisheries Center provided significant contributions to the study design and sampling methodology. Len Vining, as a representative of The North Pacific Rim, provided valuable input on study design at Task Force meetings. Others who played an important role included Craig Mishler, Lisa Scarbrough, Ronald Stanek, and Janet Cohen of the Subsistence Division of the Alaska Department of Fish and Game, David Erikson of Dames & Moore, and Judy Meidinger as Exxon's native liaison.

References

[ADHSS] Alaska Dept. of Health and Social Services. 1989a. Oil spill public health advice. Anchorage AK: Division of Public Health, Section of Epidemiology. Bulletin No. 6, May 5, 1989.

[ADHSS] Alaska Dept. of Health and Social Services. 1989b. Oil spill public health advice - Report No. 2. Anchorage AK: Division of Public Health, Section of Epidemiology. Bulletin No. 8, July 14, 1989.

Babcock MM, Irvine G, Harris P.M., Cusick JA, Rice SD. 1996. Persistence of oiling in mussel beds three and four years after the *Exxon Valdez* oil spill. In: Proceedings of the Exxon Valdez Oil Spill Symposium; 2–5 Feb 1993; Anchorage, AK; Bethesda MD: American Fisheries Society.

Frost KJ, Manen CA, Wade TL. 1994. Petroleum hydrocarbons in tissues of harbor seals from Prince William Sound and the Gulf of Alaska. In: Loughlin TR, editor. Marine mammals and *Exxon Valdez*. San Diego CA: Academic Press. p 331–358.

Galt JA, Lehr WJ, Payton DL. 1991. Fate and transport of the *Exxon Valdez* oil spill. *Environ Sci Technol* 25:202–209.

Harris PM, Rice SD, Babcock MM, Brodersen CC. 1996. Within-bed distribution of *Exxon Valdez* crude oil in Prince William Sound blue mussels and underlying sediments. In: Proceedings of the Exxon Valdez Oil Spill Symposium; 2–5 Feb 1993; Anchorage, AK; Bethesda MD: American Fisheries Society.

Meador JP, Stein JE, Reichert WL, Varanasi U. 1995. Bioaccumulation of polycyclic aromatic hydrocarbons by marine organisms. *Rev Environ Contam Toxicol* 143:79–165.

Mishler C, Cohen J. Unpublished data. Subsistence uses in six Kodiak Island Borough communities in 1989, the year of the *Exxon Valdez* oil spill. Juneau AK: Division of Subsistence, Alaska Department of Fish and Game. Technical Paper No. 201.

Roberts P, Henry CB Jr, Shigenaka G. 1998. Documentation of weathered petroleum "bioavailability" to intertidal bivalve species after the T/V *Exxon Valdez* incident. In: Proceedings of the 21st Arctic and Marine Oil Spill Program Technical Science Seminar; 10–12 June 1998; Alberta, Canada. Ottawa, ON, Canada: Environment Canada. p 939–940.

Short JW, Babcock MM. 1996. Pre-spill and post-spill concentrations of hydrocarbons in sediment and mussels in Prince William Sound, Alaska. In: Proceedings of the Exxon Valdez Oil Spill Symposium; 2–5 Feb 1993; Anchorage, AK; Bethesda MD: American Fisheries Society.

Stanek RT. 1982. Natural resource harvest at Port Graham and English Bay, 1982: An interim report. Juneau AK: Division of Subsistence, Alaska Department of Fish and Game. Technical Paper No. 32.

Stanek RT. 1985. Patterns of wild resource use in English Bay and Port Graham, Alaska. Juneau AK: Division of Subsistence, Alaska Department of Fish and Game. Technical Paper No. 104.

Stratton L. 1990. Resource harvests and use in Tatitlek, Alaska. Juneau AK: Division of Subsistence, Alaska Department of Fish and Game. Technical Paper No. 181.

Stratton L, Chisum EB. 1986. Resource use patterns in Chenega, Western Prince William Sound: Chenega in the 1960s and Chenega Bay 1984-1986. Juneau AK: Division of Subsistence, Alaska Department of Fish and Game. Technical Paper No. 139.

[USFDA] U.S. Food and Drug Administration. 1989. Summary of analyses of subsistence seafood from pilot study. Washington DC: Center for Food Safety and Applied Nutrition, U.S. Food and Drug Administration.

Varanasi U, Stein JE, Nishimoto M. 1989. Biotransformation and disposition of polycyclic aromatic hydrocarbons (PAH) in fish. In: Varanasi U, editor. Metabolism of polycyclic aromatic hydrocarbons in the aquatic environment. Boca Raton FL: CRC Press. p 94–149.

Varanasi U, Brown DW, Hom T, Burrows DG, Sloan CA, Field LJ, Stein JE, Tilbury KL, McCain BB, Chan S-L. 1993. Survey of Alaskan subsistence fish, marine mammal, and invertebrate samples collected 1989-1991 for exposure to oil spilled from the *Exxon Valdez*. Seattle WA: NOAA Tech. Memo. NMFS F/NWC-12.

Wolfe DA, Hameedi MJ, Galt JA, Watabayashi G, Short J, O'Claire C, Rice S, Michel J, Payne JR, Braddock J, Hanna S, Sale D. 1994. The fate of the oil spilled from the *Exxon Valdez*. *Environ Sci Technol* 28:561A–568A.

CHAPTER 7

Exposure of Alaskan Subsistence Shellfish to Oil Spilled from the *Exxon Valdez*

Donald W. Brown, Douglas G. Burrows, Catherine A. Sloan, Ronald W. Pearce, Susan M. Pierce, Jennie L. Bolton, Karen L. Tilbury, Katherine L. Dana, Margaret M. Krahn, Sin-Lam Chan, Usha Varanasi*

The oil spilled from the *Exxon Valdez* raised concerns among native Alaskans that their subsistence seafood (fish, marine mammals, and invertebrate organisms) was contaminated with petroleum (Varanasi et al. 1990). In response to the concerns of the villagers, the National Oceanic and Atmospheric Administration (NOAA) entered into memoranda of understanding with Exxon, and subsequently with the Alaska Department of Fish and Game (ADF&G), to analyze subsistence foods sampled from sites near native Alaskan villages and from reference areas for selected aromatic compounds (ACs) found in spilled oil (see Chapter 6 and Chapter 8 this volume; Varanasi et al. 1993a).

The Prudhoe Bay crude oil (PBCO) spilled from the *Exxon Valdez* was analyzed at the beginning of the study to determine the composition of the ACs that could be present in samples of subsistence foods (Appendix 1). Petroleum, such as PBCO, contains a variety of alkylated ACs, as well as the alkylated dibenzothiophenes typical of the North Slope crude oils (Clark and Brown 1977; Fedorak and Westlake 1981, 1983). However, spilled oil is degraded in time by physical, chemical, and microbial processes, so the aromatic fraction of the weathered oil will contain those ACs that are most resistant to weathering (e.g., highly alkylated naphthalenes, phenanthrenes and dibenzothiophenes) (Boehm et al. 1981; Atlas et al. 1981). These refractory compounds comprise a group of ACs that can be monitored in certain marine biota as indicators of exposure to petroleum. For example, mollusks have only a limited ability to metabolize ACs (Moore et al. 1989), so these compounds are bioconcentrated in their tissues (Neff 1979; James 1989; Livingstone 1991). Consequently, mollusks exposed to ACs can serve as a source of these contaminants to subsistence gatherers, as well as to biota that feed on the mollusks.

---

*Mr. Brown is an analytical chemist with 30 years experience analyzing samples for environmental pollutants. Mr. Brown and his associates at the Northwest & Alaska Fisheries Center (now the Northwest Fisheries Science Center) analyzed samples of biota collected following the *Exxon Valdez* spill and reported their data to the Alaska Oil Spill Health Task Force.

Evaluating and Communicating Subsistence Seafood Safety in a Cross-Cultural Context: Lessons Learned from the Exxon Valdez Oil Spill
L. Jay Field et al., editors. © 1999 Society of Environmental Toxicology and Chemistry (SETAC). ISBN 1-880611-29-5

The concentrations of ACs in four target mollusk species will be the main focus of this chapter. The results of analyses of mollusk samples collected in 1989 to 1994 from 24 sampling areas (88 sampling stations), as well as two reference areas, are reported. Temporal trends of the concentrations of ACs in mollusks were evaluated to determine if evidence of petroleum decreased with time. Patterns of relative concentrations of ACs (i.e., fingerprints) (Atlas et al. 1981; Boehm et al. 1981) in petroleum from the *Exxon Valdez* and in extracts of selected mollusk samples were compared to determine if oil spilled from the *Exxon Valdez* might have been the source of ACs in the mollusks.

Methods

Samples of marine biota were collected under two programs using similar protocols; these protocols are described fully in Chapter 6. Species and site summaries are detailed by Varanasi et al. (1993a). As explained in Chapter 6, the sampling was done in a manner similar to that of subsistence gatherers collecting mollusks for food. The protocols for the chemical analyses (Appendix 1) consisted of three major steps: 1) extraction, 2) liquid chromatography to separate the analytes from the tissue matrix, and 3) determination of ACs using gas chromatography/mass spectrometry (GC/MS). The ACs listed in Table 7-1 can be divided into the low-molecular-weight ACs (LACs) (i.e., two- and three-ring ACs) and the high-molecular-weight ACs (HACs) (i.e. four- to six-ring ACs). This division allows us to classify the ACs into: 1) the more water-soluble and acutely toxic compounds, LACs and 2) the less water-soluble and more chronically toxic compounds, HACs (NRC 1985). Method precision and accuracy were demonstrated by quality control measures that included the use of internal standards, standard reference materials, method blanks, replicate analyses, interlaboratory exercises, and instrument calibration checks.

Mollusks were collected from 1989 to 1994 from a number of sampling areas (Chapter 6; Varanasi et al. 1993a). Mussels (*Mytilus edulis*), butter clams (*Saxidomus giganteus*), littleneck clams (*Protothaca staminea*), and chitons (order *Neoloricata*) were the primary target invertebrate species. The largest number of samples was collected from the Chenega (Figure 7-1) and Windy Bay (Figure 7-2) sampling areas (227 samples and 183 samples, respectively) because these were the two subsistence food-collection areas suspected to be most impacted by the spill. In 1991, these were the only areas sampled. At most sampling areas, more than one sampling station (i.e., beach area) was chosen (Chapter 6).

The sum of the concentrations of the ACs listed in Table 7-1 is used in this chapter to discuss the extent of contamination of mollusks. The concentrations of ACs are on a wet-weight basis, and all data are included in Varanasi et al. (1993b). The contamination of mollusks by ACs is discussed below, both in terms of mean concentrations for an area, which represent a general level of contamination, and concentrations in individual samples, which represent worst-case situations.

Table 7-1 Aromatic contaminants (aromatic hydrocarbons and dibenzothiophenes) determined in edible tissue in the Exxon/Alaska Department of Fish and Game/NOAA subsistence fish, marine mammal, and shellfish studies

2- and 3-ring aromatic compounds (LACs)[1]	4- to 6-ring aromatic compounds (HACs)
Naphthalene (NPH)	Fluoranthene (FLA)
C1-naphthalenes (C1NPH)[2]	Pyrene (PYR)
C2-naphthalenes (C2NPH)	C1-fluoranthenes/pyrenes (C1FLA)
C3-naphthalenes (C3NPH)	Benz[a]anthracene (BaA)
C4-naphthalenes (C4NPH)	Chrysene (CHR)
Acenaphthylene (ACY)	C1-chrysenes/benz[a]anthracenes (C1CHR)
Acenaphthene (ACE)	C2-chrysenes/benz[a]anthracenes (C2CHR)
Fluorene (FLU)	C3-chrysenes/benz[a]anthracenes (C3CHR)
C1-fluorenes (C1FLU)	C4-chrysenes/benz[a]anthracenes (C4CHR)
C2-fluorenes (C2FLU)	Benzo[b]fluoranthene (BbF)
C3-fluorenes (C3FLU)	Benzo[k]fluoranthene (BkF)
Phenanthrene (PHN)	Benzo[a]pyrene (BaP)
C1-phenanthrenes/anthracenes (C1PHN)	Indeno[1,2,3-cd]pyrene (IDP)
C2-phenanthrenes/anthracenes (C2PHN)	Dibenz[a,h]anthracene (DBA)
C3-phenanthrenes/anthracenes (C3PHN)	Benzo[ghi]perylene (BZP)
C4-phenanthrenes/anthracenes (C4PHN)	
Dibenzothiophene (DBT)	
C1-dibenzothiophenes (C1DBT)	
C2-dibenzothiophenes (C2DBT)	
C3-dibenzothiophenes (C3DBT)	

[1]Lower molecular weight ACs = LACs; higher molecular weight ACs = HACs.
[2]C1-, C2-, etc. are abbreviations for methyl-, dimethyl/ethyl-, etc., respectively

A statistical package (GT2 comparison-interval graphs) was used to evaluate temporal changes of the concentrations of ACs in mollusks. The GT2 comparison interval for each mean is calculated based on the number of samples for that mean, the variability about that mean, and the number of means being compared (Gabriel 1978; Sokal and Rohlf 1981). The advantage of using GT2 plots with comparison intervals is that they provide a graphic depiction of significant differences between means (i.e., the comparison intervals overlap when the means are not significantly different [$p \leq 0.05$]).

Results and Discussion

Aromatic compounds in mollusks

Mussels, butter clams, littleneck clams and chitons were collected from 88 stations for subsistence studies from 1989 to 1994. The concentrations of ACs found in samples from these stations ranged widely from not detected to about 18,000 ng/g (Varanasi et al. 1993b) but exceeded 100 ng/g at only 14 of the 88 sampling stations (Table 7-2). The concentrations of ACs in mollusk samples from the 74 other

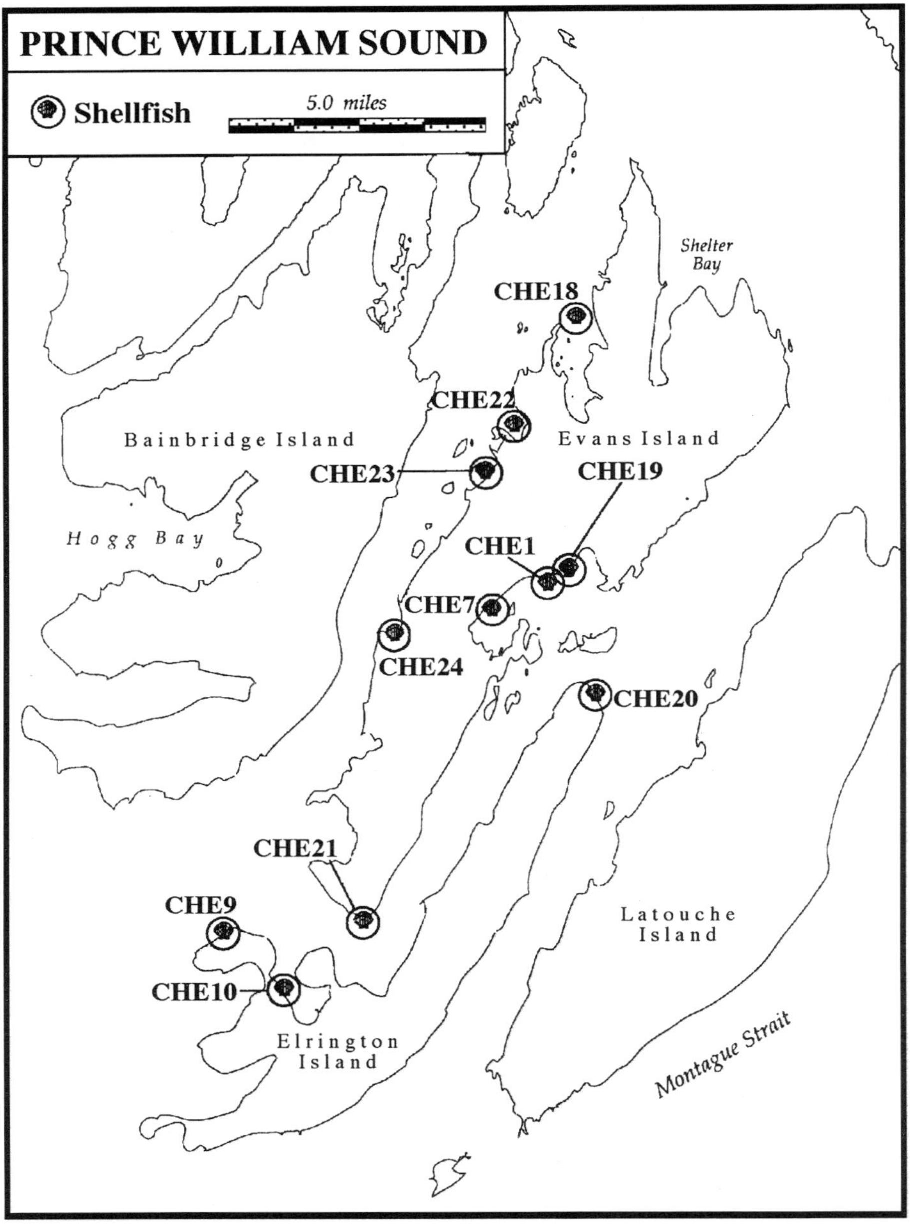

Figure 7-1 Shellfish sampling stations in the vicinity of Chenega Bay

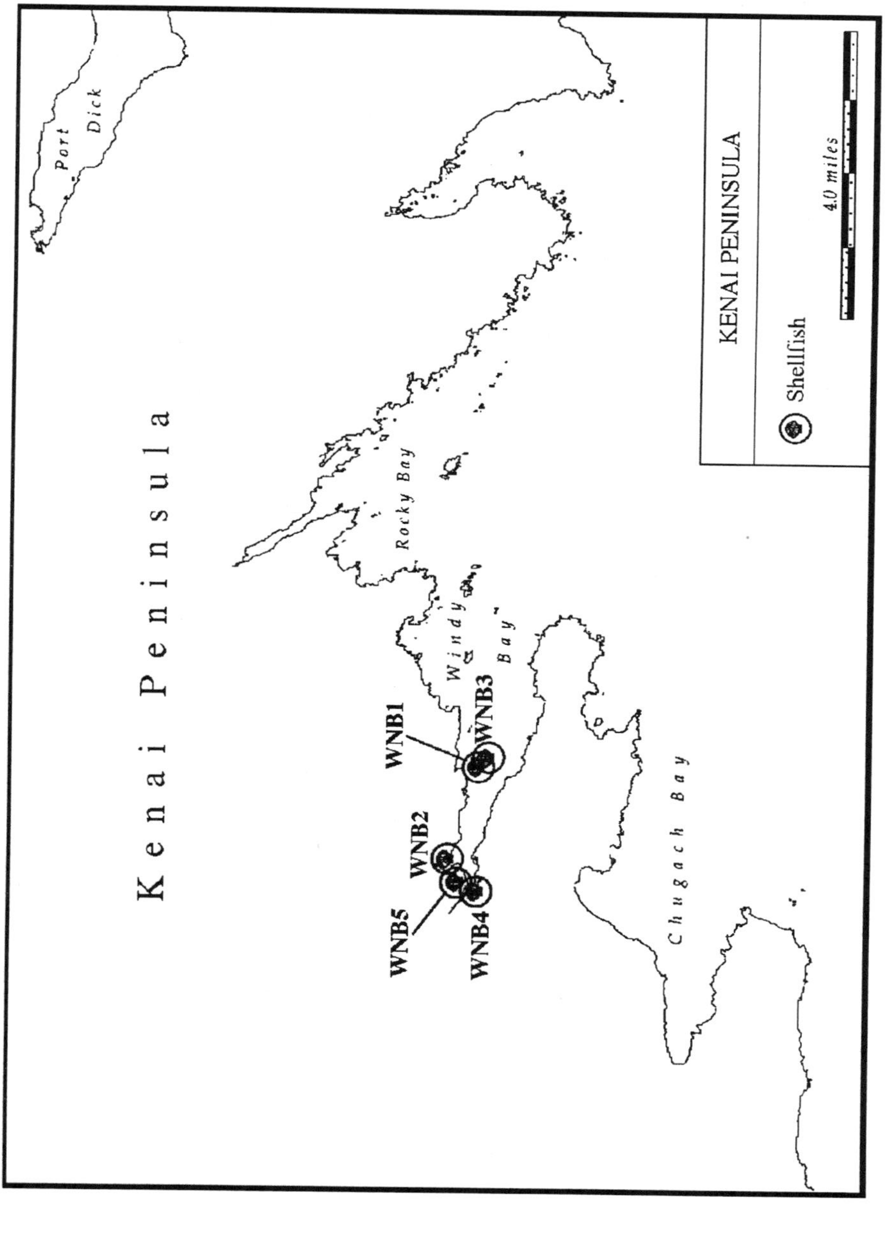

Figure 7-2 Shellfish sampling stations in Windy Bay

sampling stations were quite low; most were much lower than 100 ng/g. The stations that had one or more mollusk samples with concentrations of ACs in moderately ($\sum$ACs = 100 to 1000 ng/g) or highly contaminated ($\sum$ACs >1000 ng/g) categories are shown in Table 7-2; the results from other stations are combined and listed as other sites. Stations CHE7, WNB1, WNB3, and KOD3 (Figures 7-1 through 7-3) had the most samples in the moderately or highly contaminated categories. The concentrations of ACs in many of the invertebrate samples from the above stations were in the uncontaminated category, and most of the mean concentrations of ACs in these samples fell in either the uncontaminated or minimally contaminated categories. Only 25 of the more than 1000 invertebrate samples analyzed were considered highly contaminated (>1000 ng/g). Of these 25 samples, all were mussels or clams except for one sample of chitons. The highest mean concentrations were in mollusks from stations WNB1 and WNB3 (Table 7-3). None of the invertebrates from stations sampled in 1993 to 1994 was highly contaminated and only one station (CHE28, a new station) had samples that contained AC concentrations in the moderately contaminated category. The emphasis herein will be on those areas in which samples were moderately to highly contaminated.

Aromatic compounds in mussels

Sites with the highest mean concentrations of ACs in mussels during the 1989 to 1991 studies (Table 7-3) were Chenega stations CHE7 (1990: 640 ± 830 ng/g) and CHE10 (1990: 1100 ± 620 ng/g); Windy Bay stations WNB1 (1989: 8400 ± 8800 ng/g) and WNB3 (1990: 1600 ± 2100 ng/g); and Kodiak station KOD3 (1989: 1700 ng/g; 1990: 630 ± 200 ng/g). Of the 367 mussel samples collected during the 1989 to 1991 study, only 15 samples (4%) were highly contaminated and all were from the Chenega, Windy Bay, and Kodiak sampling areas (Varanasi et al. 1993a). A total of 47 mussel samples (13%) were moderately contaminated and were from the Old Harbor and Chignik sampling areas, in addition to the above areas. However, of these 47 mussel samples, many were in the low range of the moderately contaminated category (i.e., the concentrations of ACs were < 200 ng/g in 28 of the 47 samples). Even at the more contaminated Windy Bay stations WNB1 and WNB3, only 15 of the 32 moderately or highly contaminated mussel samples had concentrations > 200 ng/g.

The mean concentrations of ACs in most mussel samples collected in 1993 to 1994 were near background levels (< 10 ng/g; Table 7-3). The highest mean concentrations of ACs in mussels collected during these later sampling periods were found in samples from Chenega station CHE28 on the northern tip of Chenega Island (autumn 1994: 113 ± 42 ng/g; n = 3) and Tatitlek station TAT1 (summer 1994: 35 ± 8.3 ng/g; n = 3). The source of the ACs in mussels from CHE28 was likely petroleum-contaminated gravel that had been transferred to the beach prior to mussel sampling. In contrast, the source of ACs in the TAT1 mussels appeared to be products of combustion because these mussels contained a large proportion of high-molecular-weight ACs. Of the stations sampled in 1989 to 1991 that had elevated concentra-

Table 7-2 Total number of samples of target species (butter clams, chitons, littleneck clams, and mussels) by concentration category

	Number of samples containing ACs			
	Concentration range			
Station no.	Not contaminated (<10ng/g)	Minimally contaminated (10-99 ng/g)	Moderately contaminated 100-1,000 ng/g	Highly contaminated (>1,000ng/g)
Tatitlek				
T1	0	7	2	0
Chenega Bay				
CHE1	8	24	6	0
CHE7	0	14	28	3
CHE10	16[6]	22	2	1
CHE24	9	0	1	0
CHE28	0[3]	0[1]	0[3]	0
Windy Bay				
WNB1	6	7	0	4
WNB2	4	6	2	0
WNB3	22[8]	37	20	8
Kodiak				
K7	0	2	1	0
KOD3	0	4	17	9
Old Harbor				
OHA4	5	17	4	0
Chignik				
CHG1	3	4	2	0
CHG3	4	3	3	0
Other sites	486[165]	110[25]	0	0
Total samples	563[182]	257[26]	88[3]	25

The sites at which the concentrations of ACs exceeded 100 ng/g wet weight in at least one sample are listed individually; results from all other sites are combined. Numbers in brackets are for 1993 and 1994 samples; other numbers are for 1989–1991 samples.

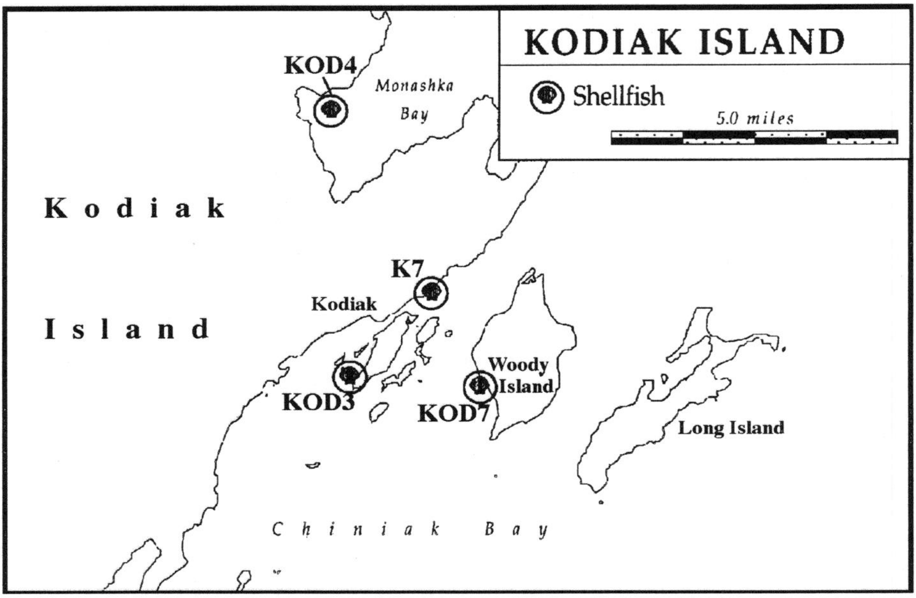

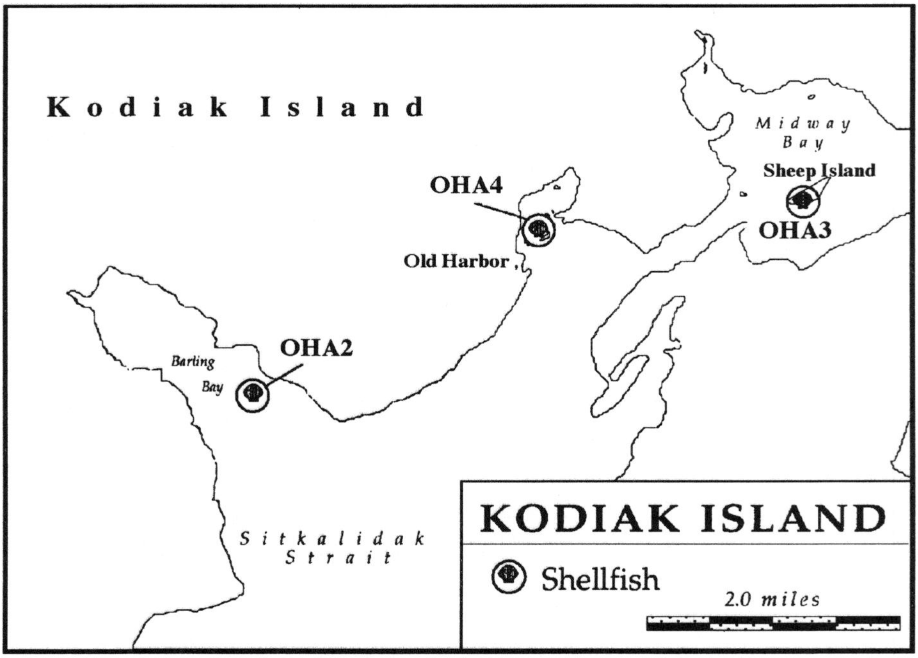

Figure 7-3 Shellfish sampling stations in Kodiak and Old Harbor

Table 7-3 Mean concentrations ± standard deviation (ng/g, wet weight) of aromatic contaminants (number of samples analyzed in parentheses) in the four target invertebrate species by area, station, and year collected

		Species				
Village Sampling area/station	Year	Mussels	Butter clams	Littleneck clams	Chitons	Other biota*
Reference Areas						
Angoon						
AGN1	1989	0.8 ± 0.6 (2)			1 ± 0.02(2)	
AGN2	1989		0.5(1)			(1)
Yakutat						
YAK1	1990	3 ± 2 (6)	1 ± 1 (6)	0.8 ± 0.3 (6)		
YAK5	1990				1 ± 0.3 (6)	
Prince William Sound						
Tatitlek						
T1	1990	23 ± 7 (3)	62 ± 46 (6)			
TAT1	1989	nd (1)				
TAT1	1990	6 ± 5 (7)	8 ± 12 (7)	4 ± 2 (4)		
TAT1	1993S	5.3 ± 2.4 (3)				
TAT1	1993F	3.7 ± 1.1 (3)				
TAT1	1994S	35 ± 8.3 (3)				
TAT1	1994F	2.7 ± 1.4 (3)				
TAT2	1990	9 ± 3 (4)	12 ± 6 (3)	4 ± 2 (2)		
TAT5	1989	2 ± 1 (6)			0.6 ± 0.9 (2)	
TAT9	1993S	4.2 ± 0.2 (3)		4.7 ± 1.6 (3)		
TAT9	1993F	1.7 ± 1.1 (3)		3.2 ± 1.2 (3)		
TAT9	1994S	1.1 ± 0.2 (3)		0.8 ± 0.1(3)		
TAT9	1994F	4.6 ± 2.0 (3)		3.9 ± 5.3 (3)		
Chenega Bay						
CHE1	1989	190 ± 51 (5)	30 ± 16 (2)			
CHE1	1990	24 ± 35 (6)	33 ± 46 (7)	18 ± 18 (4)	4 ± 5 (2)	
CHE1	1991	78 ± 18 (4)	20 ± 7 (4)	16 ± 4 (4)		
CHE7	1990	640 ± 830 (8)	330 ± 340 (9)	120 ± 44 (16)		
CHE7	1991	78 ± 33 (4)	110 ± 27 (4)	61 ± 5 (4)		
CHE9	1990	34 ± 12 (4)			0.4 ± 0.9 (4)	
CHE9	1991	1 ± 1 (4)			0.6 ± 0.2 (4)	
CHE10	1990	1,100 ± 620 (3)	27 ± 10 (8)	18 ± 11 (4)	2 ± 0.3 (2)	
CHE10	1991	23 ± 11 (8)	5 ± 3 (8)	11 ± 18 (8)		
CHE10	1993S	4.0 ± 0.6 (3)				
CHE10	1993F	5.0 ± 0.1 (3)				
CHE11	1990					(4)
CHE18	1991					(3)
CHE19	1991				2(1)	
CHE20	1991				nd (1)	
CHE21	1991				1 ± 2 (8)	
CHE22	1991	0.8 ± 0.5 (8)		3 ±3 (4)		
CHE23	1991	2 ± 3 (8)		0.6 ± 0.09 (4)	0.5 ± 0.2 (3)	
CHE24	1991	37 ± 100 (8)	0.4 (1)	0.4 (1)		
CHE25	1993S	4.2 ± 0.2 (3)				
CHE27	1994S	3.0 ± 1.9 (3)	1.4 ± 0.3 (3)			
CHE27	1994F	0.6 ± 0.2 (3)	1.4 ± 0.7 (2)	1.6 ± 2.1 (3)		
CHE28	1994S	2.5 ± 2.2 (3)		1.1 ± 0.7 (3)		
CHE28	1994F	113 ± 42 (3)				750 (1)

Table 7-3 continued

		Species				
Village Sampling area/station	Year	Mussels	Butter clams	Littleneck clams	Chitons	Other biota*
Lower Cook Inlet						
Port Graham/ Nanwalek						
PTG1	1989	2 ± 2 (6)		29 (1)	0.5 ± 0.3 (3)	(1)
PTG1	1990	2 ± 2 (21)		nd (1)	0.2 ± 0.3 (9)	(2)
PTG4	1989	9± 7 (4)				(1)
PTG4	1990	5 ± 2 (3)		20 (1)	4 ± 1 (2)	(6)
PTG4	1993S	9.3 ± 1.2 (3)		12 ± 3.5 (3)		
PTG4	1993F	6.0 ± 1.0 (3)		9.0 ± 4.4 (3)		
PTG4	1994S					1.4 (1)
PTG4	1994F			11 ± 3.5 (2)		1.4 ± 0.6 (3)
PTG8	1990				nd (7)	
PTG8/9	1990				0.7 ± 0.6 (3)	
PTG8/9	1994S	1.6 ± 0.6 (3)			0.5 ± 0.1 (3)	
PTG8/9	1994F	2.1 ± 0.9 (3)			1.3 ± 0.6 (3)	
PTG9	1990				nd (4)	
PTG10	1990				2 ± 1 (8)	(2)
PTG12	1993S				6.3 ± 0.8 (3)	
PTG12	1993F				3.3 ± 0.6 (3)	
PGT13	1994S					1.4 ± 0.1 (3)
PTG13	1994F					3.2 ± 0.8 (3)
NAN1	1993S	3.4 ± 0.1 (3)				
NAN1	1993F	3.8 ± 0.1 (3)				
NAN2	1993S	4.3 ± 0.3 (3)				
Windy Bay						
WNB1	1989	8,400 ± 8,800 (3)			2,900 ± 4,000 (2)	(1)
WNB1	1991	18 ± 12 (8)			0.6 ± 0.5 (4)	
WNB2	1989			960 (1)		
WNB2	1990	51±55 (6)				(18)
WNB2	1991	14 ± 26 (5)				(5)
WNB3	1990	600 ± 2,100 (24)			10 ± 25 (12)	(1)
WNB3	1991	110 ± 170 (38)			5 ± 8 (13)	
WNB3	1993S	4.9 ± 1.1 (3)				
WNB3	1994S	1.4 ± 0.9 (2)				
WNB3	1994F	2.7 ± 1.5 (3)				
WNB4	1990	23 ± 11 (8)		50 ± 21 (5)		(7)
WNB4	1991	10 ± 1 (5)		7 ± 2 (3)		(7)
WNB5	1991	20 ± 18 (5)		17 ± 2 (5)		(1)

Table 7-3 continued

Village Sampling area/station	Year	Species: Mussels	Butter clams	Littleneck clams	Chitons	Other biota*
Port Dick						
PTD1	1990	9 (1)		6 ± 1 (6)		(2)
Chugach Bay						
CHB1	1990				4 ± 3 (7)	
Port Chatham						
PTC1	1990			5 ± 3 (5)		
PTC2	1990	11 ± 10 (2)			3 ± 1 (9)	(2)
Pointe Bede						
BED1	1990				1 ± 0.6 (7)	(5)
Kasitsna Bay						
KAS1	1989	0.9 ± 0.3 (2)	3(1)		2(1)	
KAS1	1990			10 ± 2 (6)		(9)
Sadie Cove						
SAD1	1990	2 ± 0.4 (2)		4 ± 0.8 (5)		(5)
Kodiak Island						
Kodiak						
KOD3	1989	1,700 (1)	460 (1)	250 ± 150 (2)	190 ± 99 (2)	
KOD3	1990	630 ± 200 (4)	1,200 ± 680 (12)	310 ± 83 (4)	43 ± 14 (4)	
KOD4	1989					(1)
KOD5	1989					(1)
KOD7	1990		9 ± 5 (4)	7 ± 2 (4)	1 ± 1 (4)	
K7	1990	89 ± 31 (3)				(1)
Chiniak						
CHI1	1989	nd (1)	0.8 ± 0.6 (3)	2 ± 1 (2)		
CHI1	1990	5 ± 2 (7)	2 ± 2 (2)			
CHI2	1989	nd (1)	0.5 ± 0.3 (4)	1 (1)	0.9 ± 0.5 (5)	(3)
CHI2	1990	4 ± 3 (5)	10 ± 14 (6)	12 ± 6 (4)	1 ± 1 (4)	(1)
CHI3	1989					(1)
CHI7	1990	9 ± 7 (4)				
Old Harbor						
OHA2	1989					(1)
OHA3	1989	nd (1)	2 ± 0.9 (5)	3 (1)	1 ± 1 (3)	(1)
OHA3	1990	5 ± 3 (5)	5 ± 4 (11)	2 ± 2 (4)	0.2 ± 0.5 (7)	(6)
OHA3	1994F		20 ± 5.0 (3)			
OHA4	1989		150 ± 150 (5)	220 (1)		
OHA4	1990	120 ± 190 (5)	17 ± 9 (9)	24 ± 22 (6)		

Table 7-3 continued

		Species				
Village Sampling area/station	Year	Mussels	Butter clams	Littleneck clams	Chitons	Other biota*
Akhiok						
AKH2	1989	0.3 (1)	0.2 ± 0.2 (3)		1 (1)	
AKH2	1994S		2.0 ± 0.7 (3)			
AKH2	1994F		6.7 ± 4.2 (3)			
AKH3	1989	0.4 (1)		0.5 (1)		
AKH3	1990	10 ± 8 (4)	2 ± 0.3 (3)	2 ± 1 (6)		(1)
AKH6	1990	1 ± 1 (4)				
AKH6	1994S					8.3 ± 1.5 (3)
AKH6	1994F					7.3 ± 0.6 (3)
Karluk						
KAR1	1989	nd (1)			0.2 (1)	
KAR1	1990	nd (4)				
KAR2	1989	0.3 ± 0.06 (3)	0.3 (1)		nd (1)	
KAR2	1990	5 ± 9 (4)	0.6 ± 0.4 (4)	3 ± 2 (4)		
KAR2	1993S	7.6 ± 6.5 (3)				
KAR2	1994S	0.8 ± 0.4 (3)	1.8 ± 1.9 (3)			
KAR2	1994F	0.3 ± 0.6 (3)	5.7 ± 2.1 (3)			
Larsen Bay						
LAB1	1989	1 (1)	2 ± 2 (3)		1 ± 0.6 (2)	(1)
LAB1	1990		16 ± 9 (6)			
LAB2	1989		3 ± 2 (4)		0.4 (1)	
LAB2	1990	10 ± 4 (4)	2 ± 1 (6)	2 ± 1 (4)		(2)
LAB3	1989					(1)
LAB4	1989					(4)
LAB9	1990					(1)
LAB10	1990		34 ± 4 (2)	17 ± 5 (3)		(4)
LAB10	1994F		3.1 (1)			
LAB11	1990				8 (1)	
LAB15	1993S	4.5 ± 0.1 (3)				
LAB15	1993F	3.1 ± 1.3 (4)				
LAB16	1994F		10 ± 6.1 (5)			
Port Lions						
PTL1	1989		2 ± 0.6 (5)	3 ± 0.5 (2)	1 ± 0.6 (3)	(1)
PTL1	1990	29 ± 21 (10)	15 ± 13 (7)	12 ± 5 (10)		
PTL1	1993S	5.7 ± 0.6 (3)				
PTL1	1993F	3.3 ± 0.6 (3)				
PTL1	1994F		4.3 ± 0.6 (3)			
PTL2	1989		3 ± 1 (2)		0.7 ± 0.6 (2)	(1)
PTL2	1990	15 ± 8 (4)	23 ± 5 (4)	20 ± 7 (4)	0.2 ± 0.5 (4)	(4)
PTL4	1989					(3)
PTL5	1989					(1)
PTL9	1990					(2)
PTL10	1994F		12 ± 2.5 (3)			

Table 7-3 continued

Village Sampling area/station	Year	Mussels	Butter clams	Littleneck clams	Chitons	Other biota*
		Species				
Ouzinkie						
OUZ2	1989	0.9 (1)	0.4 ± 0.6 (2)	0.8 ± 0.3 (2)	0.3 ± 0.3 (2)	
OUZ2	1990	3 ± 1 (4)	4 ± 1 (4)	3 ± 1 (4)	5 ± 7 (4)	
OUZ2	1993S	3.3 ± 1.6 (3)	7.0 ± 4.0 (3)			
OUZ2	1993F	12 ± 13 (2)	3.6 ± 0.6 (3)			
OUZ3	1989		8 (1)			
OUZ3	1990	20 (1)	19 ± 22 (8)	3 ± 1 (2)		(1)
OUZ3	1993S	5.7 ± 1.5 (3)				
OUZ3	1993F	7.0 ± 4.4 (3)				
OUZ4	1989		3 (1)			
OUZ4	1990	10 ± 8 (4)	13 ± 3 (4)	7 ± 2 (4)	2 ± 0.2 (4)	
OUZ7	1990				nd (1)	
OUZ9	1990		22 ± 20 (6)			(1)
OUZ11	1994S		4.1 ± 1.1 (3)			
OUZ11	1994F		3.3 ± 0.48 (3)			
Alaska Peninsula						
Chignik						
CHG1	1990	42 ± 46 (9)				
CHG3	1990	40 ± 54 (10)				
Ivanof Bay						
IVB1	1990					(1)
IVB2	1990					(1)
IVB3	1990	5 ± 7 (9)	1 ± 0.8 (3)			
Perryville						
PER1	1990				8(1)	
PER3	1990	1 ± 1 (9)				
Kashvik Bay						
KAT1	1990					(4)
Koyuktolik						
KOY1	1994S	1.2 ± 0.4 (3)				
KOY1	1994F	0.1 ± 0.1 (3)				

nd = not detected
* Other biota sampled include species such as crab, shrimp, and herring roe on kelp.

tions of ACs in mussels, only two of the sites (CHE10 and WNB3) were sampled again in 1993 to 1994. In contrast to the earlier results, mussels from these sites had low concentrations of ACs (Table 7-3). For example, in 1993, mean AC concentrations in mussels from CHE10 were 4.0 ± 0.6 (n = 3) and 5.0 ± 0.1 (n = 3) in the summer and fall, respectively.

Aromatic compounds in clams

The sites with the highest mean concentrations of ACs in butter clams during the 1989 to 1991 studies (Table 7-3) were Chenega station CHE7 (1990: 330 ± 340 ng/g), Kodiak station KOD3 (1989: 460 ng/g; 1990: 1200 ± 680 ng/g) and Old Harbor station OHA4 (1989: 150 ± 150 ng/g). Based on the concentrations of ACs in individual samples collected during 1989 to 1991 (Varanasi et al. 1993a), nine butter clam samples (4.3%) of the 208 samples collected were highly contaminated with ACs (eight from the Kodiak KOD3 sampling station and one from Chenega station CHE7, all collected in 1990). The ACs in clams from CHE7, KOD3, and OHA4 probably were acquired from local sources rather than from the spilled oil (Varanasi et al. 1993a). A total of 18 butter clam samples (8.2%) were moderately contaminated with ACs, all from the Tatitlek, Chenega, Kodiak, and Old Harbor sampling areas. Concentrations of ACs in most of the butter clam samples (87%) were in the uncontaminated or minimally contaminated categories.

Butter clams collected during the 1993 to 1994 study were not contaminated with ACs. Mean concentrations were near or less than 10 ng/g, except for three samples collected from Old Harbor station OHA3 (autumn 1994: 20 ± 5 ng/g) and one sample (mixed butter and littleneck clams) from Chenega station CHE28 (autumn 1994: 750 ng/g). Concentrations of ACs in the OHA3 samples were low (near background levels) and probably resulted from local sources, whereas the ACs in clams from CHE28 may have been contaminated by the same gravel that was the probable source of contamination for the mussels from that site. None of the stations that had elevated concentrations of ACs in butter clams in 1989 to 1991 was sampled again in 1993 to 1994.

None of the 175 littleneck clam samples collected during the 1989 to 1991 study was highly contaminated with ACs, and only 21 samples (12%) of littleneck clams were moderately contaminated with ACs (Varanasi et al. 1993b). During the 1993 to 1994 study, concentrations of ACs in the 26 littleneck clam samples were at or near background levels (Table 7-3).

Aromatic compounds in chitons and other invertebrates

During the 1989 to 1991 study, only one sample (0.5%) of the 183 chiton samples collected was highly contaminated with ACs (Windy Bay station WNB1, 1989: 5800 ng/g) and two samples (1%) were moderately contaminated (Kodiak station KOD3, 1989: 190 ± 99 ng/g). The concentrations of ACs in all the other chiton samples (98%) were in the uncontaminated or minimally contaminated categories, similar to those for Yakutat, the reference area. Chitons collected during the 1993 to 1994 study (12 samples) were not contaminated with ACs (Table 7-3).

A total of 132 samples of a variety of other tissues and invertebrate samples, including clam species other than those discussed above, crab, limpets, sea urchins, snails, shrimp, kelp, and herring roe on kelp were analyzed for ACs during the 1989 to 1991 study. Of these samples, 72% were not contaminated with ACs, 26% were minimally contaminated with ACs, 2% were moderately contaminated with ACs, and none were highly contaminated with ACs.

Patterns of Aromatic Compounds in Petroleum and Invertebrates

The concentrations of individual ACs can vary greatly among petroleums, refined products, and other sources; therefore, the relative concentrations of individual ACs in samples can be indicative of their source. To compare the concentrations of individual ACs among the various biota samples, the relative concentrations of selected ACs are graphed by normalizing the peak area of each AC to the area of one specific alkyl-substituted phenanthrene (C2PHN) component. For example, the patterns of the relative concentrations of selected ACs in petroleum, petroleum products, nonpoint sources such as combustion processes (e.g., ACs from an urban marine sediment), and other materials such as creosote (from coal tar) that may have been associated with the sampling sites are shown in Figures 7-4 through 7-7. Comparing the graphs, it can be seen that the relative concentrations of the more volatile components, such as naphthalene (NPH), and the less volatile components, such as benzo[a]pyrene (BaP), varied in the different products. For example, the PBCO collected from the sea surface 11 days following the spill had lost some of the more volatile and water-soluble components (e.g., NPHs) relative to the C2PHN component in fresh PBCO (Figure 7-4); however, the patterns of the other ACs were similar. The composition of ACs in a sample collected from a patch of oil from the beach at Snug Harbor, Prince William Sound in July 1990, about 15 months after the *Exxon Valdez* spill (not shown), was quite similar to the 11-day weathered PBCO, except that there were lower levels of NPH, C1- and C2NPHs in the Snug Harbor samples. The lack of continued weathering could have resulted from several factors (e.g., an outer layer or crust could have formed that somewhat sealed the material from further weathering, or the tar mat may have been in the high intertidal zone and thus less exposed to wave action and other degradation processes).

The patterns of ACs from Cook Inlet crude oil and Kuwaiti crude oil (Figure 7-5) were found to be similar to that of PBCO except for proportions of the dibenzothiophenes (DBTs). Prudhoe Bay crude oil contains a considerably higher proportion of DBTs than does the Cook Inlet crude; the DBTs were mostly absent in the Cook Inlet crude. In contrast, the proportions of DBTs were much higher in

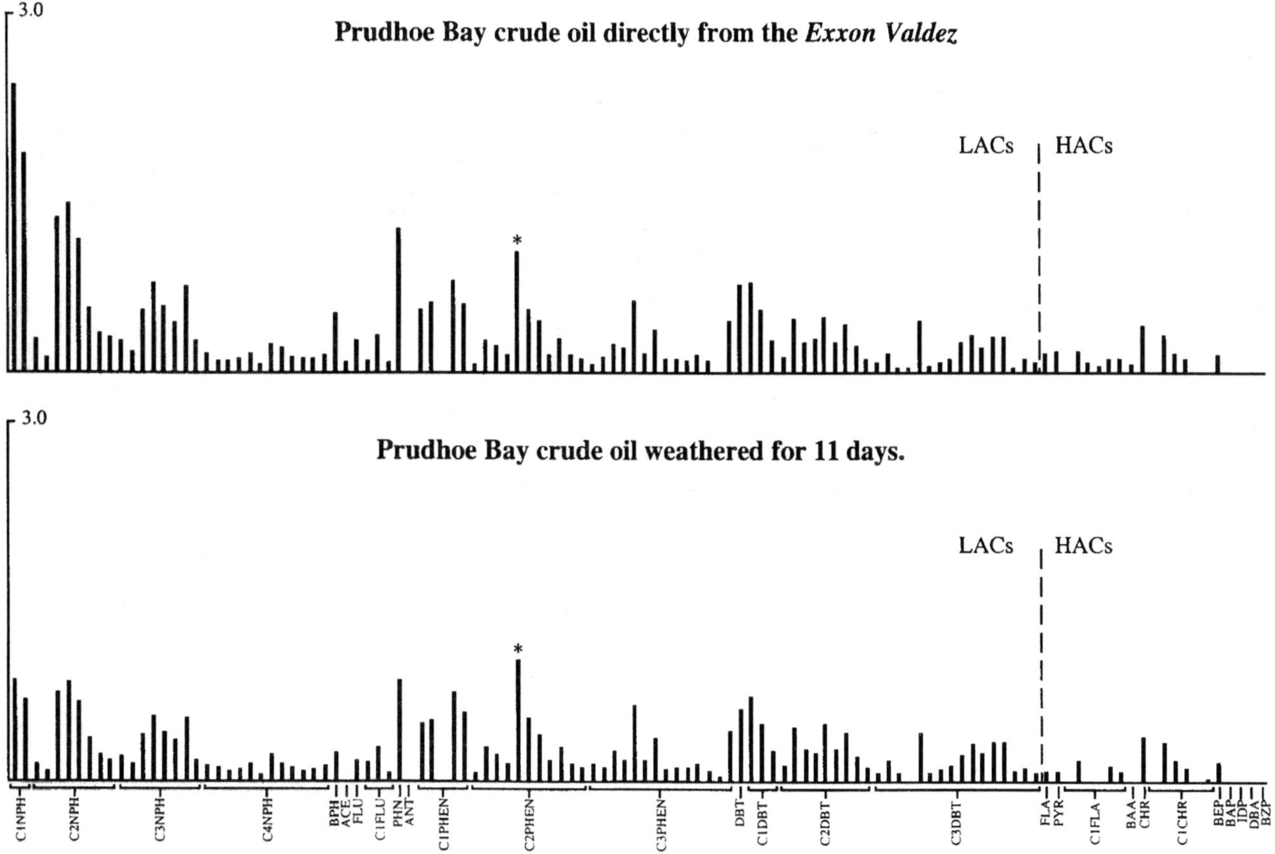

Figure 7-4 Pattern graphs of ACs with instrument peak areas normalized to the peak area of one of the C2 phenanthrene isomers (*) for weathered and unweathered PBCO. BPH = biphenyl; ANT = anthracene; BEP = benzo[e]pyrene

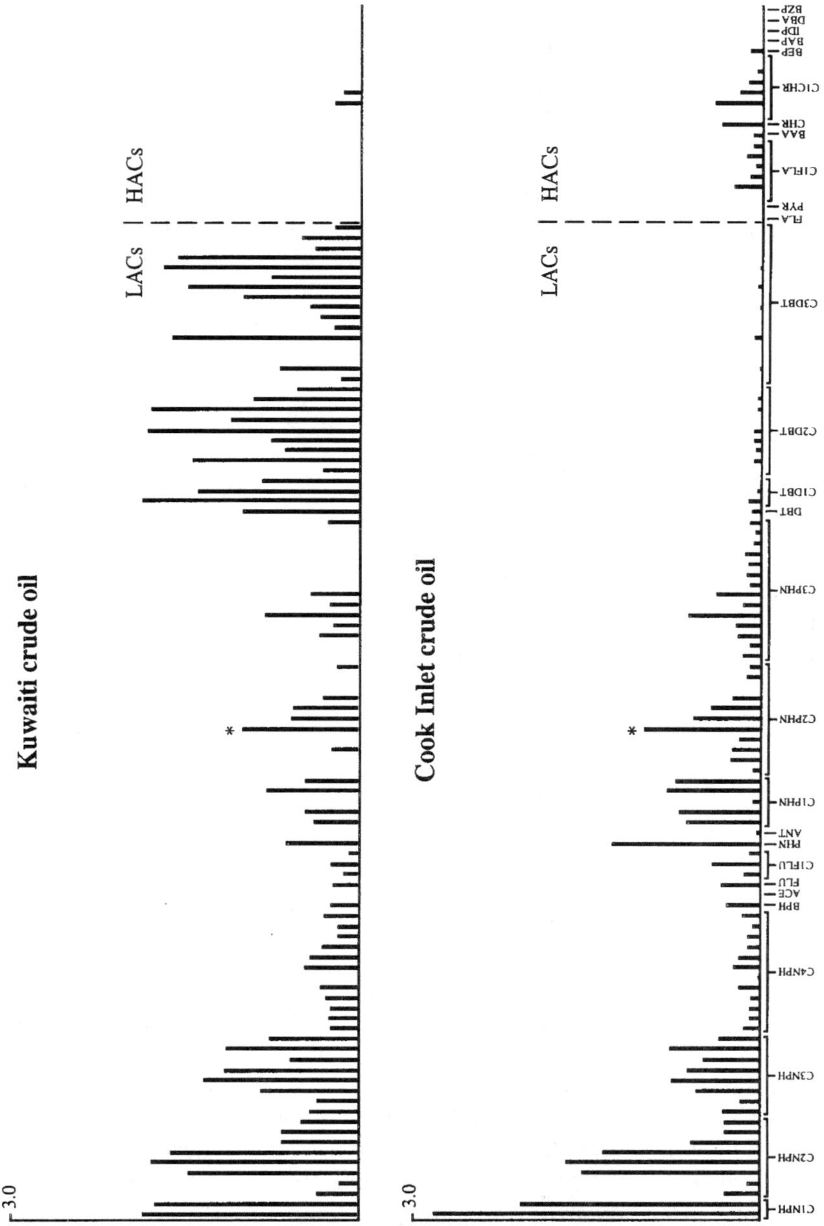

Figure 7-5 Pattern graphs of ACs with instrument peak areas normalized to the peak area of one of the C2-phenanthrene isomers (*) for fresh Kuwaiti crude oil and fresh Cook Inlet crude oil

Kuwaiti crude than in PBCO. The No. 2 fuel oil pattern (Figure 7-6) appeared somewhat similar to the PBCO pattern, even though No. 2 fuel oil basically comprises a distilled fraction of crude oil. A pattern of creosote is included (Figure 7-6) because mollusks from Chenega station CHE7 were collected near creosoted pilings, suggesting that the ACs in those samples may have been from creosote. Phenanthrene, fluoranthene, and pyrene, three major components of creosote, are also major components in combustion products, as shown in an extract of marine sediment from a contaminated urban area (Duwamish Waterway, Seattle WA; Figure 7-7), but are not major components of PBCO.

Comparing patterns of ACs in samples of biota with characteristic patterns of the various petroleum products may provide useful information about possible sources of contamination. However, certain limitations of such pattern-matching techniques become readily apparent. For example, several sources of ACs may be present at a given site (e.g., spilled oil, diesel fuel, creosote). In addition, petroleum ACs released into the environment undergo a variety of changes such as evaporation, bacterial degradation, photooxidation and other forms of weathering. Furthermore, biota may accumulate, metabolize, or depurate individual ACs at different rates. As a result, interpreting patterns of ACs in biota, especially when these ACs are from a mixture of petroleum sources, may be very difficult.

Patterns of ACs were similar in selected mussel samples from Chenega and Windy Bay (Figure 7-8). These patterns contain many of the alkyl-substituted components typical of petroleum, and, they show considerable losses of the more volatile and water-soluble components of the LACs (Figure 7-4). Additionally, the patterns of ACs in mussels from Windy Bay stations WNB1 and WNB3 over time (from 1989, 1990, and 1991; see Varanasi et al. 1993a for graphs) showed a continuing increase in the relative concentrations of the C4-substituted phenanthrenes and dibenzothiophenes, as well as some of the HACs (e.g., chrysenes, which are important components of PBCO). Petroleum from the spill was known to impact both of these areas in Windy Bay; thus, the spilled petroleum was probably the source of the ACs in the mollusks even though the patterns in the fresh PBCO and the mollusks are not identical.

The pattern of ACs in mollusk samples from Chenega station CHE10 appeared to be from multiple sources. For example, a mussel sample from CHE10 (Figure 7-9) contained many of the alkyl-substituted components typical of petroleum and similar to those found in the mussels from CHE1 as well as in samples from WNB1 and WNB3, where the spilled oil was observed. A tar mat on the beach at CHE10, assumed to be from the spilled oil, could account for the petroleum ACs in the mussels. In addition to the petroleum ACs, the pattern of ACs in mussels from CHE10 (Figure 7-9) contained compounds indicative of combustion products (e.g., phenanthrene, fluoranthene, pyrene, and benz[a]anthracene) and were similar to those found in the Duwamish sediment extract. Thus, the contaminants in biota from this site may be from a mixture of sources.

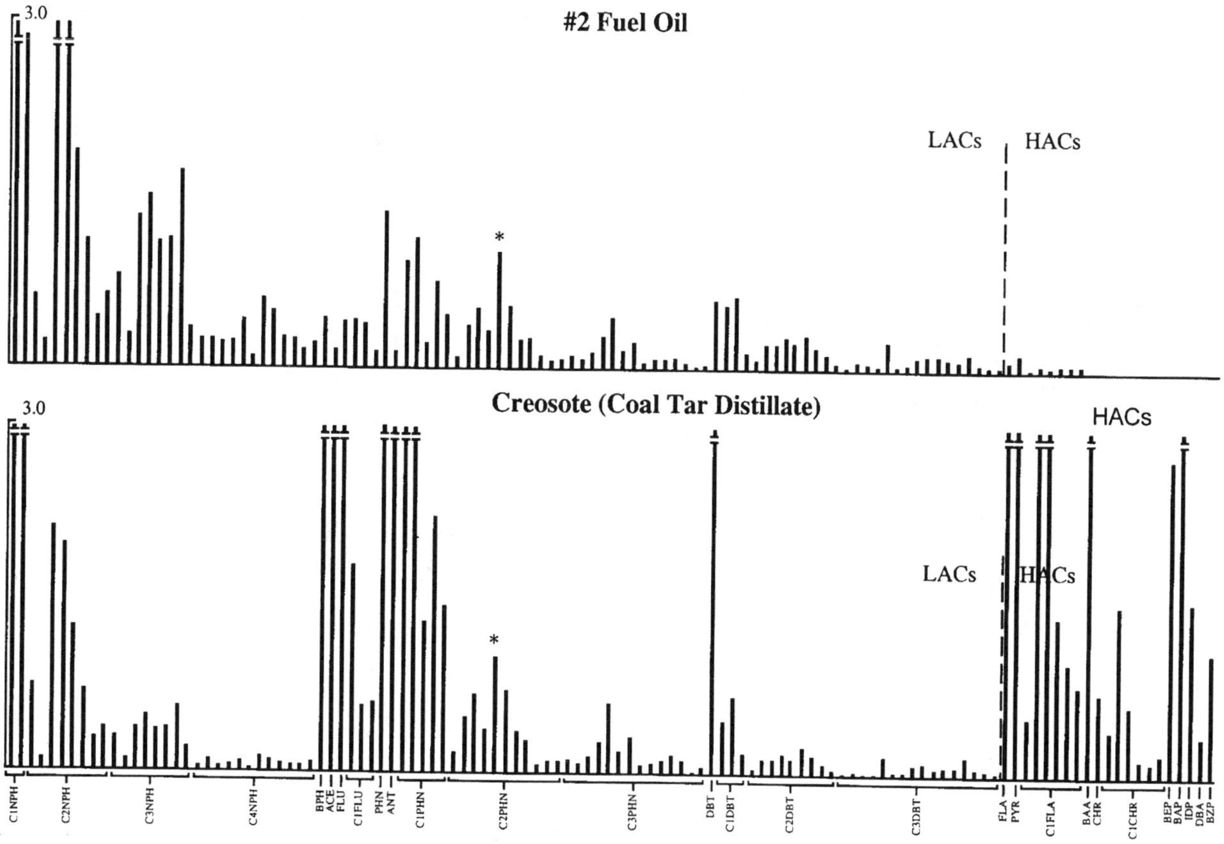

Figure 7-6 Pattern graphs of ACs with instrument peak areas normalized to the peak areas of one of the C2-phenanthrene isomers (*) for #2 fuel oil and creosote

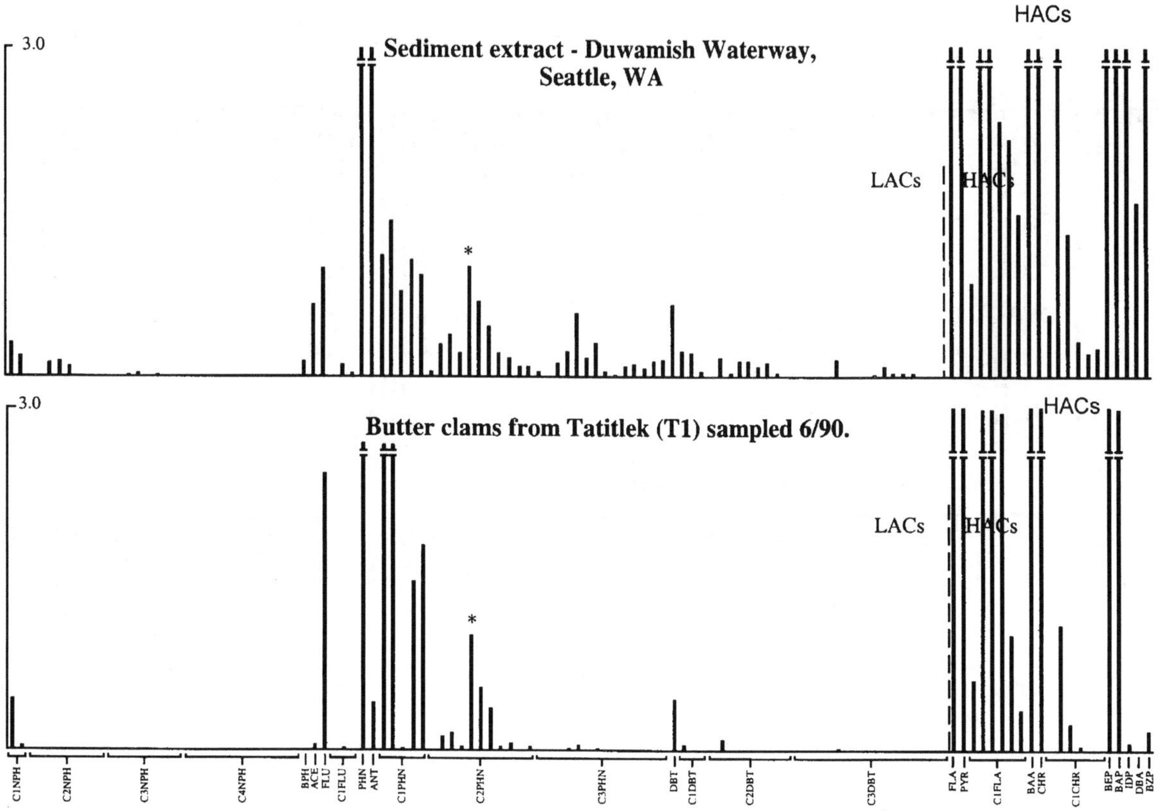

Figure 7-7 Pattern graphs of ACs with instrument peak areas normalized to the peak areas of one of the C2-phenanthrene isomers (*) for Duwamish Waterway sediment extract and butter clams from Tatitlek (T1) sampled June 1990

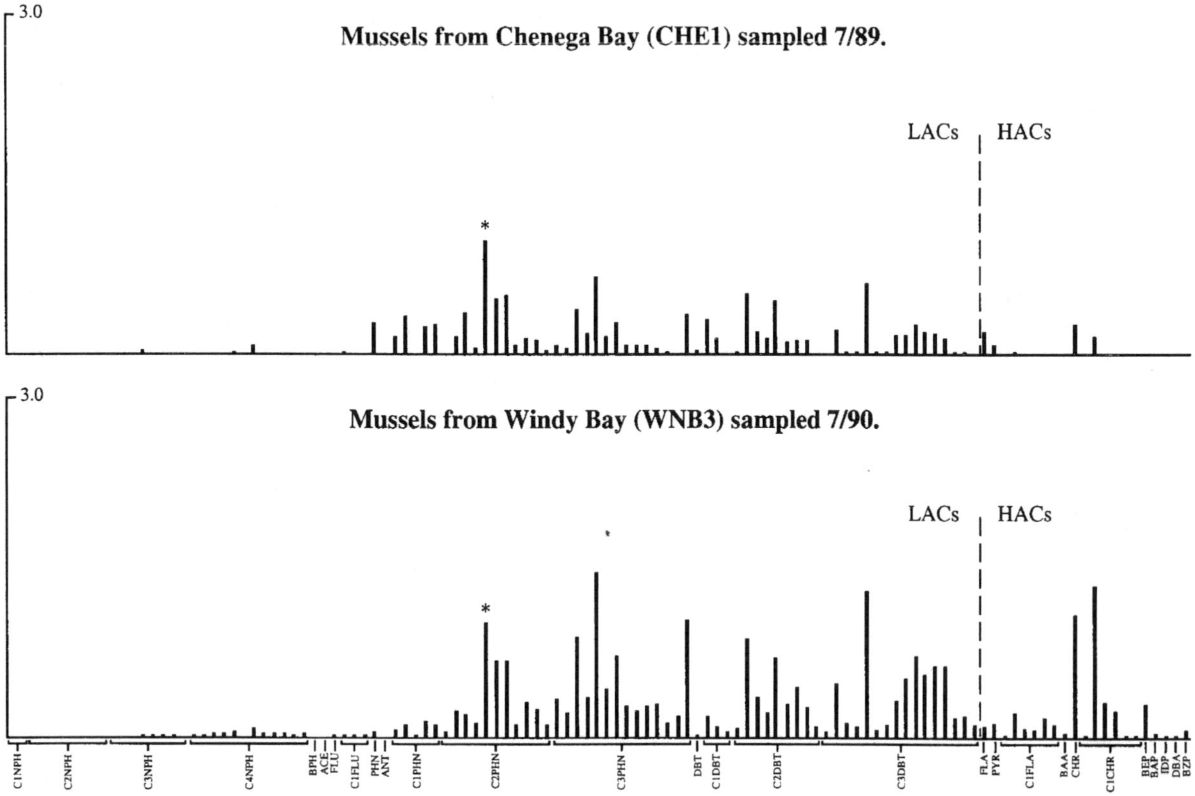

Figure 7-8 Pattern graphs of ACs with instrument peak areas normalized to the peak area of one of the C2-phenanthrene isomers (*) for mussels from CHE1 sampled July 1989 (sample no. 60-44) and WNB3 sampled July 1990 (sample no. 60-1733)

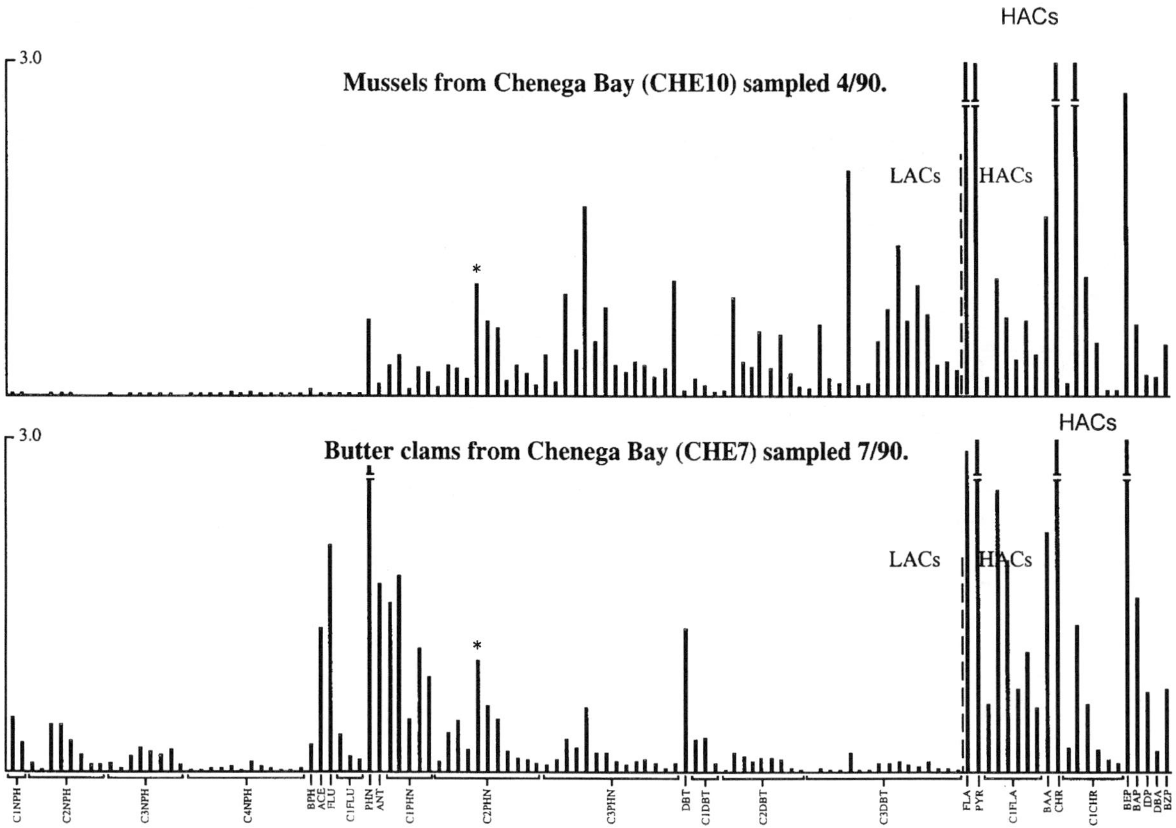

Figure 7-9 Pattern graphs of ACs with instrument peak areas normalized to the peak areas of one of the C2-phenanthrene isomers (*) for mussels from CHE10 sampled April 1990 (sample no. 60-1514) and butter clams from CHE7 sampled July 1990 (sample no. 60-1753)

Concentrations of ACs were high in some invertebrate samples that were not observed to have been exposed to the spilled PBCO. The pattern of ACs in a butter clam sample from Chenega station CHE7 (Figure 7-9) was somewhat similar to that for the mussel sample from CHE10, but the CHE7 sample contained fewer of the alkyl-substituted or petroleum-related components. In addition, the pattern for ACs in the butter clam sample from CHE7 was very similar to the patterns for creosote (Figure 7-6) and for combustion products (e.g., Duwamish sediment extract; Figure 7-7). Creosoted pilings were found in the CHE7 area where the butter clam samples were collected and may have been one source of ACs in the clams. Again, it is important to observe that when more than one hydrocarbon source is present at a site, the sources of ACs in biota from that site are difficult to establish. However, our study was designed to determine the extent of contamination in mollusks from areas where subsistence food was collected. If potential sources of contamination were to be rigorously evaluated, the study design would have been different.

Tatitlek station T1, located east of the spill site, was not suspected to have been exposed to the spilled PBCO, though samples from these stations contained ACs. The patterns of ACs in butter clams from Tatitlek station T1 (Figure 7-7) contained the ACs indicative of combustion products but were relatively free of the alkyl-substituted phenanthrenes and dibenzothiophenes found in PBCO and in the Windy Bay mussels. Thus, these clams were probably not exposed to ACs from the *Exxon Valdez* spill.

As noted earlier, mollusks from two Kodiak Island stations (KOD3 and OHA4) were moderately or highly contaminated with ACs. The patterns of ACs in a mussel sample from each station (Figure 7-10) were very similar to the patterns of ACs in mussel samples from WNB3 (Figure 7-8) except for slightly higher relative amounts of the more volatile and water-soluble components of ACs in the KOD3 and OHA4 samples. Also, the concentrations of chrysenes were lower in the two samples from KOD3 and OHA4 than in the WNB3 sample, and the concentrations of fluoranthene and pyrene (indicative of combustion products) were higher in the KOD3 and OHA4 samples than in the WNB3 sample. The patterns of ACs in samples of butter clams (March 1990) and littleneck clams (April 1990) collected from station KOD3 (see Varanasi et al. 1993a for figures), were nearly identical to that for mussels collected at the same station in April 1990 (Figure 7-10). Also, for butter clams collected at three different times at KOD3 in 1990 (March, May, and September; see Varanasi et al. 1993a for figures) the pattern of the ACs typical of petroleum in these samples over the relatively short period of time remained quite consistent. If a one time exposure had occurred, the concentrations of ACs in the clams would be expected to decrease with time. The consistent pattern of petroleum-related ACs in these samples would imply that the clams were being continually exposed to sources of ACs other than the oil spilled from the *Exxon Valdez*. Furthermore, these patterns suggest that the mussels and two clam species collected

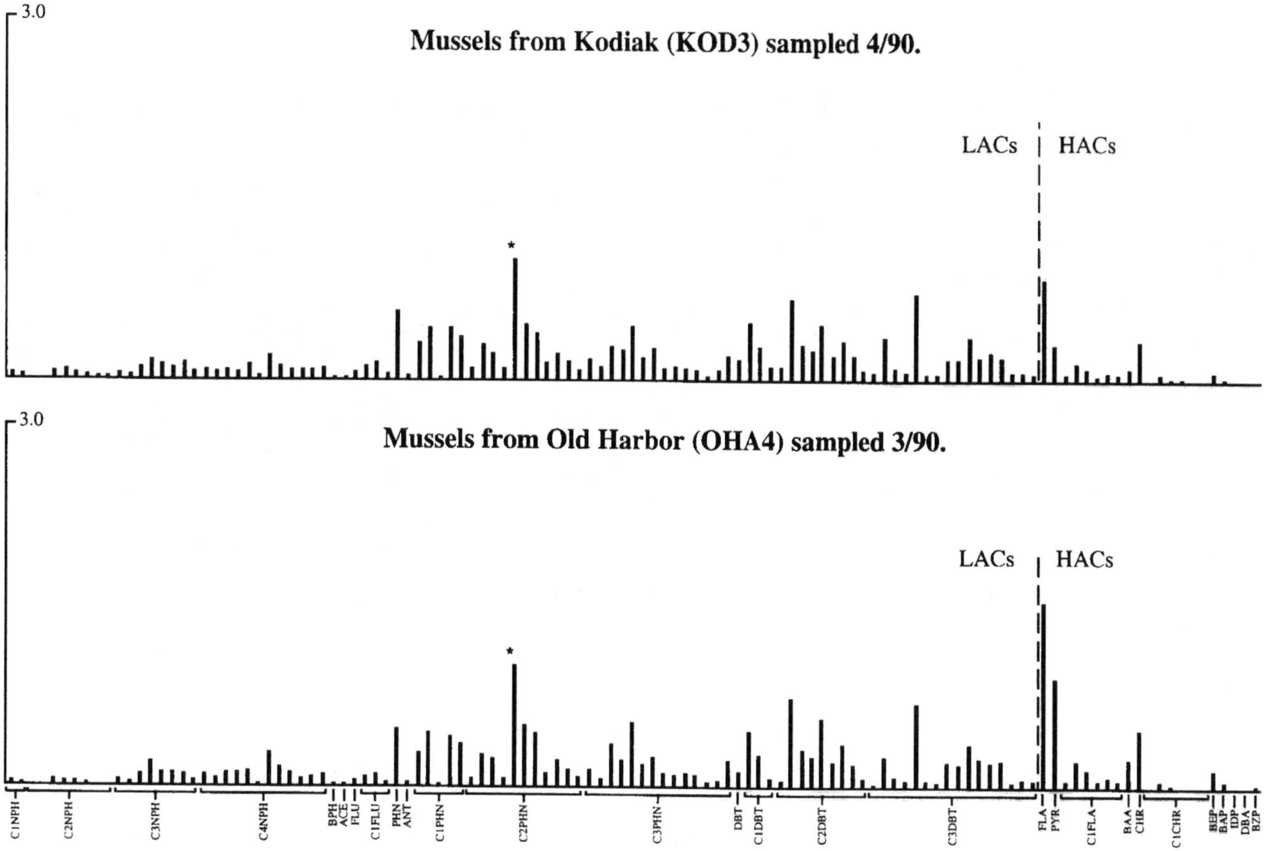

Figure 7-10 Pattern graphs of ACs with instrument peak areas normalized to the peak area of one of the C2-phenanthrene isomers (*) for mussels from KOD3 sampled April 1990 (sample no. 60-1846) and from OHA4 sampled March 1990 (sample no. 60-1158)

from station KOD3 were exposed to the same source of ACs and that their uptake and depuration processes were similar.

The preceding examples of comparing patterns illustrate the need to consider the ambiguities involved when attempting to match the patterns of ACs in samples of biota to specific sources. When comparing patterns, only similarities or differences can be pointed out, and absolute conclusions based solely on pattern comparisons can be difficult to make, especially when a mixture of sources is present. In many instances, a pattern for an environmental sample should not be firmly linked to a particular source unless the study was appropriately designed and all the variables were considered. Also, caution is needed when correlating patterns in biota to potential sources because the patterns may not exactly match because of differential uptake, depuration, or metabolism of ACs by biota. However, even with the above considerations, careful use of pattern matching techniques can be a useful tool when considering potential sources of contamination by ACs.

Temporal changes in concentrations of aromatic compounds in mollusks

Several factors are important when evaluating temporal trends of the concentrations of ACs at a site (e.g., the number of samples of each species analyzed from a station, the number of sampling events at each site, and the sample collection scheme). Furthermore, when a beach is exposed to petroleum in a single episode such as a spill, the petroleum weathers over time (e.g., by evaporation or oxidation) and results in decreased levels of ACs available to mollusks. On the other hand, in an active harbor that is continuously contaminated by petroleum-related spills due to maritime activities, a continuous supply of ACs would be available for uptake by mollusks. In 1989 to 1991, most sampling sites were chosen according to subsistence users' concerns about oil contamination of shellfish at sites they wanted to harvest. In 1993, sampling was designed to include one site for establishing trends and one new site for each subsistence community. In 1994, the emphasis was changed to sampling important sites not previously sampled because this time period probably would be the last sampling opportunity. Thus, repeated sampling of the same sites to assess temporal variations in concentrations of ACs in edible tissues was limited by these sampling objectives and by limited funding for the project. Bearing in mind these limitations, the data were evaluated using GT2 statistics.

Time-related trends in AC concentrations were found at some stations but not at others (Varanasi et al. 1993a). The only stations that had moderately or highly contaminated mollusks—which would be an important aspect for assessing recovery from oiling—in the 1989 to 1991 study that were resampled in 1993 to 1994 were CHE10 and WNB3. Mussels were collected from CHE10 in 1990, 1991, and 1993 and from WNB3 in 1990, 1991, 1993, and 1994. When concentrations of ACs in mussels from station CHE10 were evaluated statistically, a significant decline in AC concentrations was found (Figure 7-11), both from 1990 to 1991 and from 1991 to 1993. The concentrations of ACs in mussels from WNB3 were significantly lower in 1994 (mean concentrations <10 ng/g) compared with those collected in 1990 and 1991 (Figure 7-12). As noted above, WNB3 was visibly impacted by the spilled oil and a residual tar mat may have been the source of AC exposure to some of the mussels from this site.

The concentrations of ACs in mussels and clams from some stations at Chenega, Windy Bay, Kodiak, and Old Harbor also were evaluated statistically to determine if the concentrations of ACs declined during the 1989 to 1991 study period, even though the number of times samples were collected from a station were limited, restricting the extent that temporal trends could be evaluated. For example, the concentrations of ACs in mussels collected from Chenega station CHE1 in June 1991 were not significantly different from concentrations in samples collected in August 1989 (Varanasi et al. 1993a). In other words, there was no continuous declining trend in the concentrations of ACs in mussels at CHE1 over this period, which was also true for ACs in mussels from CHE7. These results for both CHE1 and CHE7 suggest that the mussels were continually being exposed to a source of ACs. As discussed above, PBCO may not have been the source of ACs in invertebrates at CHE7. In contrast, there was a significant decline in the concentrations of ACs in mussel samples collected in 1991 from CHE9 compared with 1990.

Mussel samples from WNB1 collected in April 1991 had significantly lower concentrations of ACs than those collected in 1989 (Varanasi et al. 1993a), but there was no significant continual trend of declining concentrations of ACs in mussels at Windy Bay station WNB2. However, the high standard deviations for the mean concentrations of ACs in the WNB2 samples showed that some mussel samples were highly exposed to ACs while some were exposed to ACs very little. This large variability in concentrations of ACs contributed to the lack of statistically significant trends at this station.

The concentrations of ACs in butter clams from Chenega stations CHE1, CHE7, and CHE10 were also evaluated for temporal changes (see figures in Varanasi et al. 1993a). Most butter clam samples from Chenega station CHE1 were minimally contaminated or uncontaminated with ACs, and there was no significant continual decline in the concentrations of ACs in these samples over time (Varanasi et al. 1993a). The concentrations of ACs in butter clams from CHE7 were moderate and were significantly higher in the samples collected in February 1990 than in those collected in April 1990 and June 1991. However, the concentrations of ACs in the samples collected in February 1990 were not significantly different from those collected in June 1990. Therefore, a local source of ACs may be responsible for the inconsistent temporal trends in the concentrations of ACs at CHE7. Although concentrations of ACs were generally low in butter clam samples from CHE10, significantly lower concentrations of ACs were found in butter clams collected in August 1991 compared with those collected in April 1990.

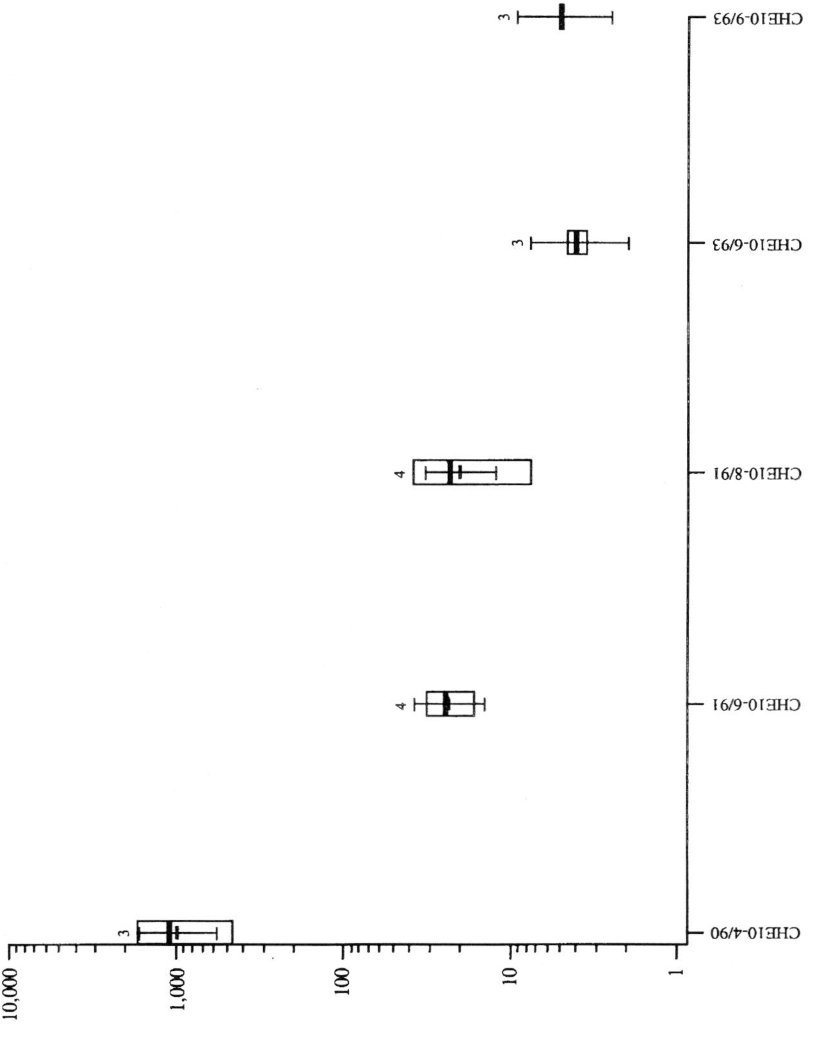

Figure 7-11 Mean concentration and GT2 comparison intervals for total ACs in mussels from Chenega Bay station CHE10 by month and year. Arithmetic mean [▬] concentrations (wet weight) ± 1 SD [□], geometric mean [—] ± comparison interval [⌶], and number of samples.

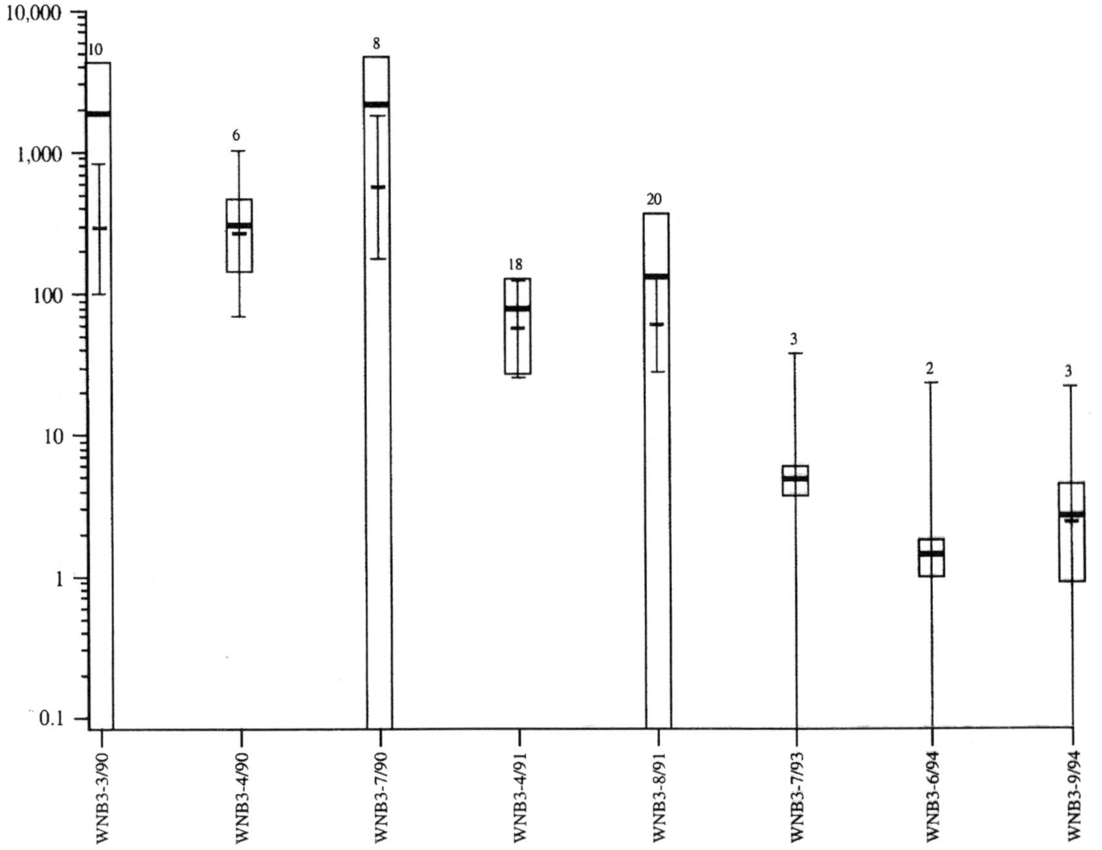

Figure 7-12 Mean concentrations and GT2 comparison intervals for total ACs in mussels from Windy Bay station WNB3 by month and year. Arithmetic mean [▬] concentrations (wet weight) ± 1 SD [☐], geometric mean [▬] ± comparison interval [ ], and number of samples.

The concentrations of ACs in butter clams from Kodiak station KOD3 did not decline significantly over the four sampling events in 1990 and three of the four mean concentrations of ACs were in the highly contaminated category (Figure 7-13). As discussed earlier, sources other than the oil from the *Exxon Valdez* spill might be the reason for the high concentrations of ACs in butter clams from KOD3. Further investigation is warranted to try to determine the source of ACs in these clams.

Overall, most of the littleneck clam samples were not contaminated or were minimally contaminated, and there was no statistically significant decline in concentrations of ACs. Littleneck clams from the two sample collections from Kodiak station KOD3 were moderately contaminated; however, the concentrations of ACs showed no statistical difference between the two collections. The concentrations of ACs were significantly lower in littleneck clams from Windy Bay station WNB4 in April 1991 than in those collected in July 1990 (Varanasi et al. 1993a).

Lessons Learned

The knowledge gained from our experiences related to this spill and from other similar incidents gives us the basis to address many issues that should be considered when designing a study to answer questions of concern for similar environmental emergencies. Questions to be answered on the basis of pertinent chemical analyses include those related to human health concerns (e.g., consumption of contaminated seafood), recovery of natural resources (e.g., temporal changes in contamination levels), injury to natural resources, and identification of the source.

Typically, rapid response is most important following an oil spill. However, one of the first responses to this type of emergency should be to develop a detailed sampling and analysis plan (SAP). The SAP should address

- the types (i.e., individual or composited) and numbers of samples needed;
- sample-collection criteria, including temperatures to be maintained during transportation and storage;
- chain-of-custody procedures;
- the analytical methods to be used and a list of analytes to be determined;
- quality assurance procedures; and
- data completion time requirements, data reporting format, and extent of data interpretation required.

Also, issues of statistical power (e.g., the number of samples per sampling event, the frequency and duration of sampling) should be addressed during the study design stage.

The sampling plan should include criteria for selection of sample stations and criteria for sample collection (e.g., "mussels will be collected along a 10 meter line from point A to B at tidal elevation X", or, as in this study, "mollusk samples will be

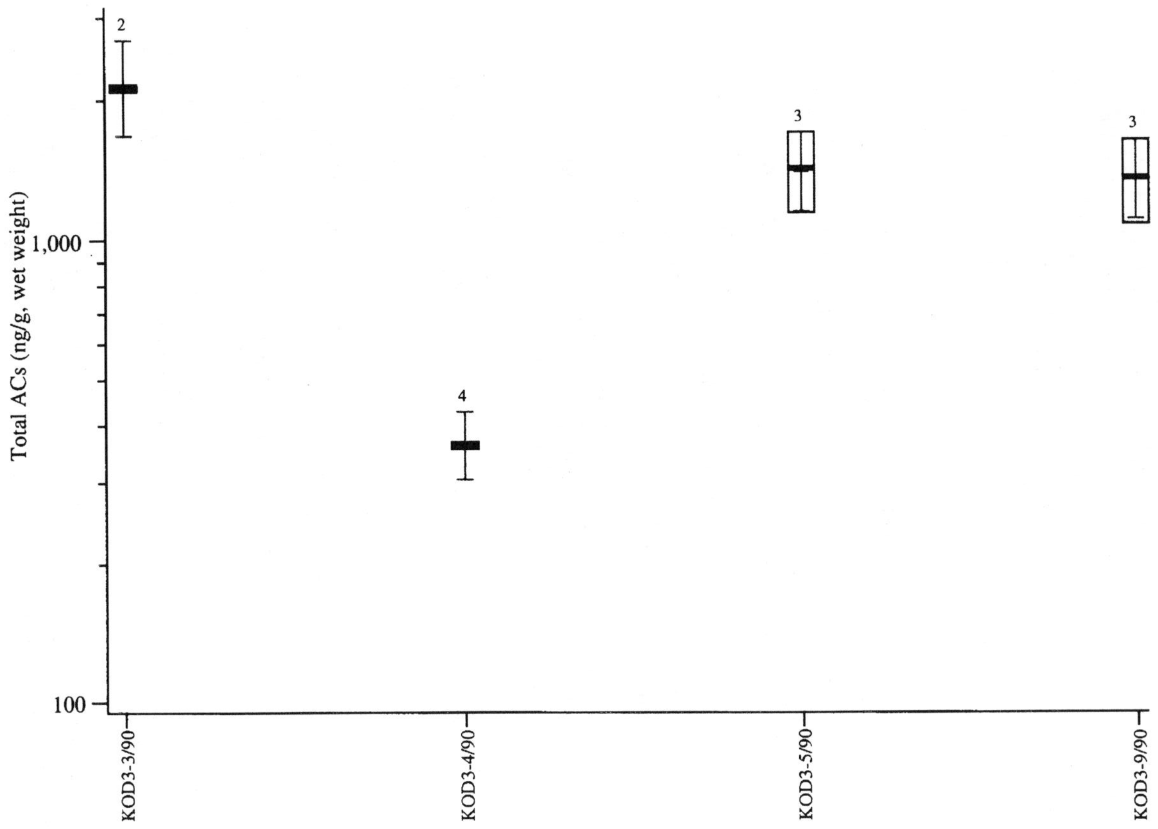

Figure 7-13 Mean concentrations and GT2 comparison intervals for total ACs in butter clams from Kodiak station KOD3 by year. Arithmetic mean [▬] concentrations (ng/g wet weight) ± 1 SD [▭] and geometric mean [▬] ± comparison interval [ ], and number of samples.

collected as subsistence hunters would gather them for consumption"). The criteria should specify measures to prevent sample contamination and the sample temperatures to be maintained during transport and storage (e.g., samples will be stored on ice until they can be frozen, shipped packed in dry ice, and stored at –80 °C until analyzed). In most cases, sampling should be designed to determine the persistence of the oil (i.e., temporal trends). When collecting samples (e.g., sediment or mollusks) to evaluate temporal trends, a very specific sampling station and sample-collection scheme (e.g., random collection along a transect at a selected tidal elevation) must be established to include a sampling schedule that will detect changes in chemical concentrations over a selected time period. Furthermore, it may be necessary to analyze samples from appropriate reference areas in order to draw statistically valid conclusions.

A chain-of-custody form should be formatted so that all relevant information about the samples and sample handling can be documented, and it should include space for special observations (e.g., presence or absence of oil, type of beach). Furthermore, if oil or another substance is observed, a sample of that substance should be collected. For example, it was reported that there was a sheen around creosoted pilings where mollusks were sampled at Chenega station CHE7, and the sample collectors believed that mollusks from that site were contaminated by creosote. Because no sample of creosote was collected at the sampling site, laboratory analysts had to obtain a sample of creosote locally and analyze it to compare patterns to those of the samples. However, if a sample of the sheen material had been collected, the pattern of ACs in that material could have been compared to patterns for mollusk samples.

It is important to establish an analysis scheme that will effectively answer the posed questions in a timely and cost effective manner so that managers can make informed decisions. The standard method for analyzing sediment and tissues for the presence of petroleum-related ACs involves solvent extraction, liquid chromatography to separate the analytes from other compounds, and the use of GC/MS for qualitative and quantitative analysis (e.g., Appendix 1). In this subsistence study, each sample was analyzed for about 270 components or peaks, with each peak representing one or more compounds. This procedure is relatively costly and time consuming, but it results in precise concentrations for individual analytes. Screening methods for ACs in sediment and tissue samples that are rapid and relatively inexpensive were recently described by Krahn and Stein (1998). The screening method for ACs in tissue consists of solvent extraction and analysis of the extract using high-performance liquid chromatography (HPLC) with fluorescence detection. Data interpretation is rapid because only two to three component peaks are determined to measure the extent of ACs contamination. The HPLC screening method results in concentrations for classes of ACs (e.g., naphthalene equivalents that are an estimate of the sum of the concentrations of naphthalene and the alkyl-substituted naphthalenes), whereas GC/MS analysis results in more precise and more accurate concentrations of naphthalene and individual alkyl substituted naphthalenes. The screening method can be calibrated so that data can be presented in concentration units of a spilled oil. On an emergency basis, data for six to eight samples could be reported within 48 hours of receipt of samples, compared with about two weeks for the standard GC/MS method. In general, samples can be screened for ACs for about 20% of the cost of detailed GC/MS analysis. If ACs are present based on the HPLC screening method, some source-related information also will be evident from the chromatographic patterns (e.g., petroleum, refined products, products of combustion).

In developing a SAP for a future oil-spill response, a tiered approach using screening methods in conjunction with standard GC/MS methods should be considered. For example, the first tier would be to use an HPLC screening method to analyze all samples for ACs. If the concentrations of ACs by the screening method are below a predetermined significant concentration, there would be no need for additional analyses. For example, in this study, sample concentrations of 10 to 99 ng/g were categorized as minimally contaminated. Therefore, if the tiered approach had been applied to this subsistence study and it was decided that samples that had < 100 ng/g ACs would not be analyzed by the GC/MS method, about 90% of the samples would not have been analyzed by GC/MS.

It is important to have an appropriate quality assurance plan in place prior to the start of chemical analyses. Specific analytes should be chosen to answer established questions related to toxicity, potential sources of contamination, and temporal trends in concentrations. An appropriate level of analytical sensitivity should be chosen (i.e., appropriate target-detection limits). Quality assurance performance criteria should include at least the use of control materials (preferably standard or certified reference materials), method blanks, solvent blanks, certified calibration standards, and replicate sample analyses.

Finally, timely communication of test results—combined with data interpretation that provides proper background for the evaluation and understanding of the results—is important to resource managers who must make decisions of political and economic importance (e.g., reopening of closed fisheries).

Acknowledgments—We appreciate the encouragement and support from Dr. Charles Ehler, John Robinson, and Dr. Richard Berry for this study. We also thank Lew Consiglieri, Ann Hayward-Walker, L. Jay Field, Dr. Tom Nighswander, and Tim Reilly and Dave Schmidt and his staff of field biologists from Dames & Moore. Dr. James Fall, Ronald T. Stanek, Pippa Coiley, Rita Miraglia, Lisa Scarbrough, and Craig Mishler of the Alaska Department of Fish and Game (ADF&G) provided valuable assistance. We also acknowledge the assistance of numerous other staff in several segments of the National Oceanic and Atmospheric Administration (NOAA) and ADF&G. A number of EC Division scientists ably assisted this study in the sample analyses and data management. In alphabetical order they are Nicolaus Adams, Stacie Aspey, Lisa Bogatzki, Daryle Boyd, Richard Boyer, Kristin Bryant, Tho Dang, Jennifer Fisher, Barbara French, Rebecca Hastings, Deborah Holstad, Stephanie Johansen, Thomas Merculief, Hannah Morris, Andrew Nalin, David Rees, Eunice Schnell, John Shields, and Dana Whitney. The authors thank Paul Robisch and Tom Hom for reviewing this manuscript.

References

Atlas RM, Boehm PD, Calder JA. 1981. Chemical and biological weathering of oil, from the *Amoco Cadiz* spillage, within the littoral zone. *Estuarine Coast Shelf Sci* 12:589–608.

Boehm PD, Fiest DL, Elskus A. 1981. Comparative weathering patterns of hydrocarbons from the *Amoco Cadiz* oil spill observed at a variety of coastal environments. International Symposium on the *Amoco Cadiz*: Fates and Effects of the Oil Spill. Paris, France: Centre National pour l'Exploitation des Oceans. p 159–173.

Clark Jr RC, Brown DW. 1977. Petroleum: properties and analyses in biotic and abiotic systems. In: Malins DC, editor. Volume I, Effects of petroleum on Arctic and subarctic marine environments and organisms. New York: Academic. p 1–89.

Fedorak PM, Westlake DWS. 1981. Microbial degradation of aromatics and saturates in Prudhoe Bay crude oil as determined by glass capillary gas chromatography. *Can J Microbiol* 22:432–443.

Fedorak PM, Westlake DWS. 1983. Microbial degradation of organic sulfur compounds in Prudhoe Bay crude oil. *Can J Microbiol* 29:291–296.

Gabriel KR. 1978. A simple method of multiple comparisons of means. *J Am Stat Assoc* 73:724–729.

James MO. 1989. Biotransformation and disposition of PAH in aquatic invertebrates. In: Varanasi U, editor. Metabolism of polycyclic aromatic hydrocarbons in the aquatic environment. Boca Raton FL: CRC. p 69–92.

Krahn MM, Stein JE. 1998. Assessing exposure of marine biota and habitats to petroleum compounds. *Anal Chem* 70:186–192.

Livingstone DR. 1991. Organic xenobiotic metabolism in marine invertebrates. In: Gilles R, editor. Volume 7, Advances in comparative and environmental physiology. Berlin Heidlelberg, Germany: Springer-Verlag. p 46–118.

Moore MN, Livingstone DR, Widdows J. 1989. Hydrocarbons in marine molluscs: biological effects and ecological consequences. In: Varanasi U, editor. Metabolism of polycyclic aromatic hydrocarbons in the aquatic environment. Boca Raton FL: CRC p 69–92.

Neff JM. 1979. Polycyclic aromatic hydrocarbons in the aquatic environment. Essex, England: Applied Sciences.

[NRC] National Research Council. 1985. Oil in the sea: inputs, fates, and effects. Washington D.C: National Academy Press.

Sokal R, Rohlf F. 1981. Biometry, 2d edition. San Francisco CA: W.H. Freeman.

Varanasi U, Brown DW, Hom T, Burrows DG, Sloan CA, Field LJ, Stein JE, Tilbury KL, McCain BB, Chan S-L. 1993a. Volume I: Survey of Alaskan subsistence fish, marine mammal, and invertebrate samples collected 1989-91 for exposure to oil spilled from the *Exxon Valdez*. NOAA Tech. Memo. NMFS F/NWC-12. 110 p.

Varanasi U, Brown DW, Hom T, Burrows DG, Sloan CA, Field LJ, Stein JE, Tilbury KL, McCain BB, Chan S-L. 1993b. Volume II: Supplemental information concerning a survey of Alaskan subsistence fish, marine mammal, and invertebrate samples collected 1989-91 for exposure to oil spilled from the *Exxon Valdez*. NOAA Tech. Memo. NMFS F/NWC-13. 173 p.

Varanasi U, Chan S-L, MacLeod WD Jr, Stein JE, Brown DW, Burrows DG, Tilbury KL, Landahl JT, Wigren CA, Hom T, Pierce SM. 1990. Survey of subsistence fish and shellfish for exposure to oil spilled from the *Exxon Valdez*. First Year: 1989. NOAA Tech. Memo. NMFS F/NWC-191. 151 p.

Chapter 8

Measuring the Exposure of Subsistence Fish and Marine Mammal Species to Aromatic Compounds Following the *Exxon Valdez* Oil Spill

Tom Hom, Donald W. Brown, John E. Stein, Usha Varanasi*

The *Exxon Valdez* oil spill (EVOS) in Prince William Sound, Alaska brought about the temporary closure of several commercial fisheries (i.e., halibut, salmon, herring) and the oiling and death of numerous marine mammals such as harbor seals and sea otters. It was highly likely that many fish and marine mammals were exposed to petroleum-related contaminants by migration through oiled areas or through ingestion of contaminated food sources. A high proportion of dietary protein for native Alaskans comes from the edible tissues of fish and marine mammals collected for subsistence. Consequently, concern was raised over the potential effects on human health from ingestion of petroleum-contaminated tissues of aquatic species used for subsistence by native Alaskans.

Prudhoe Bay crude oil (PBCO) contains complex mixtures of aromatic compounds (ACs), including polycyclic aromatic hydrocarbons (PAHs) and sulfur-containing ACs (e.g., dibenzothiophenes) (Krahn et al. 1993). Some of these petroleum-related ACs are suspected of being toxic or carcinogenic to humans (Dipple et al. 1984). Previous studies (Varanasi and Gmur 1981; Solbakken et al. 1984; Stein et al. 1984; Varanasi et al. 1989) have shown that marine organisms can readily take up aromatic contaminants, including PAHs and structurally related heterocyclic compounds, from their environment. Marine organisms that are most susceptible to exposure to these chemicals are those inhabiting polluted waterways near urban centers or areas contaminated by environmental accidents such as the EVOS. Unlike invertebrate species such as mollusks, fish have the capacity to biotransform PAHs to polar metabolites that are released from the liver and concentrated into bile for

*Mr. Tom Hom is a research chemist and Division Coordinator for the Environmental Conservation Division of the Northwest Fisheries Science Center. Mr. Hom coordinates studies on the metabolic fate and effects of organic contaminants on marine biota. His area of expertise is the uptake, accumulation, and disposition of these contaminants in fish and marine mammals, with the findings of these studies used to assess potential adverse biological effects. Mr. Hom received his B.S. and M.S. in chemistry from Montana State University and the University of Washington, respectively.

Evaluating and Communicating Subsistence Seafood Safety in a Cross-Cultural Context: Lessons Learned from the Exxon Valdez Oil Spill
L. Jay Field et al., editors. © 1999 Society of Environmental Toxicology and Chemistry (SETAC). ISBN 1-880611-29-5

excretion (Varanasi and Gmur 1981; Varanasi et al. 1985). For marine mammals, comparatively less data are available on the uptake and fate of PAHs. Several studies, however, have shown that pinnipeds and cetaceans contain the same hepatic enzyme systems found in terrestrial mammals and fish that can convert PAHs to excretable metabolites and limit the accumulation of the parent compounds or their metabolites in tissues (Addison et al. 1986; Goksøyr et al. 1988). The normal detoxifying mechanism of the liver, however, can be circumvented during diving periods of marine mammals; during these periods, contaminants could accumulate in brain and other extrahepatic tissues.

Because teleosts and marine mammals rapidly metabolize PAHs, extensive chemical analysis of tissues from these animals for parent PAHs would provide misleading information about exposure to petroleum-related compounds. However, the finding of high concentrations of PAH metabolites in bile of fish exposed to radiolabeled PAHs led to the development of a method (Krahn et al. 1984, 1986) that measures fluorescent aromatic compounds (FACs) in bile by high pressure liquid chromatography (HPLC). The method provides a rapid, semiquantitative means of assessing exposure of fish and marine mammals to PAHs and was used previously to evaluate exposure of fish to ACs from an oil spill on the Columbia River (Krahn et al. 1986) and in other laboratory and field studies. Additionally, the use of biliary FACs for estimating exposure of fish to ACs from petroleum was validated using fish collected from Prince William Sound shortly after the EVOS (Krahn et al. 1992). Several metabolites of ACs were identified by gas chromatography/mass spectroscopy (GC/MS) in bile of salmon and pollock captured in Prince William Sound several months after the spill. These AC metabolites were also present in bile of a Pacific halibut injected with weathered PBCO. In contrast, these metabolites were not present in the bile of fish collected from reference sites not affected by crude oil. Moreover, a significant correlation ($r = 0.93$, $p \leq 0.0001$) was found between the sum of individual biliary metabolites determined by GC/MS and the concentrations of FACs in bile determined by HPLC with fluorescence detection.

In response to the concern of Alaska Natives that their subsistence seafood was contaminated by oil, we utilized the relatively inexpensive HPLC analyses of bile to assess the extent of petroleum-derived exposure of aquatic species sampled after the spill. The results of FACs in bile were used to prioritize corresponding edible muscle samples for detailed analyses of parent ACs by GC/MS. The results of analyses of edible flesh of fish were then evaluated by the Alaska Oil Spill Health Task Force and the U.S. Food and Drug Administration to assess the potential risk to Alaska Natives of consuming seafood from their traditional fishing sites following the spill. In addition to fish, bile of marine mammals from areas impacted by the EVOS was analyzed to assess exposure to ACs. The results of bile and detailed analyses by GC/MS of tissues were compared to assess the potential for accumulation of parent ACs, since marine mammals may accumulate significant levels of parent PAHs, even if present at low concentrations, due to their potential disposition into lipid-rich blubber. Further, the findings of this study will also provide guidance in choosing the proper analytical approaches, in terms of time- and cost-effectiveness, for future petroleum-related catastrophes in marine environments.

Sample Collection and Analysis of Bile and Edible Tissue

Locations of native subsistence villages are shown in Figure 8-1. Various fish species were caught using a combination of hook-and-line, longline, or gill nets by the consulting firm of Dames & Moore and the Alaska Department of Fish and Game (ADF&G) near these sites. Details of locations of where subsistence fish were sampled have been presented in Varanasi et al. (1993). Marine mammals were sampled from sites in Prince William Sound, the Gulf of Alaska, and Lower Cook Inlet on the Kenai Peninsula. The majority of marine mammals were collected by ADF&G as part of the Natural Resource Damage Assessment (NRDA) studies. Harbor seals (*Phoca vitulina*) and Steller sea lions (*Eumetopias jubata*) were selected

Figure 8-1 Map of selected native Alaskan subsistence fishing sites sampled in Prince William Sound, 1989 and 1990

on the basis of their degree of external oiling—where those most heavily oiled represented the worst-case scenario—and not specifically for subsistence (Frost et al. 1994). Two additional harbor seals and one Steller sea lion were collected by NOAA as part of the Marine Mammal Tissue Archival Program (MMTAP).

The fish species were selected in cooperation with representatives from Alaska Native villages; fish were caught in areas generally used by native fishermen. Field collections of biological samples were designed to minimize the possibility of external contamination of samples. Bile contents taken from gall bladders of fish and marine mammals were transferred to individual, solvent-rinsed 4-ml vials and frozen as soon as possible. Muscle fillets of individual fish were double-wrapped in aluminum foil (prebaked at 180 °C for one hour), placed in locking freezer bags, and put on ice before freezing. Both bile and muscle were then transferred under chain-of-custody protocols to our laboratory and stored at –80 °C until analyzed.

The analytical methods used in the subsistence study have been previously described (Krahn et al. 1986, 1988; Burrows et al. 1990; Sloan et al. 1993), and details of their use in this study are described in Appendix 1. Briefly, the HPLC bile screening method was used to provide an estimate of exposure of fish to petroleum-related ACs. The results of bile screening were then used to prioritize corresponding muscle tissue for analysis of parent ACs by more time-consuming and costly GC/MS methods. A ranking factor, depending on the degree of exposure indicated by the bile FAC results, was used to determine GC/MS analyses of individual or composited muscle tissue. Generally, in most cases where bile FACs were high, analysis of muscle tissue by GC/MS was done on an individual basis. Conversely, muscle tissues were composited for detailed analysis when FAC results indicated little or no exposure to ACs. The ranking criteria are described in detail in Appendix 1.

Site and temporal comparisons of the concentrations of biliary FACs for fish were statistically evaluated using GT2 comparison interval plots (Gabriel 1978; Sokal and Rohlf 1981). The GT2 comparison intervals are similar to confidence intervals, but are more closely related to an analysis of variance. The comparison interval for each mean was calculated based on the number of samples for that mean, the variability of that mean, and the number of means being compared. Comparison intervals of means that do not overlap were considered significantly different. Statistical comparisons of other results were done using analysis of variance or Student's t-test; the significance level for these tests was set at $p \leq 0.05$.

Fish

Aromatic compounds in edible muscle tissue

The concentrations of ACs in muscle tissue of selected salmonid and bottomfish species, reported as the sum of low- and high-molecular-weight ACs and the alkylated ACs (∑ACs, listed in Table 8-1) are summarized in Table 8-2. The results of muscle analyses of other fish species (e.g., sockeye and chum salmon, dolly varden, rock sole, rockfish) collected in this study have been reported previously (Varanasi et al. 1993). Site comparisons were not statistically evaluated because of the low amounts of ∑ACs detected in the majority of muscle samples analyzed by GC/MS.

Table 8-1 Aromatic compounds (ACs) determined in tissues of salmon, bottomfish, and marine mammals sampled after the EVOS by GC/MS[1]

Low-molecular weight ACs (LACs, 2–3 rings)	High-molecular-weight ACs (HACs, > 3 rings)
naphthalene	fluoranthene
acenaphthylene	pyrene
acenaphthene	benz[a]anthracene
fluorene	chrysene
phenanthrene	benzo[b]fluoranthene
dibenzothiophenes	benzo[k]fluoranthene
	benzo[a]pyrene
Alkylated LACs	indeno[1,2,3-c,d]pyrene
C1-C4 naphthalenes	dibenz[a,h]anthracene
C1-C3 fluorenes	benzo[g,h,i]perylene
C1-C4 phenanthrenes/anthracenes	
C1-C3 dibenzothiophenes	*Alkylated HACs*
	C1 fluoranthenes/pyrenes
	C1-C4 chrysenes/benz[a]anthracenes

[1] C1-, C2-, C3-, and C4- are abbreviations for alkylated groups such as methyl, dimethyl/ethyl, or trimethyl/butyl that are substituted on the aromatic ring.

Low concentrations of ∑ACs were detected in muscle of salmonids and bottomfish collected from sites in Prince William Sound and Lower Cook Inlet and most sites along Kodiak Island. Mean concentrations of ∑ACs in muscle tissue ranged from not detected to 34 ng/g wet weight for all fish species sampled. Of the several hundred muscle samples analyzed in 1989 and 1990 for individual ACs by GC/MS, only 16 salmon (< 6% of the total fish analyzed) had concentrations of ∑ACs in muscle exceeding 10 ng/g (Figure 8-2). Interestingly, most muscle samples containing the higher concentrations (14 to 100 ng/g wet weight) of ∑ACs were in pink salmon from Kodiak. Detailed analyses of bivalve species sampled from Kodiak revealed AC patterns that suggested the availability of an AC source unrelated to the oil spilled from the *Exxon Valdez* (Chapter 7). Further, GC/MS analyses of these fish showed that of the total ∑ACs detected in muscle tissue, the amount resulting from

Table 8-2 Concentrations (ng/g wet weight) of ∑ACs in muscle of salmon and bottomfish sampled after the EVOS[1,2]

	Pink salmon		Coho salmon		Halibut		Pacific cod	
Site	1989	1990	1989	1990	1989	1990	1989	1990
Angoon (reference)	2.0 ±0.1 (2)		3.0 ±1.0 (3)		0.4 (1)		0.6 (1)	
Yakutat (reference)					4.0 ±3.9 (6)			
Tatitlek	0.01 ±0.02 (6)		9.0 ±7.7 (7)		nd (2)		nd (1)	nd (4)
Ouzinkie	2.0 ±1.7 (10)	nd (1)[3]	3.0 ±2.3 (8)	0.5 ±0.3 (3)	0.3 ±0.5 (5)	1.0 ±2.0 (2)		3.0 (1)
Chiniak	1.0 ±1.4 (13)				1.0 ±0.4 (2)			
Port Lions	0.7 ±0.8 (10)	8.0 ±8.3 (2)	1.0 ±1.1 (6)		0.3 ±0.3 (4)			1.0 ±1.4 (2)
Port Graham/ Nanwalek	0.1 ±0.3 (7)	0.4 ±1.1 (5)	0.6 ±0.8 (6)			0.1 ±0.1 (2)		nd (1)
Old Harbor	0.6 ±1.2 (18)	0.9 ±1.1 (8)			0.7 ±0.6 (3)		0.4 ±0.5 (2)	1.0 (1)
Larsen Bay	2.0 ±3.4 (15)	0.5 ±0.5 (2)			0.4 ±0.3 (5)		0.4 ±0.1 (2)	0.7 (1)
Kodiak	31 ±34 (15)	34 ±42 (3)			0.4 ±0.5 (3)			
Chenega Bay	2.0 ±4.3 (21)	0.9 ±0.7 (5)			0.1 ±0.1 (4)	3.0 ±3.7 (2)	0.1 ±0.1 (4)	1.0 ±1.0 (6)

[1]The concentration of ∑ACs from each site is expressed as the mean ± SD. Of the total ∑ACs detected in individual muscle, the amount resulting from high-molecular-weight ∑ACs (listed in Table 8-1) ranged from 0 to < 10%.
[2]Numbers in parentheses indicate the number of samples analyzed.
[3]nd indicates that the analyte was not detected above the detection limit (0.01 to 1.0 ng/g wet weight).

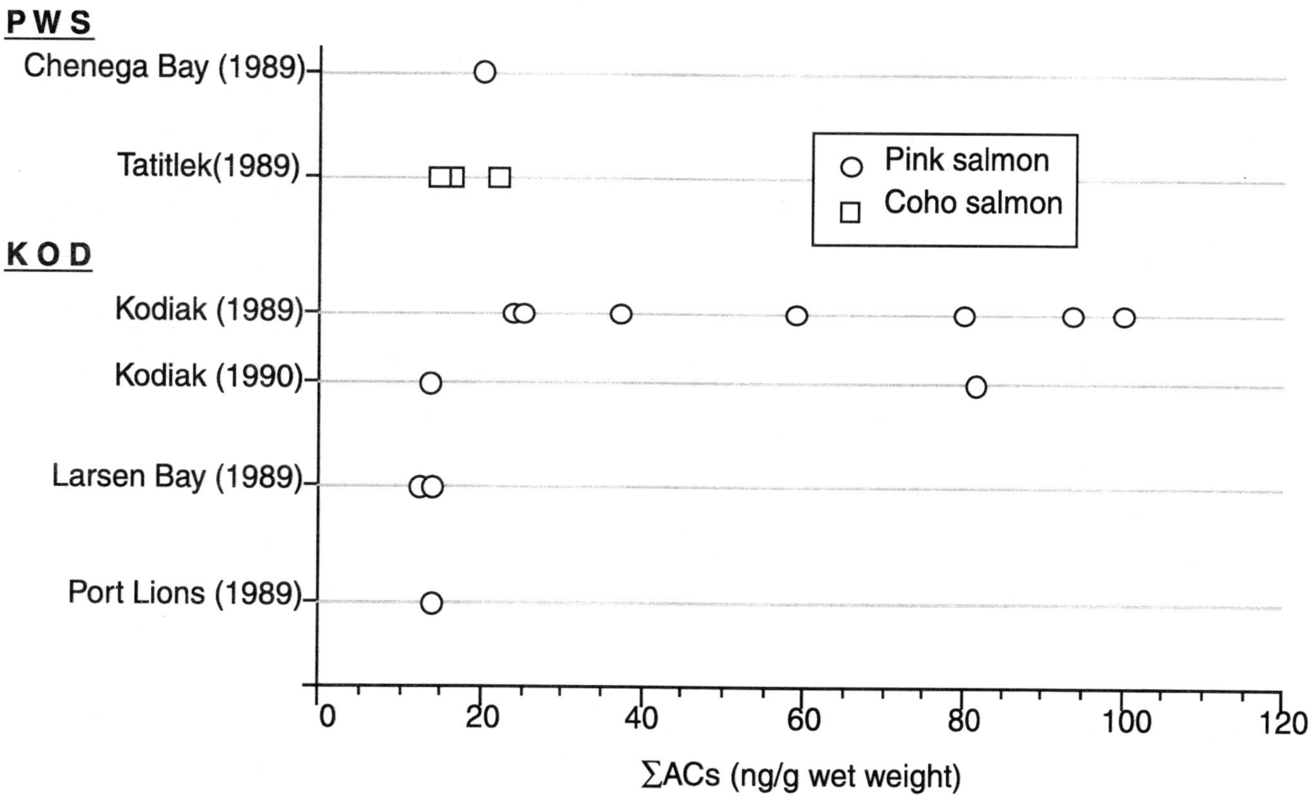

Figure 8-2 Concentrations (ng/g wet weight) of aromatic compounds ($\sum$ACs) exceeding 10 ng/g wet weight in edible muscle tissues of individual salmon sampled from subsistence sites in 1989 and 1990. PWS and KOD indicate areas of Prince William Sound and Kodiak Island, respectively.

high-molecular-weight ACs (listed in Table 8-1) ranged from 0 to < 10% of the total ACs measured. Certain high-molecular-weight ACs are known to be carcinogenic in experimental animals; however, the health risk from consuming edible flesh of these subsistence fish would be negligible (Chapter 9).

The concentrations of ∑ACs in individual muscle samples of several pink salmon (ranging from not detected to 100 ng/g wet weight) and coho salmon (ranging from not detected to 22 ng/g wet weight) were generally higher than in bottomfish. However, the mean concentrations of ACs in most fish muscle sampled from subsistence sites were < 35 ng/g wet weight (Table 8-2). For example, in muscle of halibut and Pacific cod, the mean concentrations of ∑ACs were ≤ 3 ng/g wet weight in fish sampled from all subsistence sites in both years (Table 8-2). Further, mean concentrations of ∑ACs in muscle of these bottomfish were similar to concentrations of ∑ACs found in a halibut and Pacific cod from Angoon and Yakutat, the designated reference sites in southeast Alaska.

Although sufficient samples of muscle from pink salmon and Pacific cod were collected in both sampling years to allow evaluation of temporal changes, comparisons among concentrations of ∑ACs in edible muscle were difficult because of the low amounts of ∑ACs detected in many of the samples. For example, mean concentrations of ∑ACs in muscle of pink salmon from Port Graham/Nanwalek, Old Harbor, Larsen Bay, and Chenega Bay were < 3 ng/g wet weight in both sampling years (Table 8-2). At Kodiak, the mean concentrations of ∑ACs in muscle of fish were substantially elevated (> 30 ng/g wet weight) relative to levels in fish from the other sites but did not change significantly over time. Mean concentrations of ∑ACs in muscle were 31 ± 34 ng/g wet weight and 34 ± 42 ng/g wet weight in 1989 and 1990, respectively. These results, as well as those for FACs in bile of fish and data from analyses of shellfish from Kodiak (Chapter 7), suggest exposure of marine species from Kodiak to a source of ACs other than spilled oil from the *Exxon Valdez*.

Fluorescent aromatic compounds in bile

Bile was analyzed for FACs by HPLC/UV-Fluorescence at excitation/emission wavelength pairs for phenanthrenes and naphthalenes because these compounds are present in high proportions in PBCO (Varanasi et al. 1993). Because the concentrations of biliary FACs at phenanthrene and naphthalene wavelength pairs were highly correlated ($r = 0.91$, $p = 0.0001$), only the concentrations measured at the phenanthrene wavelength pair are reported. The concentrations of biliary FACs are reported on the basis of milligrams of biliary protein. Recent studies (Collier and Varanasi 1991) have shown that such a normalization can account, to a large extent, for changes in the concentrations of biliary FACs caused by differences in the feeding status of fish. The results of analyses of bile for FACs from pink salmon (*Oncorhynchus gorbuscha*), coho salmon (*Oncorhynchus kisutch*), Pacific halibut (*Hippoglossus stenolepis*), and Pacific cod (*Gadus macrocephalus*) collected in 1989 and 1990 were adapted from earlier NOAA reports and Technical Memoranda (Varanasi et al. 1990, 1993) and are summarized in Figures 8-3 and 8-4.

Concentrations of FACs determined in bile of other salmon (i.e., sockeye, chum, chinook) and bottomfish (i.e., yellowfin sole, rockfish, rock sole, greenling, flounder) sampled in 1989 and 1990 are not shown in detail here. Results of analyses of these fish species have been reported previously by Varanasi et al. (1990, 1993).

Site differences

Exposure of subsistence fish to spilled oil from the *Exxon Valdez* was assessed by measuring the concentrations of biliary FACs by HPLC/fluorescence. Salmon and bottomfish sampled from selected subsistence sites exhibited a wide range of FACs in their bile; the concentrations of biliary FACs measured in individual fish in 1989 and 1990 ranged from 10 to 17,000 ng phenanthrene equivalents (Es)/mg bile protein. Fish containing high concentrations of biliary FACs were probably exposed to petroleum-related ACs. The highest mean concentrations of biliary FACs detected in subsistence fish species were collected from sites near Chenega Bay, located in Prince William Sound and in the path of spilled oil. For example, in 1989, the mean concentrations of biliary FACs in pink salmon from Chenega Bay were significantly higher than levels in fish from all other subsistence sites except Kodiak (Figure 8-3). No significant differences in biliary FAC concentrations among pink salmon from Chenega Bay or Kodiak and Angoon, the reference site, were observed. This was due to a single pink salmon from Angoon with a biliary FAC level (12,000 ng phenanthrene Es/mg bile protein) that was 4- to 20-fold higher than levels in the other three pink salmon (1800 ± 1300 ng phenanthrene Es/mg bile protein) sampled from the reference site. However, the concentrations of biliary FACs were significantly higher in pink salmon from Chenega Bay when compared with Angoon, if the reference sample showing the high biliary FAC value was removed from the dataset. Furthermore, mean FAC concentrations in bile of coho salmon (530 ng phenanthrene Es/mg bile protein) and chinook salmon (490 ng phenanthrene Es/mg bile protein) from Angoon were considerably lower than FAC concentrations in pink salmon from Chenega Bay and Kodiak after the spill. Additionally, concentrations of biliary FACs in pink salmon from Chenega Bay and Kodiak were also significantly higher than levels in fish from Tatitlek, a site not in the path of the oil spill.

As with pink salmon, high concentrations of biliary FACs also were found in Pacific halibut and Pacific cod from Chenega Bay in 1989 (Figure 8-3). The concentrations of FACs in bile of halibut from Chenega Bay were significantly higher than levels in halibut from Angoon, the reference site (Figure 8-3). Further, significantly higher concentrations of biliary FACs were also observed in halibut from Ouzinkie and Port Lions compared with levels in halibut from Angoon. No statistical comparison could be made with halibut from Kodiak because only one fish was sampled; however, this fish also exhibited an elevated biliary FAC concentration (7400 ng

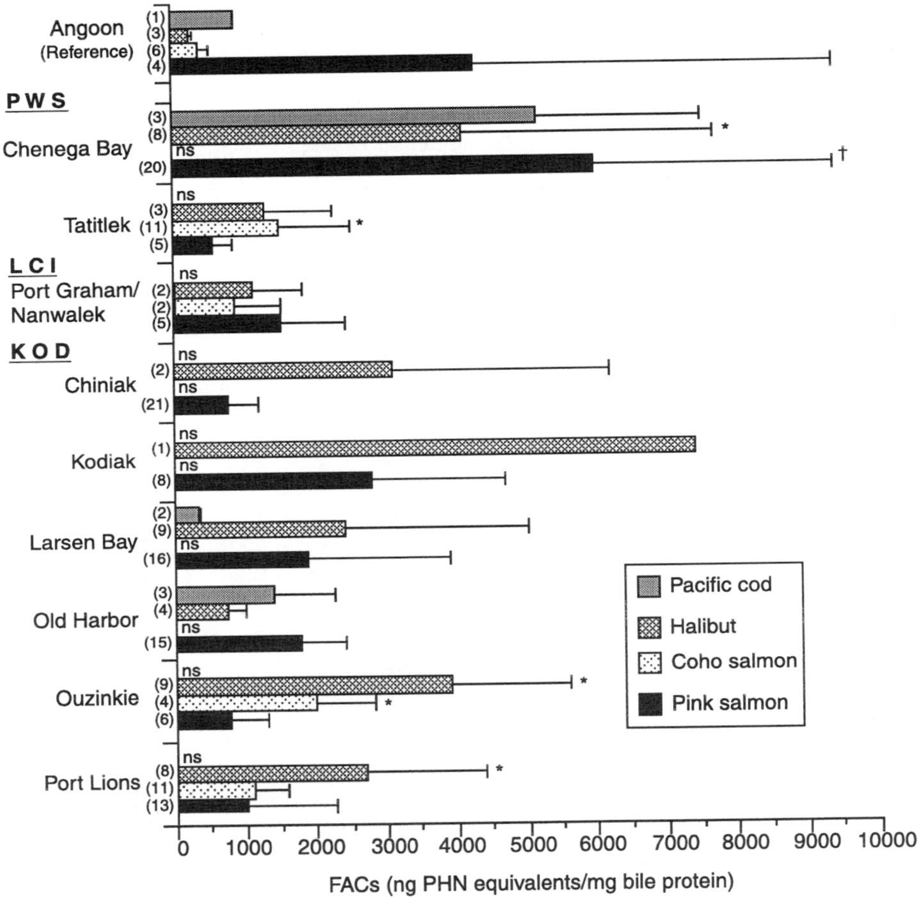

Figure 8-3 Concentrations (mean ± SD) of FACs (ng phenanthrene Es/mg bile protein) in salmon and bottomfish sampled from Alaskan fishing sites in 1989. Numbers in parentheses indicate number of samples analyzed; ns indicates a fish species that was not sampled; PWS, LCI, and KOD indicate areas of Prince William Sound, Lower Cook Inlet, and Kodiak Island, respectively; asterisks (*) denote a value that is significantly higher than the measured value in fish from Angoon, the designated reference site, by GT2 comparison intervals; dagger (†) denotes a value that is significantly higher than the measured value in fish from all other sites except Kodiak and Angoon, by GT2 comparison intervals.

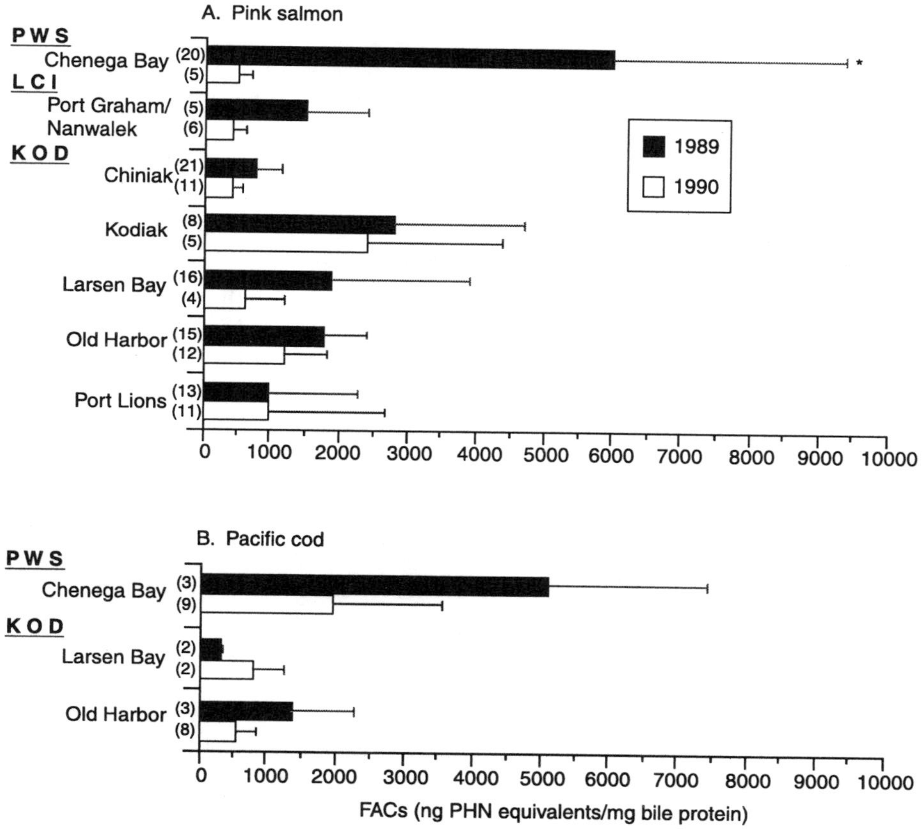

Figure 8-4 Mean concentrations (mean ± SD) of FACs (ng phenanthrene Es/mg bile protein) in (A) pink salmon and (B) Pacific cod sampled from Alaskan fishing sites in 1989 and 1990. PWS, LCI, and KOD indicate areas of Prince William Sound, Lower Cook Inlet, and Kodiak Island, respectively; numbers in parentheses indicate number of samples analyzed; asterisks (*) denote a value that is significantly different than the measured value in 1990 by GT2 comparison intervals.

phenanthrene Es/mg bile protein) compared with levels in halibut from the reference site.

Pacific cod sampled from Chenega Bay also exhibited high concentrations of biliary FACs compared with cod from the reference site, Angoon. Although statistical comparisons could not be made with cod from Angoon because only one fish was collected, the concentration of FACs in the bile of this fish (480 ng phenanthrene Es/mg bile protein) was much lower than those in cod from Chenega Bay (5200 ± 2300 ng phenanthrene Es/mg bile protein) (Figure 8-3).

In 1989, concentrations of biliary FACs in individual coho salmon sampled from five sites ranged from 140 to 4900 ng phenanthrene Es/mg bile protein (Figure 8-3). Unfortunately, no coho salmon were sampled from Chenega Bay or Kodiak, precluding comparisons of FAC levels with the other species sampled from these oil-affected sites. Concentrations of biliary FACs were significantly higher in coho salmon from Ouzinkie and Tatitlek than in fish from Angoon, the reference site.

Generally, fish captured in areas within Prince William Sound that were in the path of the spilled oil exhibited the highest levels of biliary FACs. Additionally, most fish captured at sites along Kodiak Island (i.e., Kodiak, Ouzinkie, Chiniak, Port Lions) also contained elevated concentrations of FACs in bile, but these concentrations were below those found in fish from Chenega Bay. Further, relatively higher concentrations of biliary FACs were found in fish captured at sites in the path of the spilled oil, compared with concentrations in fish captured at Angoon, the designated reference site in southeast Alaska not affected by the EVOS. In a separate but related study, Collier et al. (1993) reported that several subtidal fish species caught in sites heavily contaminated by spilled crude oil contained significantly higher concentrations of biliary FACs than did fish sampled in areas that showed signs of little or no oiling.

Temporal changes in biliary FACs

Pink salmon and Pacific cod were the only species collected in sufficient numbers in both sampling years to allow evaluation of temporal changes. Comparisons among other salmon and bottomfish species were not possible because of small sample size or lack of corresponding data from 1989.

The presence of FACs in bile of fish indicates a relatively recent (within several weeks) exposure of fish to PAHs (Collier and Varanasi 1991). In the present study, significantly lower levels of biliary FACs in 1990, compared with 1989, were observed in pink salmon from Chenega Bay. At Chenega Bay, a 10-fold decrease (from 6000 ± 3400 to 490 ± 230 ng phenanthrene Es/mg bile protein) in mean concentrations of FACs was observed in bile of pink salmon in 1990 relative to those sampled in 1989 (Figure 8-4A). Additionally, a trend of decreasing concentrations of biliary FACs in pink salmon in 1990, compared with 1989, was also observed at most of the other subsistence sites sampled. For example, relatively smaller decreases in FACs from 1989 to 1990 were observed in pink salmon from Port Graham/Nanwalek (3.6-fold decrease), Chiniak (1.6-fold decrease), Old Harbor (1.5-fold decrease), and Larsen Bay (3.0-fold decrease) (Figure 8-4A). Similar findings of markedly reduced biliary FACs in subtidal fish sampled in 1990, compared with 1989, from sites heavily oiled by the spill also were reported by Collier et al. (1993). Thus, the findings of lower concentrations of biliary FACs in the subsistence fish suggested decreased availability for uptake of petroleum-related ACs at most sites one year after the oil spill. In contrast, concentrations of biliary FACs in pink salmon from the Kodiak site, a harbor with high commercial fishing-vessel traffic and fueling facilities, remained at a relatively high level in both 1989 and 1990, indicating no change in bioavailability of ACs in both sampling years.

Pacific cod were collected in both years at only a few subsistence sites. Pacific cod sampled in consecutive years from Chenega Bay and Old Harbor also showed declines (> 2-fold) in mean concentrations of biliary FACs, but these were not significant by GT2 comparison intervals. An increase in biliary FACs from 1989 to 1990 was observed in Pacific cod from Larsen Bay; however, only two fish were sampled in each year (Figure 8-4B).

Relationship between biliary FACs and ACs in muscle

Comparison of the concentrations of FACs in bile to the concentrations of $\sum$ACs in corresponding muscle tissue of salmon and bottomfish showed no significant correlation ($r = 0.06$, $p = 0.40$) (Figure 8-5). Although levels of biliary FACs in several fish species sampled from oiled sites indicated significant exposure of fish to ACs, edible muscle tissues in fish were found to have concentrations of ACs that rarely exceeded the relatively low concentration of 30 ng/g wet weight. This finding was especially exemplified in fish from Chenega Bay, where fish showed the highest exposure to petroleum-related ACs in bile (6000 ± 3400 ng phenanthrene Es/mg bile protein), but still contained minimal amounts of $\sum$ACs in corresponding muscle tissue (1.6 ± 4.3 ng/g wet weight). These results strongly suggest that the efficient metabolism of ACs by fish greatly limits the accumulation of parent ACs in extrahepatic tissues such as muscle.

Marine Mammals

Aromatic compounds in mammalian tissues

Selected samples of blubber, liver, and muscle from 33 harbor seals, including those visibly oiled (Figure 8-6) or collected from heavily oiled sites, and 10 Stellar sea lions were analyzed for ACs because these tissue types are usually collected for subsistence food by native Alaskans. The AC results for individual specimens have been reported elsewhere (Frost et al. 1994). Mean concentrations of $\sum$ACs in tissues of

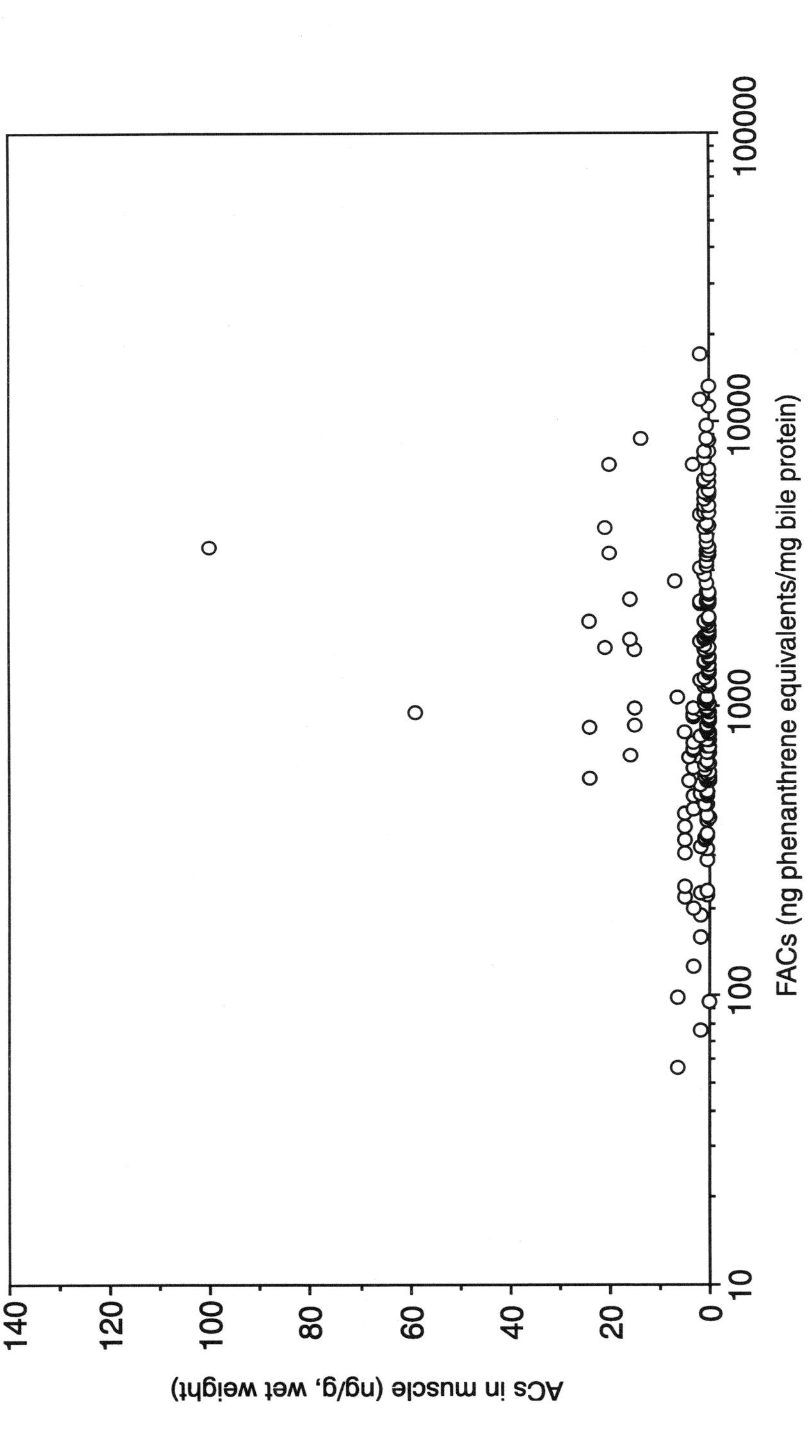

Figure 8-5 Relationship between FACs (ng phenanthrene Es/mg bile protein) in bile and total ACs (ng/g wet weight) in corresponding edible muscle determined in salmon and bottomfish sampled from Alaskan fishing grounds in 1989 and 1990. Concentrations of FACs in bile are plotted on a semi-logarithmic scale.

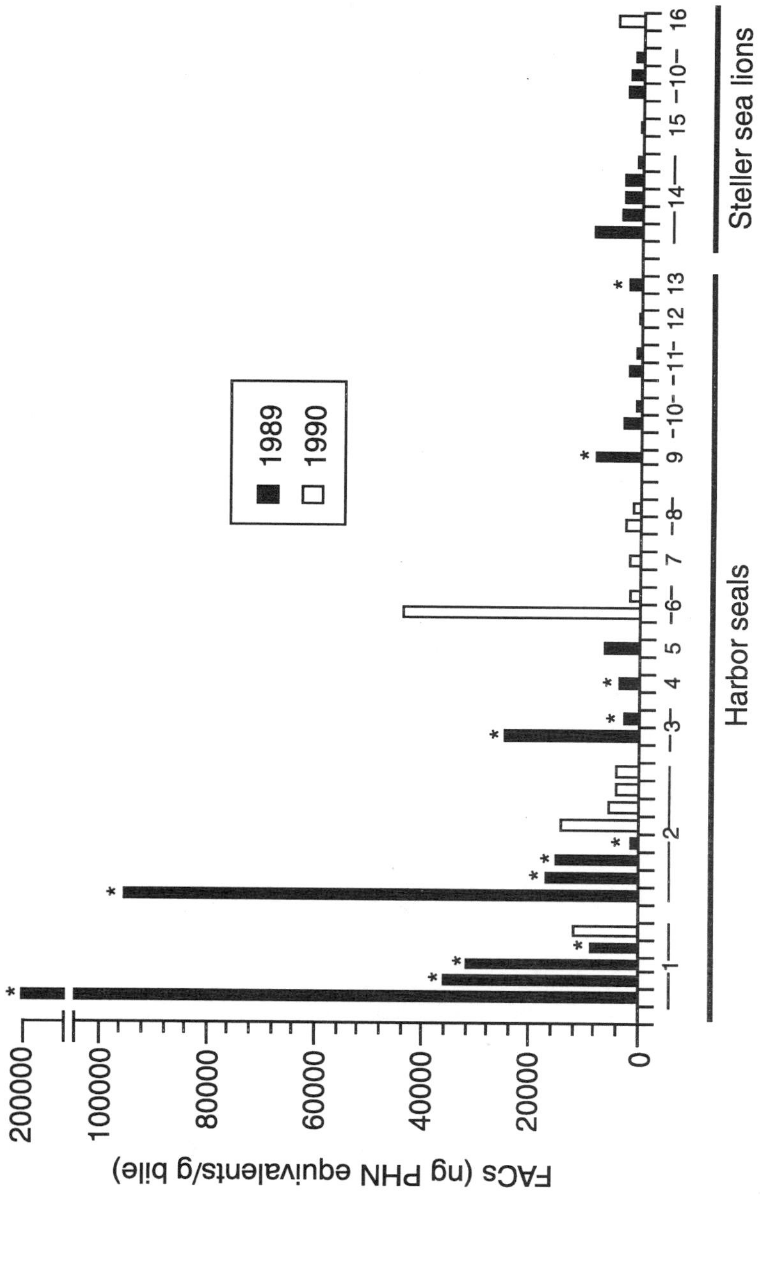

Figure 8-6 Concentrations of biliary FACs (ng phenanthrene Es/g bile) in individual harbor seals and Steller sea lions from Alaskan fishing sites. Site identifications: 1) Bay of Isles, 2) Herring Bay, 3) Seal Island, 4) Applegate Rocks, 5) Agnes Island, 6) NE Eleanor Island, 7) New Year Island, 8) Galena Bay, 9) W. Amatuli-Barren Island, 10) Ushagat Island-Barren Island, 11) Perenosa Bay-Afognak, 12) Big Fort Island, 13) Perl Island, 14) The Needles, 15) Chiswell, and 16) Flat Island. Sites 1–8 and 14 are located in Prince William Sound, and remaining sites are located along the Gulf of Alaska. Asterisk (*) indicates that the animal was visibly oiled.

marine mammals sampled from sites in Prince William Sound, the Gulf of Alaska, and the outer Kenai are summarized in Table 8-3.

Similar to fish, the ability to effectively metabolize ACs by marine mammals limited the accumulation of these compounds in the tissues. With a few exceptions, the concentrations of $\sum$ACs measured in corresponding tissues, including blubber, liver, and muscle were relatively low. The highest concentrations of $\sum$ACs were found in blubber of harbor seals from Herring Bay (range 85 to 800 ng/g wet weight) and the Bay of Isles (range 63 to 460 ng/g wet weight) in Prince William Sound; both of these sites were heavily oiled in 1989 (Table 8-3). By 1990, however, concentrations of $\sum$ACs (< 70 ng/g wet weight) in blubber of harbor seals from these sites had declined considerably, suggesting a decrease in the exposure to ACs. For Stellar sea lions collected in 1989 and 1990, only one blubber sample (17 ng/g wet weight) in an animal from Flat Island in the Gulf of Alaska contained AC concentrations >10 ng/g wet weight. Generally, concentrations of $\sum$ACs in liver and muscle of harbor seals and Stellar sea lions were lower than corresponding blubber tissue (Table 8-3). Moreover, concentrations of $\sum$ACs in liver and muscle of these animals compared favorably with levels measured in the muscle of salmon and bottomfish sampled for subsistence.

The accumulation of ACs exceeding 10 ng/g wet weight in various tissues from individual harbor seals is illustrated in Figure 8-7. Generally, ACs were primarily deposited in blubber tissue of these marine mammals. Highest concentrations of $\sum$ACs were found in blubber of visibly oiled harbor seals from Herring Bay (800 ng/g wet weight) and the Bay of Isles (460 ng/g wet weight). In contrast, only one muscle (16 ng/g wet weight) and one liver (15 ng/g wet weight) sample from harbor seals from Seal Island and Herring Bay (1990), respectively, contained $\sum$AC concentrations > 10 ng/g wet weight. Generally, the lipid content in selected marine mammals is highest in blubber (50 to 90%), followed by liver (5 to 7%), and lowest in muscle (< 3%) tissue (J. Bolton, personal communication). Previous studies have shown a correlation between accumulation of chlorinated hydrocarbons, such as polychlorinated biphenyls (PCBs), and the lipid content in tissues (Waid 1986; Varanasi et al. 1992). Accordingly, the accumulation of some nonpolar ACs into lipid-rich tissue, particularly blubber, is possible in marine mammals inhabiting oiled sites.

Fluorescent aromatic compounds in bile

As with fish, the bile of marine mammals was analyzed for concentrations of FACs to assess exposure of these animals to ACs from oil spilled from the *Exxon Valdez*. Unlike fish, we have not determined whether biliary protein can be used as a normalizing factor to account for differences in bile composition in marine mammals. Thus, concentrations of biliary FACs in marine mammals are expressed as ng phenanthrene Es/g bile. Additionally, because of the limited number of animals

Table 8-3 Concentration of ∑ACs (mean ± SD) in tissues of harbor seals and Steller sea lions sampled after the EVOS[1]

Village/Sampling site[2]	Year sampled	Blubber	Liver	Muscle
Harbor seal				
Prince William Sound				
Herring Bay	1989	280 ± 350 (4)	0.5 ± 1.0 (4)	0.3 ± 0.6 (3)
Herring Bay	1990	26 ± 29 (4)	4.0 ± 8.0 (4)	0.6 ± 1.0 (4)
Bay of Isles	1989	200 ± 190 (4)	0.7 ± 0.9 (4)	5.0 ± 4.0 (4)
Bay of Isles	1990	69 (1)	nd (1)[3]	0.8 (1)
Seal Island	1989	18 ± 8.0 (2)	nd (2)	12 ± 6.0 (2)
Applegate Rocks	1989	6 (1)	nd (1)	1 (1)
Agnes Island	1989	12 (1)	nd (1)	0.4 (1)
New Year Island	1990	2 (1)	3 (1)	nd (1)
Little Green Island	1990	2.0 ± 2.0 (4)	6.0 ± 2.0 (4)	—[4]
Galena Bay	1990	7.0 ± 4.0 (2)	3.0 ± 2.0 (2)	nd (2)
NE Eleanor Island	1990	15 ± 1.0 (2)	nd (2)	4.0 ± 5.0 (2)
W. Amatuli Island-Barren Island	1989	nd (1)	nd (1)	nd (1)
Gulf of Alaska				
Ushagat Island-Barren Island	1989	2.0 ± 1.0 (2)	3 ± 4 (2)	nd (2)
Perenosa Bay-Afognak	1989	4 (1)	4 (1)	nd (1)
Perenosa/Seal Bay	1989	nd (1)	5 (1)	0.4 (1)
Big Fort Island	1989	9 (1)	nd (1)	nd (1)
Outer Kenai				
Perl Island	1989	2 (1)	6 (1)	nd (1)
Steller sea lion				
Prince William Sound				
The Needles	1989	0.4 ± 0.4 (5)	2.0 ± 1.8 (5)	0.6 ± 0.4 (5)
Gulf of Alaska				
Chiswell Island	1989	0.6 (1)	nd (1)	0.7 (1)
Flat Island	1990	17 (1)	1 (1)	0.5 (1)
Ushagat Island-Barren Island	1989	0.7 ± 0.4 (3)	3.0 ± 3.0 (3)	nd (3)

[1]Numbers in parentheses indicate number of samples analyzed.
[2]All animals, with the exception of harbor seals from New Year Island, and Galena Bay and the Steller sea lion from Flat Island, were sampled by the ADF&G for NRDA; the others were collected for NOAA's MMTAP.
[3]nd = not detected by GC/MS.
[4]No samples were analyzed.

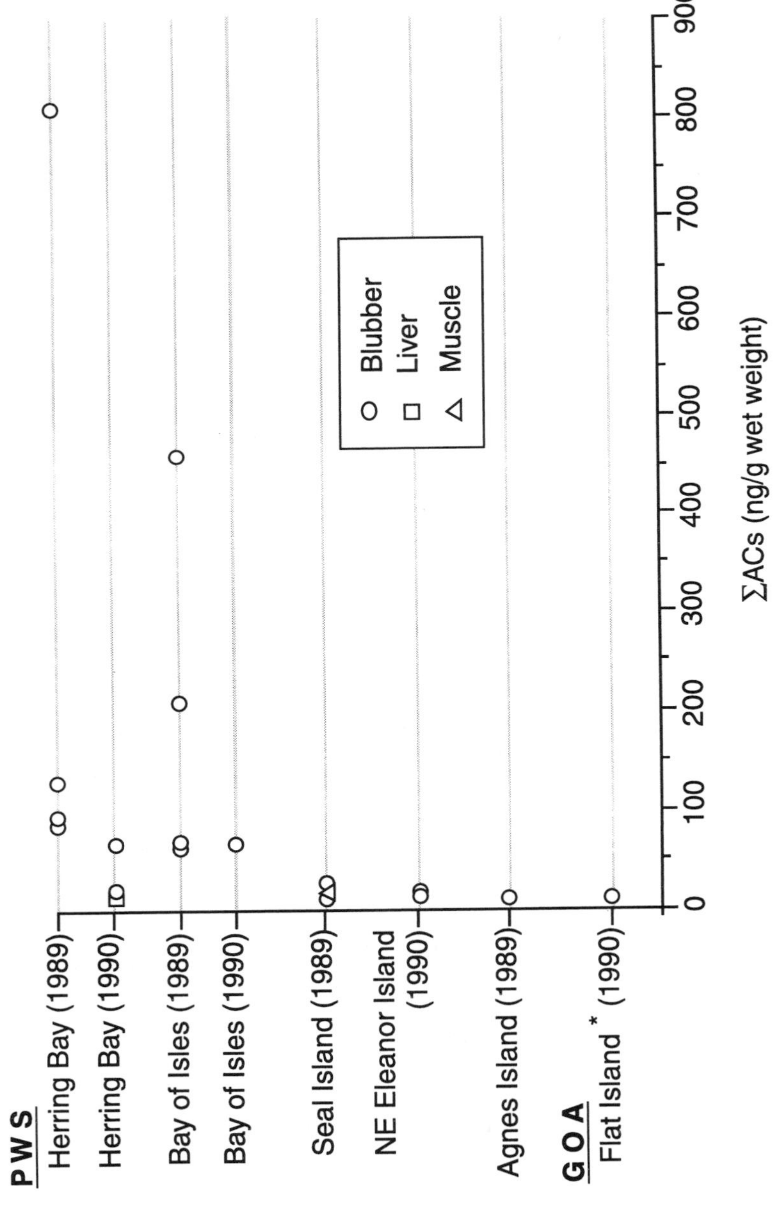

Figure 8-7 Concentrations (ng/g wet weight) of $\sum$ACs exceeding 10 ng/g wet weight in blubber, liver, and muscle tissue of individual marine mammals sampled from Prince William Sound in 1989 and 1990. Asterisk (*) indicates a location in the Gulf of Alaska from which a Steller sea lion was sampled; harbor seals were sampled at all other sites.

sampled at any of the selected areas, no statistical analyses for site comparisons were done.

The results of bile analyses of harbor seals collected in 1989 and 1990 have been previously reported (Varanasi et al. 1993; Frost et al. 1994). The results of bile analyses of these marine mammals showed evidence of exposure to petroleum-related ACs after the EVOS (Figure 8-6). As with ACs in muscle, the highest concentrations of biliary FACs were found in harbor seals sampled in 1989 from the Bay of Isles (mean concentration of 72,000 ± 93,000 ng phenanthrene Es/g bile) and Herring Bay (32,000 ± 43,000 ng phenanthrene Es/g bile) in Prince William Sound. Additionally, moderate concentrations of FACs were found in seals from Seal Island (14,000 ± 16,000 ng phenanthrene Es/g bile). In contrast, relatively lower biliary FAC concentrations (170 to 8000 ng phenanthrene Es/g bile) were found in harbor seals sampled from unoiled sites in the Gulf of Alaska (Figure 8-6).

In 1990, a harbor seal sampled from NE Eleanor Island in Prince William Sound contained a relatively high FAC concentration (44,000 ng phenanthrene Es/g bile), indicating that this seal was exposed to a source of ACs shortly before capture. Additionally, relatively moderate concentrations of biliary FACs were found in individual harbor seals from Herring Bay (14,000 ng phenanthrene Es/g bile) and the Bay of Isles (12,000 ng phenanthrene Es/g bile). Other marine mammals sampled in 1990 contained concentrations of FACs in their bile of < 6000 ng phenanthrene Es/g bile (Figure 8-6).

Bile of Stellar sea lions from one site in Prince William Sound and several sites in the Gulf of Alaska were analyzed for FACs in 1989 (Figure 8-6). Compared with harbor seals from the Bay of Isles and Herring Bay, mean concentrations of biliary FACs in Stellar sea lions were considerably lower, ranging from 390 to 8500 ng phenanthrene Es/g bile. None of the Stellar sea lions sampled were visibly oiled. Unfortunately, the Stellar sea lions were not from the same sites (e.g., Bay of Isles, Herring Bay, Seal Island) from which harbor seals were sampled, preventing a direct comparison of bile results between two species of marine mammals inhabiting a common area.

Temporal changes and relationship between biliary FACs and tissue ACs

Comparison of temporal changes in exposure of marine mammals from a specific site was possible only for harbor seals and only Herring Bay and the Bay of Isles in Prince William Sound were sampled in both years. Harbor seals sampled from Herring Bay exhibited nearly a 5-fold decrease in mean biliary FAC concentrations in 1990 (6900 ± 4800 ng phenanthrene Es/g bile) compared with seals sampled in 1989 (mean of 32,000 ng phenanthrene Es/g bile). Additionally, the one seal sampled from the Bay of Isles in 1990 (1200 ng phenanthrene Es/g bile) also contained much lower biliary FACs than those sampled in 1989 (mean of 72,000 ng phenanthrene Es/g bile). Further, when combining bile results of seals sampled from all the oiled sites in Prince William Sound, Frost et al. (1994) showed a more than 3-fold decrease in biliary FAC concentrations in harbor seals collected in 1990 compared with 1989.

Because of the limited number of animals sampled, statistical analyses for comparing concentrations of biliary FACs with tissue ACs were not done. However, empirical comparisons of the data show a slight trend of higher concentrations of biliary FACs and tissue ACs in harbor seals that were visibly oiled and collected from oiled sites in Prince William Sound in 1989. For example, of the oiled harbor seals that contained the highest concentrations (e.g., > 35,000 ng phenanthrene Es/g bile) of biliary FACs, three of those animals had the highest concentrations (210 to 800 ng/g wet weight) of ACs in blubber and were from the heavily oiled sites (i.e., Bay of Isles, Herring Bay).

Discussion

Overall, the results of chemical analyses of fish and marine mammals sampled in the subsistence study showed minimal or no contamination of edible tissue by petroleum-related ACs. For comparison, the mean concentration of parent ACs in mussels collected at Windy Bay, a heavily oiled site in Prince William Sound, was nearly 10-fold higher than the highest ACs found in fish or marine mammals. This result is not surprising because earlier studies have clearly demonstrated the lack of efficient metabolism in invertebrates compared with vertebrate species. Thus, the consistency of the results from this field study and those of previous laboratory studies provided evidence of minimal accumulation of ACs in edible tissues of fish and marine mammals captured at sites affected by the spilled oil.

The results of bile analyses of fish species used for subsistence by Alaska Natives showed a wide range of exposure to petroleum-related ACs after the EVOS. The high concentrations of biliary FACs detected in salmon and bottomfish indicated that the fish were able to readily take up and metabolize ACs to polar compounds for excretion. As stated earlier, there was minimal contamination of corresponding edible muscle by ACs. These data—showing low or undetectable concentrations of ACs in muscle of fish exhibiting a substantial range in exposure to ACs—corroborated results of earlier laboratory studies. For example, laboratory studies with fish exposed to a model AC, benzo[a]pyrene, by way of water, food, or contaminated sediment showed that fish can readily take up and efficiently biotransform benzo[a]pyrene to polar metabolites that are concentrated into bile for excretion, thus limiting the accumulation of the parent compound in extrahepatic tissues such as muscle (Varanasi and Gmur 1981; Balk et al. 1984; Stein et al. 1984, 1987; Varanasi et al. 1989). These findings were important in the development of techniques (Krahn et al. 1986) to measure concentrations of AC metabolites in bile that subsequently would provide the necessary information for responding effectively to oil spills. Additionally, the results demonstrated the usefulness of rigorous laboratory studies for predicting the response of marine species to chronic or acute exposure to chemical pollution.

A major attribute of bile analysis by HPLC during environmental emergencies is its ability to estimate exposure of vertebrate species to ACs. Identifying individual xenobiotic compounds found in bile is difficult because bile consists of a complex mixture of many components and provides only a semiquantitative assessment of exposure of fish and marine mammals to ACs. Nonetheless, because ACs are quickly converted and excreted by these animals, the analysis of bile is currently the only way to determine recent exposure to petroleum-related ACs. Additionally, bile analyses provide a rapid, cost-effective means of assessing AC exposure by which many samples can be analyzed in a relatively short time period.

Conclusions and Lessons Learned

Our experience from responding to the EVOS gives us a unique perspective on guiding responses to future petroleum spills. Before the EVOS, our knowledge from laboratory studies about the uptake and biotransformation of ACS in marine biota led to development of the key analytical techniques used for the EVOS. In addition, findings from detailed laboratory studies of the fate and biotransformation of ACs in fish and invertebrates provided the necessary understanding of these processes for us to interpret the data on levels of ACs found in the wide range of subsistence species examined. The EVOS also provided a large-scale field verification of the laboratory findings and a real-world application of the analytical techniques recently developed to measure exposure of marine species to oil-related chemicals. Several specific conclusions and recommendations may be useful in guiding responses to human-health concerns in future spills.

Power in the use of screening methods

Certain analytical approaches to investigating the fate and effects of ACs in marine species were developed from research-scale studies before the EVOS. The potential of these techniques for use in a response to a spill was clear, but their utility had not been tested in a real-world situation. With EVOS, these "new" techniques, such as the HPLC bile-screening method, were used and evaluated in the subsistence studies. The bile-screening method provides rapid analyses of large sample sets and the ability to assess exposure of fish and marine mammals in a relatively short time and at a much lower cost than that of detailed analyses for parent ACs. The bile screening method was validated as a useful tool to screen individual fish and marine mammals for subsequent analysis of corresponding edible tissues by the detailed GC/MS method.

Practicality of a "tiered" approach

The findings from EVOS showed that using a "tiered" approach consisting of a series of analyses—i.e., a rapid HPLC screening method (Tier 1) followed by a more detailed and costly method (Tier 2)—is both scientifically sound and economical in its application. Screening allows collection of sufficient data that can provide a greater picture of the scope and extent of contamination of the biota and habitat affected by the spill. Moreover, rapid screening techniques can also be used to give both researchers and managers flexibility in their response to an oil spill. For example, results from a preliminary sampling can provide the necessary information needed by managers to design further sample collection or analysis. Use of the tiered approach was very successful in the rapid turnaround of analytical results to guide seafood safety decisions following the EVOS. For the EVOS study, only about 10% of the samples collected warranted detailed analyses of subsequent edible tissue using GC/MS. Screening, therefore, can be very effective in minimizing the use of more costly methods on samples with low levels of contaminants.

Field validation of laboratory studies on the fate of ACs in marine biota

Earlier laboratory studies with fish and invertebrate species exposed to ACs through several different routes (i.e., water, food, sediment) demonstrated differential metabolism by fish and invertebrates. Fish can readily take up and efficiently biotransform ACs to polar metabolites that are concentrated into bile for excretion. In contrast, invertebrate species do not have the same capacity to detoxify ACs, thus allowing the bioaccumulation of these compounds in their tissues. This rapid metabolism of ACs in fish limits the accumulation of parent compounds in tissues such as muscle. These laboratory findings were corroborated by results of the subsistence study that showed a wide range of exposure of fish to ACs from spilled oil, but little or no accumulation of these compounds in corresponding edible tissue. The combination of the laboratory findings and data from the subsistence study allowed for scientifically sound judgments on the bioavailability, disposition in tissues, and level of accumulation of oil-related chemicals in biota following a spill.

Fate of ACs in marine mammals

Before the EVOS, there was little information on the fate and effects of petroleum-related contaminants in marine mammals. Marine mammal species have biochemical pathways similar to fish for metabolizing ACs. Unlike fish, however, marine mammals have large lipid reserves, such as blubber, where ACs could potentially accumulate. Blubber is a subsistence food. The findings from the analysis of seal tissue samples showed very low accumulation of ACs in blubber, even in seals exposed to high levels of ACs, as indicated by the high levels of AC metabolites measured in bile. The increased data on seals, therefore, demonstrated that seals and, most likely, other marine mammal species can efficiently metabolize ACs to limit accumulation of parent compounds in blubber tissue. Had analyses of seal tissue samples not been done following the EVOS, it is very unlikely that this data on the fate of ACs in a marine mammal could have been collected because of constraints on conducting experiments with these protected species.

Assessment of trends and the importance of sampling design

In the aftermath of an oil spill, information on temporal and spatial trends are important to managers for decision-making about the risks to human health and about affected resources (i.e., biota, habitat). During EVOS, meeting the objectives of sampling a sufficient range of subsistence species, as well as sampling sites, was necessary to allow a robust assessment of trends. To gather sufficient data for assessing trends and other objectives, it is important to formulate a sampling design that is sound both scientifically and statistically. The quantity of marine biota collected from pertinent sites (i.e., reference, test) for monitoring over time is critical in providing sufficient power of analysis to make statistically sound comparisons or biological inferences. The estimation of statistical power should be done early in the design of a study, before the field sampling begins. Sampling schemes should provide samples sufficient to satisfy both power-of-analysis issues and the necessary archival of additional samples to avoid the expense of resampling, e.g., when more data are needed to decrease the uncertainty of conclusions or replace samples that were compromised or lost.

Frequency of seafood-safety analyses in future spills

In future oil spills, analyses of seafood safety should always be conducted, regardless of prior knowledge of spills and assessment of human health risk, since each situation has its own unique set of circumstances (i.e., type and amount of oil spilled; type of human, marine, and habitat resources affected). The infrequency of major oil spills limits the amount of information available to local communities affected by a spill for the first time. Seafood analyses are needed because the overriding perception of the affected community is that their seafood must be contaminated. The community perceives a large quantity of a "foreign substance" invading their local environment. As with EVOS, analyses of both bile and edible flesh from fish can provide conclusive data to demonstrate the level of exposure of fish to spilled oil. Bile data is important because it is generally consistent with sensory data. The data on AC metabolites in bile provide the context for communicating contamination data to the local populace for edible flesh that in most instances will show very low levels of parent ACs. The low levels of ACs in edible tissue can be explained because of our knowledge of the fate of ACs in vertebrate species. For invertebrates, the range of analyses needed depends on the circumstances of the spill. The lesson from EVOS is that the human health risk of consuming seafood is often quite low. The analyses conducted, if communicated effectively, can help to rebuild confidence in the safety of local invertebrate seafood.

Acknowledgments—We appreciate the encouragement and support of Dr. Charles Ehler and John Robinson of the National Ocean Service and Dr. Richard Berry of the NWFSC for their valuable assistance and support throughout these studies. We thank Anna Kagley and Sylvester Spencer for the analyses of fish bile by HPLC; Catherine Sloan, Doug Burrows, Jennie Bolten and Ron Pearce for performing the GC/MS analyses; Karen Tilbury and Susan Pierce for calculation and compilation of the data; and the biologists from Dames and Moore for the collection of fish samples. We also thank Dr. James Fall, Pippa Coiley, Rita Miraglia, Lisa Scarbrough, and Craig Mishler of the Subsistence Division of the Alaska Department of Fish and Game (ADF&G) for their support; and Kathy Frost, also of ADF&G, Dr. Thomas Loughlin of NMML and their colleagues for the collection of harbor seal samples under the Natural Resources Damage Assessment for the Exxon Valdez oil spill; and Dr. Paul Becker for providing the bile samples from the ringed seals. Finally, we thank Drs. David Herman and Cheryl Krone for their excellent review of this manuscript. Funding for much of this work came from the Exxon Corporation and ADF&G under a Memorandum of Understanding with NOAA.

References

Addison, RF, Brodie PF, Edwards A, Sadler MC. 1986. Mixed function oxidase activity from the harbor seal (*Phoca vitulina*) from Sable Is., N.S. *Comp Biochem Physiol* 85C:121–124.

Balk L, Meijer J, DePierre JW, Appelgren L-E. 1984. The uptake and distribution of [^{3}H]benzo(a)pyrene in the Northern pike (*Esox lucius*). Examination by whole-body autoradiography and scintillation counting. *Toxicol Appl Pharmacol* 74:430–437.

Boon JP, Arnhem EV, Jansen S, Kannan N, Petrick G, Schulz D, Duinker JC, Reijnders PJH, Goksøyr A. 1992. The toxicokinetics of PCBs in marine mammals with special reference to possible interactions of individual congeners with the cytochrome P450-dependent monooxygenase system: an overview. In: Walker CH, Livingstone DR, editors. Persistent pollutants in marine ecosystems. Oxford NY: Pergamon. 272 p.

Burrows DG, Brown DW, MacLeod Jr. WD. 1990. Improved sensitivity for aromatic hydrocarbon quantitation by sequencing GC-MS MID scan descriptors. Presented at the 38th ASMS Conference on Mass Spectrometry and Allied Topics; 3–8 June 1990; Tucson, AZ.

Collier TK, Varanasi U. 1991. Hepatic activities of xenobiotic metabolizing enzymes and biliary levels of xenobiotics in English sole (*Parophrys vetulus*) exposed to environmental contaminants. *Arch Environ Contam Toxicol* 20:462–473.

Collier TK, Krahn MM, Krone CA, Johnson LL, Myers MS, Chan S-L, Varanasi U. 1993. Oil exposure and effects in subtidal fish following the EVOS. In: Proceedings of the EVOS Symposium. p 235–238.

Dipple A, Moschel RC, Bigger CAH. 1984. Polynuclear aromatic carcinogens. ACS Chemical Carcinogens 182:41–163.

Frost KJ, Manen CA, Wade TL. 1994. Petroleum hydrocarbons in tissues of harbor seals from Prince William Sound and the Gulf of Alaska. In: Loughlin TR, editor. Marine mammals and *Exxon Valdez*. San Diego CA: Academic. p 331–358.

Gabriel KR. 1978. A simple method of multiple comparisons of means. *J Am Stat Assoc* 73:724–729.

Goksøyr A, Andersson T, Förlin L, Stenersen J, Snowberger EA, Woodin BR, Stegeman JJ. 1988. Xenobiotic and steroid metabolism in adult and foetal piked (minke) whales, *Balaenoptera acutorostrata*. *Mar Environ Res* 24:9–13.

Krahn MM, Burrows DG, Ylitalo GM, Brown DW, Wigren CA, Collier TK, Chan S-L, Varanasi U. 1992. Mass spectrometric analysis for aromatic compounds in bile of fish sampled after the EVOS. *Environ Sci Technol* 26: 116–126.

Krahn MM, Moore LK, MacLeod WD Jr. 1986. Standard analytical procedures of the NOAA National Analytical Facility, 1986: Metabolites of aromatic compounds in fish bile. NOAA Tech. Memo. NMFS F/NWC-102. 25 pp.

Krahn MM, Myers MS, Burrows DG, Malins DC. 1984. Determination of metabolites of xenobiotics in the bile of fish from polluted waterways. *Xenobiotica* 14:633–646.

Krahn MM, Wigren CA, Pearce RW, Moore LK, Bogar RG, MacLeod WD Jr, Chan S-L, and Brown DW. 1988. Standard analytical procedures of the NOAA National Analytical Facility, 1988: New HPLC cleanup and revised extraction procedures for organic contaminants. NOAA Tech. Memo. NMFS F/NWC-153. 52 p.

Krahn MM, Ylitalo GM, Buzitis J, Chan S-L, Varanasi U, Wade TL, Jackson TJ, Brooks JM, Wolfe DA, Manen C-A. 1993. Comparison of high-performance liquid chromatography/fluorescence screening and gas chromatography/mass spectrometry analysis for aromatic compounds in sediments sampled after the EVOS. *Environ Sci Technol* 27:699–708.

Sokal RR, Rohlf FJ. 1981. Biometry. 2nd ed. San Francisco CA: W.H. Freeman. 859 p.

Solbakken JE, Solberg M, Palmork KH. 1984. A comparative study on the disposition of three aromatic hydrocarbons in flounder (*Platichthys flesus*). *FiskDir Skr Ser Havunders* 17:473–481.

Sloan CA, Adams NG, Pearce RW, Brown DW, Chan S-L. 1993. Northwest Fisheries Science Center organic analytical procedures. In: Lauenstein GG, Cantillo AY, editors. Sampling and analytical methods of the National Status and Trends Program National Benthic Surveillance and Mussel Watch Projects 1984–1992, Volume IV. NOAA Tech. Memo. NOS/ORCA/ CMBAD-71.

Stein JE, Hom T, Varanasi U. 1984. Simultaneous exposure of English sole (*Parophrys vetulus*) to sediment-associated xenobiotics: Part 1 – Uptake and disposition of ^{14}C-polychlorinated biphenyls and ^{3}H-benzo(a)pyrene. *Mar Environ Res* 13:97–119.

Stein JE, Hom T, Casillas E, Friedman AJ, Varanasi U. 1987. Simultaneous exposure of English sole (*Parophrys vetulus*) to sediment-associated xenobiotics: Part 2 – Chronic exposure to an urban estuarine sediment with added ^{3}H-benzo(a)pyrene and ^{14}C-polychlorinated biphenyls. *Mar Environ Res* 22:123–149.

Varanasi U, Brown DW, Hom T, Burrows DG, Sloan CA, Field LJ, Stein JE, Tilbury KL, McCain BB, Chan S-L. 1993. Survey of Alaskan subsistence fish, marine mammal, and invertebrate samples collected 1989–91 for exposure to oil spilled from the *Exxon Valdez*. NOAA Tech. Memo. NMFS F/NWC-12.

Varanasi U, Chan S-L, McCain BB, Schiewe MH, Clark RC, Brown DW, Myers MM, Landahl JT, Krahn MM, Gronlund WD. 1989b. National Benthic Surveillance Project: Pacific Coast, Part II, Technical presentation of the results for Cycles I to III (1984–86). NOAA Tech. Memo. NMFS-NWFSC-8. 159 p.

Varanasi U, Chan S-L, MacLeod WD Jr, Stein JE, Brown DW, Burrows DG, Tilbury KL, Landahl JT, Wigren CA, Hom T. 1990. Survey of subsistence fish and shellfish for exposure to oil spilled from the *Exxon Valdez*, First Year: 1989. NOAA Tech. Memo. NMFS F/NWC-191. 151 p.

Varanasi U, Gmur DJ. 1981. Hydrocarbons and metabolites in English sole (*Parophrys vetulus*) exposed simultaneously to [^{3}H]benzo[a]pyrene and [^{14}C]naphthalene in oil-contaminated sediment. *Aquat Toxicol* 1:49–67.

Varanasi, U, Reichert WL, Stein JE, Brown DW, Sanborn HR. 1985. Bioavailability and biotransformation of aromatic hydrocarbons in benthic organisms exposed to sediment from an urban estuary. *Environ Sci Technol* 19:836–841.

Varanasi U, Stein JE, Nishimoto M. 1989. Biotransformation and disposition of polycyclic aromatic hydrocarbons (PAH) in fish. In: Varanasi U, editor. Metabolism of polycyclic aromatic hydrocarbons in the aquatic environment. Boca Raton FL: CRC Press. p 94–149.

Varanasi U, Stein JE, Reichert WL, Tilbury KL, Krahn MM, Chan S-L. 1992. Chlorinated and aromatic hydrocarbons in bottom sediments, fish and marine mammals in U.S. coastal waters:

Laboratory and field studies of metabolism and accumulation. In: Walker CH, Livingstone DR, editors. Persistent pollutants in marine ecosystems. Oxford NY: Pergamon. 272 p.
Waid J S, editor. 1986. PCBs and the environment. Volume 2. Boca Raton FL: CRC. 192 p.

CHAPTER 9

Hazard and Risk Assessment of Crude Oil in Subsistence Seafood Samples from Prince William Sound: Lessons Learned from the *Exxon Valdez*

Michael Bolger, Clark D. Carrington*

On 24 March 1989 the largest oil spill in U.S. history resulted from the accidental grounding of the *Exxon Valdez* in Prince William Sound in Alaska. As part of the oil-spill remediation efforts the Alaska Oil Spill Health Task Force (OSHTF) was charged with conducting a survey and assessment of the impact of the spill on subsistence food supplies. In 1990 the U.S. Food and Drug Administration (USFDA) conducted a risk assessment and provided an advisory opinion on the safety of aromatic hydrocarbon residues in response to a request from the OSHTF (see Appendix 3 for full text of the quantitative risk assessment).

Petroleum mixtures, such as the crude oil released by the *Exxon Valdez*, are composed of hundreds and perhaps thousands of different compounds, including alkanes (aliphatic hydrocarbons with open-chain carbon atoms), aromatic hydrocarbons (with one or more six-carbon rings), and non-organic substituents. The relative proportions of these components vary considerably among mixtures. Chemical analysis of a sample of oil from the *Exxon Valdez* spill (Guerin et al. 1989) indicated that the distributions of alkanes, aromatic contaminants (ACs), polar compounds, and trace metals in the Alaskan oil were typical of the region. Of the most toxic metals, lead was present at levels < 3 ppm; mercury concentrations were not measured.

In the months following the spill, Alaska Natives were gravely concerned that their seafood could be contaminated by spilled petroleum. In response, the National Oceanic and Atmospheric Administration (NOAA) entered into an agreement with Exxon to collect and analyze edible flesh of fish and shellfish from 13 subsistence

*Dr. Bolger is a toxicologist and head of the U.S. Food and Drug Administration's Food Contaminants Branch. He has assessed the hazards and risks of food-borne contaminants, both human-derived and natural, for over 20 years. Dr. Bolger served on the Toxicological Expert Committee for Evaluating Data Related to the Consumption of Marine Subsistence Foods for the Alaska Oil Spill Health Task Force.

Evaluating and Communicating Subsistence Seafood Safety in a Cross-Cultural Context: Lessons Learned from the Exxon Valdez Oil Spill
L. Jay Field, et al., editors. © 1999 Society of Environmental Toxicology and Chemistry (SETAC). ISBN 1-880611-29-5

fishing grounds used by Alaska Natives. Fish and shellfish samples were analyzed for the presence of ACs from petroleum, such as alkylated (in which a substance such as ethyl is substituted in the compound to make high-octane fuel) and unsubstituted aromatic hydrocarbons with two to seven benzenoid rings, as well as dibenzothiophenes (Varanasi et al. 1990).

Hazards of Exposure to Crude Oil

The acute toxicity to humans from direct exposure to petroleum mixtures is characterized by effects to the lungs, gastrointestinal tract, liver, kidneys, central nervous system, and the hematopoietic system (blood and blood-producing organs). Most effects from direct exposure are attributable to the presence of benzene and other small ACs (NRC 1982). However, other components may have direct, adverse health effects as well. Aliphatic compounds may act as asphyxiants and, through their action as fat solvents, cause dermatitis upon contact with the skin. Also, short-term (weeks to months) exposure to n-hexane may cause a peripheral neuropathy. Aliphatic hydrocarbons are generally considered to be non-mutagenic (MacFarland 1988). Assays for mutagenicity and/or carcinogenicity of smaller alkanes, cyclohexane, and a number of petroleum products have nearly all produced negative results, with the possible exception of large isoalkanes. Continuous exposure to branched alkanes with a minimum length of five carbons has been found to be nephrotoxic (toxic to kidneys) and to produce renal tumors in male, but not female, rats. An epidemiological study of dry cleaners using petroleum hydrocarbons indicated an increased risk of kidney cancer in humans (MacFarland 1988). On the other hand, the carcinogenicity of aromatic hydrocarbons is well established. Benzene is one of the few compounds clearly identified as an etiologic agent for cancer in humans (NRC 1982). In addition, some of the polycyclic aromatic hydrocarbons (PAHs) (five-ring aromatic compounds) are known to be very potent carcinogens in other mammals.

Heterocyclic aliphatic hydrocarbons, high-molecular-weight isoalkanes, and non-hydrocarbons are compounds for which information on fate, distribution, and/or toxicity is lacking (NRC 1985). Studies of different petroleum fractions show a poor correlation between PAH content and mutagenicity or carcinogenicity (Ellenton and Hallet 1981; IARC 1989). Although this lack of correlation may result from imperfect characterization of the mutagenicity of individual PAHs, other components such as the larger isoalkanes may contribute to the mutagenicity of a petroleum mixture. Of the non-hydrocarbon components, the toxicity of some of the elements such as lead and mercury have been clearly demonstrated.

The chronic hazards of an oil spill reflect the processes of biodegradation and bioaccumulation. Smaller, more water-soluble aliphatic and aromatic hydrocarbons undergo degradation readily. Larger isoalkanes, branched alkanes, and PAHs are hydrophobic and resistant to microbial degradation (McKenna 1971; NRC 1985) and can accumulate in the food chain. As a result, concerns following past oil spills about contamination of seafood have been restricted mainly to the contribution of petroleum to levels of PAHs.

Polycyclic Aromatic Hydrocarbons: Levels in Food and Estimates of Exposure

Because of the global presence of PAHs, they commonly are detected in many foods (Fazio and Howard 1983; NRC 1985). Levels of individual PAHs ranging from 0.2 to 395 µg/g have been reported for plant and plant products such as wheat, spinach, kale, dried yeast, peanuts, vegetable oils, roasted coffee, tea, and whiskey. PAHs in foods also may be generated by pyrolysis during preparation. Searing or smoking food commonly results in a 2- to 6-fold increase in PAH levels. Some foods in which PAHs have been found are summarized in Table 9-1, with ranges of PAH levels.

Table 9-1 Polycyclic aromatic hydrocarbons in foods

Source	PAH ppb (µg/kg)	B[a]P ppb (µg/kg)
Corn oil	2–10	0.4–1.0
Smoked meat and fish	10–200	0.3–60
Bakers yeast	10–350	2–40
Kale	60–500	13–48

In 1985 the National Research Council derived estimates of the relative contribution of oil-contaminated seafood to benzo[a]pyrene (B[a]P) intake as expressed on an annual basis (NRC 1985). These estimates are summarized in Table 9-2, indicating that eating food from oil-spill-contaminated waters generally approximates the B[a]P exposure from a diet composed mainly of seafood or heavily smoked foods.

Table 9-2 Sources and intake of B[a]P

Source	Annual intake of B[a]P (µg)
Air	0.05–500
Cigarette smoking	15–900
Drinking water	6–70
Normal food diet	250–500
Smoked food diet	550–3000
Seafood diet	37–1825
Oil-contaminated seafood	550–1900

Complicating the assessment of seafood contamination by petroleum is the presence of PAHs in the marine environment from other sources (NRC 1982). Although there is little, if any, natural production of PAHs, they are formed by high-temperature pyrolysis of organic material, from direct combustion of fossil fuels such as gasoline, from the burning of coal and refuse, and from forest and agricultural fires. PAHs may enter the marine environment by way of surface runoff or atmospheric fallout. Although the total marine PAH load is predominantly derived from oil spills (~75%), the most carcinogenic five-ring PAHs are usually (~ 95% for B[a]P) derived from sources other than petroleum spillage (NRC 1985).

Polycyclic aromatic hydrocarbon equivalency approach

The equivalency approach used in the relative cancer-risk assessment is a method for assessing the relative risk of a number of different compounds that are related from both a chemical and a biological activity perspective and that are present in a single-exposure source. This method has been used for other ubiquitous environmental contaminants, most notably the class of contaminants known as dioxins/furans (USEPA 1989). A major justification for the use of such an approach is that one component of known potency is used as a standard rather than calculating individual risks for each component. The concentration of each of the other components is then adjusted on the basis of its estimated, comparative potency to calculate an equivalent concentration for the standard. Summation of the equivalent concentrations produces a single number from which the risk may be estimated.

There are two rationales for using the equivalency approach in the case of a risk assessment for PAHs. First, data on the inherent in vivo, biological activity are inadequate to assess risks for individual components of the mixture of PAHs, and obtaining such data is unfeasible. However, there are data from in vitro systems, or short-term in vivo exposures, that measure a parameter considered relevant to the carcinogenic mechanism of PAHs and that permit the potency of a data-deficient component to be quantitatively related to a reference PAH, in this case B[a]P, for which a long-term study is available. The second rationale for using the equivalency approach is the uneven quality of the available data for individual components. In such cases, the potencies of the components for which there are relatively little data are highly subject to revision, whereas the potency number for a well-studied compound may be expected to be stable. Calculation of an acceptable intake based on the concentration of the component with the best-available data will be least likely to require revision. As long as the potency of the primary compound remains unchanged, the equivalency intake will be minimally affected and essentially remain unchanged. The equation by which the primary equivalents are calculated may change, but the number used to evaluate the sum will not.

While the risk calculated by this procedure is an estimate, it is invariably more reasonable than the estimates obtained either by ignoring all but a few well-described contaminants or the estimates obtained by assuming that all the congeners have equivalent potencies. The available toxicology data for B[a]P are much better than those data available for any of the other PAHs. Short-term studies for most of the compounds are available that allow approximation of potencies relative to B[a]P. Therefore, the equivalency approach is the most defensible because it relies on data that are considered the most sound and that facilitate the incorporation of future revisions in the relative potencies of the PAHs.

The relative potency of PAHs was described in two assessments: one produced by the National Institute of Public Health and U.S. Environmental Protection of the Netherlands (Slooff et al. 1989) and the other by the Environmental Protection Agency (USEPA) (ICF-Clement Assoc. 1990). Both assessments reviewed 19 studies, with five found in both documents. The Netherlands report used a linear model for calculating potency, while the USEPA report used either a two-stage (Moolgavkar and Knudson 1981) or a linear multistage model. The Clements report provided estimates for more of the compounds in question and systematically selected the best study for each compound, although it did not provide multistage estimates for either pyrene or fluoranthene. The best available study was selected for pyrene (Wislocki et al. 1986). The one study listed in the Netherlands report (Slooff et al. 1989), in which a clear tumorigenic response was observed, was therefore used to calculate a potency number for fluoranthene (Busby et al. 1984). For the alkylated PAHs, the addition of the side chains was assumed to have no effect on carcinogenic potency. Since the alkylated compounds were reported as either mixtures of fluoranthenes and pyrenes or chrysenes and benz[a]anthracenes, it was assumed that the relative proportions of the alkylated mixtures were the same as the unsubstituted compounds that were measured separately. The alkylated PAHs were not placed in any International Agency for Research on Cancer category, because there were no data (IARC 1996). Potency numbers relative to B[a]P and judged to be the best available for the nine PAHs measured in the Alaskan marine samples were derived (Bolger et al. 1996).

B[a]P equivalencies exposure from consumption of subsistence fish and shellfish

Several hundred subsistence fish and shellfish samples from 13 fishing grounds in or near Prince William Sound were analyzed for ACs, including aromatic hydrocarbons and dibenzothiophenes (Varanasi et al. 1990). Fish and shellfish samples were collected near the village of Angoon in southeast Alaska to serve as a reference. The results of this study indicated that the pattern of ACs in the fish samples was consistent with the known metabolism of aromatic hydrocarbons by fish. In mollusks, which have little ability to metabolize ACs, both alkylated and unsubstituted ACs were present, and the pattern resembled that of Prudhoe Bay crude oil. B[a]P equivalencies (B[a]PEs) in all the Alaskan fish and shellfish samples, including salmon, were below the level of detection (0.5 ppb). Most of the molluskan bivalves also failed to demonstrate detectable levels, with only a few samples

(22 out of 162) having levels varying from 1 to 49 ppb B[a]PEs. Analyses of molluskan bivalves from areas unaffected by the oil spill indicated negligible PAH levels. Levels of B[a]PEs were unsurprisingly higher in the smoked salmon, because PAHs in smoked foods are known to be generated by pyrolysis of the smoke constituents during preparation. Searing or smoking food commonly results in a 2- to 6-fold increase in PAH levels (Fazio and Howard 1983).

A survey of subsistence fish consumption was used in the assessment. The fish-consumption patterns of the village of Chenega Bay in Prince William Sound (Stratton and Chisum 1986) were surveyed. The Chenega Bay fish and shellfish data were used to estimate upper-bound lifetime risks. The Chenega Bay residents were among the most likely consumers of fish and shellfish that may have come in contact with spilled oil; therefore, the Chenega Bay data were most useful and relevant for risk assessment. The residents, 77% of whom are Alaska Natives, use traditional hunting and fishing practices to obtain a major portion of their food. The rigors of living in a cold climate increase the caloric demand, requiring a higher food intake to maintain normal body function. Fish and shellfish consumption in the isolated Alaskan communities depends on available resources, prevailing customs and tradition, and possible access to alternate food sources from outside the community.

Carcinogenic relative risk assessment

The chronic cancer bioassay for B[a]P was deemed to be the best for estimating the relative risk of carcinogenic PAHs (Brune et al. 1981). In this study, a single dosage of B[a]P was administered to a group of rats over a lifetime. Administering only one dosage level makes for a somewhat limited dose-response evaluation. However, the existence of a low incidence of treatment-related tumors that were mostly benign indicates a response at the lower end of the observable dose-response curve. This response, therefore, is at the point where a linear extrapolation was performed to a zero dose (Gaylor and Kodell 1980). The calculated time-averaged daily dose was 0.107 mg/kg bw day^{-1}, with a corresponding calculated potency of 1.75 mg/kg day^{-1}. The upper-bound relative cancer risk was not estimated for finfish, because no detectable levels were found. For molluskan bivalves, the upper-bound relative risk was estimated as 1.75×10^{-6} whereas that for smoked salmon was about 2-fold greater, or 1.5×10^{-4}.

In estimating advisory levels for B[a]PE from the *Exxon Valdez* oil spill, it was assumed that the duration of the spill's impact was a maximum of 10 years; therefore, the duration of exposure would not be for a 70-year lifetime. This assumption was based on information from other spills, particularly the *Amoco Cadiz,* that indicated that oiled environments do cleanse themselves through environmental mechanisms of oil degradation and biological recovery (NRC 1985). The advisory levels varied from 3 ppb for salmon, 5 ppb for other finfish, 11 ppb for crustaceans, to 120 ppb for molluskan bivalves. The advisory levels are concentrations that, if not exceeded for the given conditions of exposure (10 years consumption), conservatively limit the relative carcinogenic risk from ingested B[a]PE to less than one in a million. The actual risk is most probably lower than these figures suggest. Although PAHs produced by smoking fish are unrelated to the oil spill, an advisory level of 0.8 ppb could be established for smoked salmon (0.8 ppb = 34 ng B[a]PE per 45 g salmon). Since the mean concentration of B[a]PE in smoked salmon was reported to be 112 ppb, this illustrates the importance of this method of food preparation as a source of PAHs.

Conclusions and Lessons Learned

The availability of specific consumption information on the affected subsistence population was a major asset in conducting the relative cancer risk assessment. It is rare that such precise consumption and exposure information is available for assessing the potential risk of exposure to environmental contaminants. In the vast majority of cases, the potential exposure to a contaminant must be inferred based on consumption and exposure information that is not specific to the population of concern. Also, distributional information on the range of consumption of individual foods and levels of oil contaminants is critical to reducing uncertainty in the risk assessment. The survey design for obtaining specimens for analysis is also critical in reducing uncertainty in the risk estimates. Appropriate sampling should adequately reflect the likelihood of exposure and not bias the sampling by overrepresenting certain affected areas. It is critical that the assessment of potential exposure to PAHs from an oil spill be carried out in the context of overall PAH exposure, particularly from diet.

Concern for the presence of contaminants from petroleum spills in marine organisms should be primarily focused on the potential long-term health effects (i.e., carcinogenesis) of certain petroleum components, specifically PAHs. While toxic effects other than cancer are associated with other crude oil components—particularly in the case of direct exposure to petroleum mixtures—the high levels required (e.g., worker exposure) for these effects will not occur from secondary exposure through consumption of fish or shellfish unless there are obvious effects on the marine organisms themselves. In addition, because the methodology for relative cancer-risk assessment is inherently more conservative than that used for non-cancer endpoints, the focus on the PAH-induced cancer effects is the prudent and appropriate public health focus.

PAHs were not present to any significant extent in the subsistence samples that were collected and analyzed as part of the NOAA National Marine Fisheries Service subsistence survey. This is particularly the case for the numerous finfish samples where no evidence was found of the presence of PAHs. With regard to fresh salmon, the 10^{-6} risk level is at or below the detection limit of PAHs. The risk associated with consumption of unsmoked salmon is insignificant compared with the risk associated with consuming smoked salmon, since smoking significantly increases the PAH level. Shellfish, particularly bivalves, deserve particular attention in any oil spill, because it has consistently been shown that components of petroleum accumulate to a much greater extent in bivalves than in finfish. The contamination of mollusks is, therefore, a more sensitive index for exposure of a marine environment to petroleum and represents the most likely point of passage of aquatic oil spillage into human consumption. The data collected from the Alaskan spill are consistent with the view that although finfish do not accumulate toxic petroleum hydrocarbons to any significant extent, mollusks may be a source of concern.

The risk estimate presented for molluskan bivalves was predicated on the initial conservative assumption that persons at risk would consume molluskan bivalves contaminated at the level of PAH produced by the *Exxon Valdez* oil spill for a period of 10 years. Subsequent evidence gathered during the course of the study indicated that this was indeed a conservative assumption and that bivalves would not be expected to be contaminated with PAHs at this level for such an extended period of time. The lifetime carcinogenic risk is low for consumption of unsmoked salmon, other finfish, crustaceans, and even oil-contaminated molluskan bivalves.

In interpreting the relative cancer risk estimates, several points should be emphasized. First, the equivalency approach to estimating the potencies of various PAHs was based on several assumptions; thus, this approach cannot be assumed to produce exact potencies for the PAHs. Second, there are limitations in the available laboratory animal data used to estimate the potency of B[a]P and other PAHs. Third, as with most quantitative relative risk assessments for cancer, an upper-bound risk estimate has been produced with the knowledge that the actual risk is somewhere between the upper-bound estimate and zero and in reality is much closer to zero.

As with any assessment of risk associated with the contamination of food, the greater the available information, the greater the degree of accuracy and certainty. In this assessment, the greatest contribution to uncertainty arose from the use of animal bioassay data to derive estimates of potency for the individual PAHs. This uncertainty derives from two major areas: 1) uncertainty in the use and extrapolation of effects and dosages from laboratory animals to human exposure and 2) reliance on animal bioassays that used non-oral routes of exposure. The contribution of consumption and exposure information to uncertainty in the relative risk assessment was significantly less than that arising from the hazard information. This was because the consumption information was specific to the population of concern and precise analytical information was available on subsistence foods.

The equivalency approach developed and used in this assessment has proved to be a useful framework for evaluating potential effects of oil spills on food supplies in subsequent episodes. In March of 1996 an oil spill occurred off the coast of Rhode Island that significantly affected the substantial commercial fishery in the area. The state health officials responsible for assessing the public health impact of the spill contacted the USFDA for technical assistance. The equivalency approach was adopted and tailored by the state officials in assessing the impact of the spill. The primary adjustment made in the approach was the use of different seafood consumption information on species specific to the affected region.

There were major data gaps on the potential toxicity of crude oil components at the time of the *Exxon Valdez* assessment and there still are today. There is a critical need for a better animal bioassay database on crude-oil constituents and a much better characterization of the potency estimates for the major crude oil PAHs on which to base assigned toxicity equivalents. A better characterization of the toxicity profile of the major classes of crude-oil constituents is still needed. In their 1985 review, the National Research Council identified heterocyclic aliphatic hydrocarbons and non-hydrocarbons as compounds for which information was lacking on fate and distribution and/or toxicity. High-molecular-weight isoalkanes could also be added to this list. Studies of different petroleum fractions show imperfect correlations between PAH content and the degree of mutagenicity and/or carcinogenicity, suggesting that there are other crude-oil constituents with significant biological activity that remain undescribed.

References

Bolger M, Henry S, Carrington C. 1996. Hazard and risk assessment of crude oil contaminants in subsistence seafood samples from Prince William Sound. *Am Fish Soc Symp* 18:837–843.

Brune H, Deutsch-Wenzel RP, Habs M, Ivankovic S, Schmahl D. 1981. Investigation of the tumorigenic response to benzo(a)pyrene in aqueous caffeine solution applied orally to Sprague-Dawley rats. *J Cancer Res Clin Oncol* 102:153–157.

Busby Jr WF, Goldman ME, Newberne PM, Wogan GN. 1984. Tumorigenicity of fluoranthene in a newborn mouse lung adenoma bioassay. *Carcinogenesis* 5:1311–1316.

Ellenton J A, Hallet DJ. 1981. Mutagenicity and chemical analysis of aliphatic and aromatic fractions of Prudhoe Bay crude oil and fuel oil No. 2. *J Toxicol Environ Health* 8:959–972.

Fazio T, Howard JW. 1983. Polycyclic aromatic hydrocarbons in foods. In: Bjorseth A, editor. Handbook of polycyclic aromatic hydrocarbons. New York: Marcel Dekker.

Gaylor DW, Kodell RL. 1980. Linear interpolation algorithm for low dose assessment of toxic substances. *J Environ Pathol Toxicol* 4:305–310.

Guerin MR, Griest WH, Ho C-L. 1989. Health related chemical properties of crude oil. ORNL-DWG 89–14740. Oak Ridge TN: Oak Ridge National Laboratory.

[IARC] International Agency for Research on Cancer. 1989. Crude oil. In: IARC monographs on the evaluation of carcinogenic risks to humans. Volume 45, Occupational exposures in petroleum refining: Crude oil and major petroleum fields. Geneva, Switzerland: World Health Organization. p 119–158.

International Agency for Risk on Cancer [IARC]. 1996. IARC monograph on the evaluation of carcinogenic risks to humans. Volume 65, Preamble. Geneva, Switzerland: World Health Organization. p 9–32.

ICF-Clements Associates. 1990. Comparative potency approach for estimating the cancer risk associated with exposure to mixtures of polycyclic aromatic hydrocarbons. Prepared under USEPA contract 68-02-4403.

MacFarland HN. 1988. Toxicology of petroleum hydrocarbons. In: Weaver NK, editor. The petroleum industry. Volume 3(3), Occupational medicine: State of the art reviews. Philadelphia PA: Manley and Belfus. p 445–454.

McKenna EJ. 1971. Microbial degradation of normal and branched alkanes. In: Degradation of synthetic organic molecules in the biosphere. Washington DC: National Academy Press. p 73–79.

Moolgavkar SH, Knudson AG. 1981. Mutation and cancer: a model for human carcinogenesis. *J Natl Cancer Inst* 66:1037–1052.

[NRC] National Research Council. 1982. Drinking water and health, Volume 4. Washington DC: National Academy Press.

[NRC] National Research Council. 1985. Oil in the sea. Inputs, fates and effects. Washington DC: National Academy Press.

Slooff W, Janus JA, Matthijen AJCM, Montizaan GK, Ros JPM, editors. 1989. Integrated criteria document: PAHs report 758474011. Bilthoven: The Netherlands: National Institute of Public Health and Environmental Protection.

Stratton L, Chisum EB. 1986. Resource and use patterns in Chenega, western Prince William Sound: Chenega in the 1960s and Chenega Bay 1984–1986. Technical paper 139. Anchorage AK: Alaska Dept. of Fish and Game, Division of Subsistence.

[USEPA] U.S. Environmental Protection Agency. 1989. Interim procedures for estimating risks associated with exposures to mixtures of chlorinated dibenzo-p-dioxins and -dibenzofurans (CDDs and CDFs) and 1989 update. Washington DC: USEPA.-625/3–89/016.

Varanasi U, Chan S-L, MacLeod WD, Stein JE, Brown DW, Burrows DG, Tilbury KL, Landahl JL, Wigren CA, Hom T, Pierce SM. 1990. Survey of Subsistence Fish and Shellfish for Exposure to Oil Spilled from the *Exxon Valdez*. Summary. Cycles I-III. Environmental Conservation Division, Northwest Fisheries Science Center, National Marine Fisheries Service, NOAA. Seattle WA. 7 February 1990.

Wislocki PG, Bagan ES, Lu AYH, Dooley KL, Fu PP, Han-Hsu H, Beland FA, Kadlubar FF. 1986. Tumorigenicity of nitrated derivatives of pyrene, benz[a]anthracene, chrysene, and benzo[a]pyrene in the newborn mouse assay. *Carcinogenesis* 7:1317–1322.

Chapter 10

The Communication of Health Risk from Subsistence Food in a Cross-Cultural Setting: Lessons from the *Exxon Valdez* Oil Spill

Thomas S. Nighswander, Nancy Peacock

> *Mega-disasters are probably necessary to advance the cause of civic science, even though, tragically, they leave many martyrs in their wake. . . . What we can never know is how far the learning experience in the convulsive aftermath of such events creates institutional change of sufficient quality so as to prevent similar possible events.*
> —Timothy O'Riordan (1996)

This chapter reviews the intensive efforts of the Oil Spill Health Task Force (OSHTF) and state and federal agencies to communicate information and advice about the health and safety of subsistence seafood following the *Exxon Valdez* oil spill (EVOS). We discuss the growing base of interdisciplinary knowledge and understanding about risk assessment and risk communication that has emerged in the years since the EVOS as the background for explaining the OSHTF's communication strategies. Finally, we evaluate the major lessons that can be drawn from our interactions with Alaska Native communities in the oil-spill area at the time of the spill, particularly within a cross-cultural context. At the most fundamental level, the major issues were

- the cultural conflicts between the local populace and outside experts—in our case, the conflicting scientific paradigms of Alaska Natives and Western scientists that can exacerbate risk-communication problems;
- the wide qualitative scope of risk perceived by the Alaska Natives versus the narrower technical risk parameters within which the experts were operating (e.g., cancer endpoints);
- the generic problems inherent in communicating risk to the public during a technological disaster scenario; and
- the confusion wrought by multiple studies being conducted simultaneously (i.e., confidential damage-assessment studies by both Exxon and the trustees and the subsistence study conducted under the auspices of the OSHTF by the Alaska Department of Fish and Game [ADF&G], Exxon, and the National Oceanic and Atmospheric Administration [NOAA]).

The fundamental issue for the OSHTF was to inform and advise the residents of these villages about the safety of subsistence seafood resources that were actually or

Evaluating and Communicating Subsistence Seafood Safety in a Cross-Cultural Context: Lessons Learned from the Exxon Valdez Oil Spill
L. Jay Field et al., editors. © 1999 Society of Environmental Toxicology and Chemistry (SETAC). ISBN 1-880611-29-5

potentially exposed to *Exxon Valdez* oil. Although the basic food-safety message was consistent throughout the three years of reporting to the villages—that all finfish and all mollusks collected from non-oiled beaches were safe to eat—many villagers were reluctant to share the scientists' and health community's confidence in the safety of this food.

Risk as a Culturally Framed Concept

To begin to discuss risk communication, one must first define the terms "risk" and "risk analysis." Risk is "a combination of the probability, or frequency, of occurrence of a defined hazard and the magnitude of the consequences of the occurrence" (Warner 1992 cited in Jones and Hood 1996). In this sense, hazard becomes a component within risk. Selecting which risks and hazards will be most important is a complex, controversial social process.

As Jones and Hood (1996) explain, there is a close analogy between the beliefs and interpretations of cause-effect relationships affecting the "environment" and different views of how ecosystems work (e.g., the Native versus the Western paradigm). Thus, "risk can be said to comprise perceptions about the loss potential associated with the interrelationships among humans and between humans and their natural (physical), biological, technological, behavioral and financial environments—a complex that may conveniently be termed the *risk environment*" (Jones and Hood 1996:3). O'Riordan (1996) also asserts that risk is reflective of the social order of justice and opportunity (i.e., the metaphor of risk can be a weapon of frustration and protest for society's powerless).

Risk Perception and the Alaska Native World-View

The perception of risk by Alaska Natives differed in unexpected and complicated ways from that of the outside experts who arrived at Prince William Sound armed with their sampling and testing and interpretive methodologies. These differences resulted from the conflict between the Alaska Native paradigm and the Western scientific paradigm. Undeniably, the most important factor at play in the reactions of Alaska Natives to the oil spill, cleanup, and ecological and subsistence food-safety considerations was the way in which Alaska Natives assess their environment. Their assessment is synecological observing the whole environment (e.g., water, shoreline, vegetation, marine and land animals) as a vast network of interrelationships in which an abnormal observation in one part indicates to the ill health of the whole. In contrast, the Western scientific approach selects samples of specific subsets of the environment for scrutiny, according to a prescribed design, draws specific conclusions based on analyses of those samples, and then makes carefully bounded extrapolations of their conclusions to other parts of the environment. According to Hild (1994),

> The scientific community works to compartmentalize the world in an attempt to study its various pieces and how they work. They report on *a* level of *a* contaminant in *a* tissue of *an* animal . . . [in contrast] the Native community historically observes the local ecosystem and its patterns in order to understand specific effects. They have passed on through their oral histories and practices the information needed for daily survival. They understand from their observations that large cycles and patterns exist with people as part of an undivided whole, and that if any part is contaminated in any way then the entire system is out of balance.

Although the Native paradigm is highly empirical, Alaska Natives also sense danger in the invisible. To them, the waters following the EVOS were poisoned, regardless of whether there was visible oil. This perhaps explains why, ironically, Native leaders were demanding Western scientific studies to evaluate oil contamination in their subsistence resources. They clearly did not trust the initial advisory health bulletins' advice that sensory testing was the best way to determine the safety of their seafood.

In some cases, residents found support for their continued concerns about particular animals, as well as a broader suspicion about the ubiquitous nature of the oil in the water or the insidiousness of its effects. For example, the finding of a damage-assessment study (Patten et al. 1998) that the population of harlequin ducks had declined following the spill confirmed the observations by Chenega Bay residents of fewer harlequin ducks. Harlequins feed in intertidal areas, some of which were heavily oiled. However, Patten's hypothesis that ingestion of oil-contaminated food may have caused a breeding failure in harlequin ducks was not supported by later research, leading to the conclusion that the lack of suitable breeding habitat, even before the spill, was the limiting factor in western Prince William Sound (Rosenberg and Petrula 1997).

In another instance in 1989, hunters from Chenega Bay noted unusual behavior in seals, who appeared disoriented and were noticeably less fearful of humans than in the past. At necropsy, seals from this area were found to have brain lesions associated with oiling, which probably accounted for the abnormal behavior (Lowry et al. 1994; Spraker et al. 1994).

Subsistence living functions best when the biocultural relationship is predictable. For example, when salmon return to the same stream and in similar numbers every year, or sea birds return in similar numbers to the same nesting sites, a subsistence lifestyle works fairly harmoniously with the environment. The EVOS abruptly changed the environment, both extrinsically and intrinsically, in unprecedented ways within the overall historical context of the Alaska Natives. Their data sources are direct observations of the current environment compared with both their own remembered observations and the earlier observations and experiences of their elders as passed down through oral histories.

One of the village elders from Chenega Bay stated that the oil spill was worse than the tidal wave caused by the 1964 Alaska earthquake that killed 29 of his fellow villagers and led to the abandonment of the village site. The village was not reestablished at another site until 1984. The tidal wave and its aftermath, although devastating, were foreseeable to the people because these events somehow were rooted in their experiential knowledge of their environment (high winds, rough waters, etc.). Although tankers plying the waters of Lower Cook Inlet and Prince William Sound were a familiar sight to Alaska Native communities, the sudden grounding and rupture of the *Exxon Valdez* and the sight of the quickly spreading oil could not be contextualized by the people and could not be woven into their past experience or their future expectations.

Flexibility is also an essential aspect of the subsistence lifestyle for Alaska Natives. Natural fluctuations in the quantity and variety of subsistence resources necessitate adaptability by subsistence harvesters. In fact, the OSHTF reminded the Natives of this adaptability by telling them early on that they "must learn to contend with the effects of the oil spill on their resources" and "adapt to the changed conditions, just as they have adapted to changing conditions for thousands of years" (OSHTF 1990a). But even these historical adaptations themselves are based upon shared knowledge and experience, and are part of a long-term cycle within which Native culture has evolved.

The Enduring Importance of Subsistence Foods to Alaska Natives

Subsistence seafood is the predominant source of protein, as well as fatty acids and lipids, for Alaska Natives living in villages of Prince William Sound, Lower Cook Inlet, Kodiak, and the Alaska Peninsula. Just as important, the collection, preparation, storage, and sharing of this food also help to define and reinforce the culture of these coastal Alaska Natives.

However, the subsistence lifestyle has not been static, changing considerably throughout Alaska in the decades before the spill (see Kuhnlein and Receveur 1996). In the village of Chenega, for example, the economy between the 1960s and just before the spill (Stratton and Chisum 1986) had changed significantly. This change is illustrated by a per capita harvest of subsistence foods in 1985 to 1986 of 378 lbs, less than half the amount harvested before the 1964 earthquake that forced the village ("Old Chenega") to evacuate and relocate 20 years later, suggesting an increased role of cash and purchased foods in the local economy.

New Paradigms in Risk Communication

Since the EVOS, there has been greater international attention on the application of risk communication to food safety issues. For example, the process of risk analysis has been recognized by the Food and Agriculture Organization and the World Health Organization (FAO/WHO) (1998) as being comprised of three interrelated processes: risk assessment, risk management, and risk communication. They define risk communication as "an interactive process of exchange of information and opinions concerning risk and risk-related factors among risk assessors, risk managers, consumers and other interested parties."

Risk analysis, then, is a synthesis of several disciplines that, in order to be accurate as well as socially meaningful, must formally factor in both technical appraisal and social tolerance. Risk analysis has the responsibility to integrate across the natural/social science divide and to include a broader range of endpoints. For example, just because the cancer endpoint is the most sensitive in terms of measuring the toxicity of foods does not mean that it should be the sole quantitative measure of risk.

Risk analysis must acknowledge the uncertainties in both physical and social systems, e.g., uncertainties of process, laws, data collection, historical trend interpretation, and responsiveness to new findings or new input relationships. Risk analysis must pave the way for dialogues between social judgment of possible outcomes and cost-effectiveness calculations of various courses of action (O'Riordan 1996).

As the OSHTF learned, there is a distinction between preparing and disseminating risk messages and the process of communicating these messages. Clearly, communicators must recognize and overcome 1) gaps in knowledge, 2) obstacles inherent in the uncertainties of scientific risk assessment, and 3) barriers to effective risk communication. Risk communication is an integration of processes and procedures that not only must inform and educate, but also that must help develop transparent and credible decision-making processes and instill confidence in risk-management decisions (FAO/WHO 1998).

Risk communication must anticipate the "gut feelings" of alarm that are not assuaged by expert scientific judgments. Rumors about cause-and-effect relationships, although genuinely unsubstantiated, become legitimized in the minds of doubters. This acceptance of misinformation happens partly because the apparatus of scientific proof is suspect and because sometimes science cannot provide unequivocal answers. Advisory bodies need to become more vernacular rather than purely scientific.

Guidelines for groups responsible for risk communication include (Chess et al. 1994) :

- admitting that risk exists,
- acknowledging uncertainty,

- releasing information early,
- responding to all requests for information,
- considering both quantifiable and non-quantifiable factors,
- being sensitive to the distinction between voluntary and involuntary risks, and
- avoiding risk comparisons that equate the two.

The Public Perception of Risk

The concept of health risk has very different meanings depending, for example, on whether you are a citizen living near the source, an environmentalist, an elected official, or a member of the regulatory community. Each group views health risk very differently (Hazen 1996), illustrated by the difference between the *technical risk* calculated by the scientific expert and the *perceived risk* of the lay public (Johnson 1992). Technical risk is measured quantitatively using formal risk-assessment methods, as in the case of the *Exxon Valdez*. In contrast, perceived risk is qualitative and subjective, informed by an individual's prior experience with the same or a similar risk (Fessenden-Raden et al. 1987) and by many kinds and sources of information, including sensory impressions, memories and folklore, word of mouth, and the mass media. Several qualities have a moderating effect on one's perception of risk, including adverseness to risk, one's personal or family history of risk-taking, confidence in scientific and technological expertise, and the ability to put one's trust in others (whether individuals or institutions).

Preexisting and initial perceptions

Risk perception research indicates that disagreements between the general public and the science community about the magnitude of risk should not be expected to evaporate in the presence of scientific evidence. Strong initial views that an event threatens health are resistant to change and influence the way subsequent information is interpreted. New evidence appears reliable and informative only if it is consistent with one's initial beliefs; contrary evidence tends to be dismissed as unreliable, erroneous, or unrepresentative (Nisbett and Fischhoff 1980).

This feature of risk perception is still an issue in Alaska 10 years after the spill. The health risk assessment done in 1990 by the U.S. Food and Drug Administration (USFDA) (Bolger 1996) established the safety of subsistence food collected from non-contaminated beaches. Detrimental health effects from the oil spill have not been detected in the villages located in the oil-spill region (Sherry et al. 1999). But even five years after the spill, some members of the public continued to suspect a lingering health risk from the oil spill (Gary Kompkoff, Tatitlek village council president, personal communication; see Chapter 4). Lowden (1997) affirms this by citing a National Research Council report that indicates that statistics about "actual risks" do little to change preexisting "perceived risks" of people who have already made up their minds.

A number of factors associated with an event and the characteristics of that factor affect the level of public concern (Table 10-1). Using these factors to measure public concern about the EVOS, one can understand why an elder from Chenega Bay described the oil spill as more catastrophic than the 1964 earthquake that caused a tidal wave to devastate his village, and kill a significant portion of the residents. The earthquake and the subsequent tidal wave were "acts of God," familiar through the oral history of coastal Natives. The mechanisms of injury and risk were known, and the risk was immediate. All these factors led to decreased long-term public concern.

Table 10-1 Factors associated with an event and its characteristics that shape perceptions

	Event	
Factor	Increased public concern	Decreased public concern
Familiarity	Unfamiliar	Familiar
Understanding	Mechanism or process not understood	Mechanism or process understood
Uncertainty	Risk scientifically unknown or uncertain	Risk known to science
Personal control	Uncontrollable	Controllable
Voluntary exposure	Involuntary	Voluntary
Effects on children	Children specifically at risk	Children not specifically at risk
Effects' manifestations	Delayed effects	Immediate effects
Future effects	Risk to future	No risk to future
Dread	Effects dreaded	Effects not dreaded
Trust in institutions	Lack of trust in responsible institutions	Trust in responsible institutions
Media attention	Much media attention	Little media attention
Reversibility	Effects irreversible	Effects reversible
Origin	Caused by human actions or failures	Caused by acts of nature or God

Source: Covello et al. 1988

In contrast, the EVOS was unprecedented in local experience and lore. Moreover, it attracted media attention from around the world. The mechanisms of human health risks from food were not understood and, if present, were delayed and dreaded. The spill resulted from human failure, and the health risks in the eyes of Alaska Natives were scientifically uncertain. All of these factors increase public concern. Thus, one could have predicted the lasting concern that this oil spill has created.

Voluntary versus involuntary risk

According to Starr (1996), "The public will accept risks from voluntary activities (such as skiing) that are roughly 1000 times as great as it would tolerate from involuntary hazards (such as food preservatives) that provide the same level of benefits." The fact is that the frequency of significant oil spills is far less than the frequency of other hazards to people, such as crime, automobile accidents, workplace injuries, and disease. Thus, the public's generally high level of concern over spills would seem to be irrational when compared with many other dangers that are tolerated on a daily basis or that receive little attention. The explanation for this high concern, as Lowden (1997) explains, is that the public's concern over threats to the environment, such as oil spills, is not derived simply from estimates of probability and potential harm, but rather by many underlying subjective factors. Most of us think dramatically and thus measure the risk of a particular action or situation by imagining the worst that could possibly happen rather than by evaluating several risk factors by their degree of risk and probability of occurrence.

For example, in the context of the EVOS, the samples of smoked fish that are eaten frequently by Alaska Natives from the villages contained cancer-causing hydrocarbon levels hundreds of times higher than did any of the subsistence samples from the beaches (Bolger 1996). However, at several of the public village meetings, villagers were upset when this risk comparison was made. We believe their anger about this comparison was due to the involuntary nature of the spill versus the voluntary risks of their diet, particularly a diet involving highly familiar and traditional foods such as smoked fish.

The gradual partial shift among Alaska Natives from a subsistence diet to a commercial, high-fat diet is another example of a risk behavior having many features that tend not to incite public concern until they reach epidemic proportions. In fact, this dietary shift has become a very important issue to the health of Alaska Natives, not only because it is high-fat and high cholesterol but also because its lipids are very different from those found in subsistence foods. Recent significant increases in diabetes (Schraer 1997) and cardiovascular disease have been linked to this dietary shift. In a 1988 study of the Inuit diet in the Canadian Arctic conducted by the Center for Indigenous Peoples' Nutrition and Environment at McGill University, 66% of the average sources of calories for Inuit women came from store-bought foods, mostly biscuits, sugar, cookies, soft drinks, and ground beef. Not unlike the villagers of the *Exxon Valdez* spill area, a generation ago the Inuit diet was entirely traditional. Heart and kidney disease were almost nonexistent in the north until the Inuit began adding imported "convenience foods" to their diet, and the resultant diseases tend to be worse for them than for residents of the Continental U.S. However, these diseases have raised little public concern among Alaska Natives and have received little media attention in part because they are perceived as controllable and as the result of a voluntary behavior that is familiar and whose risk is well known to science.

The psychology of disaster

Following the spill, Alaska Natives of the impacted communities exhibited relatively high levels of depression (Palinkas et al. 1992 cited in Picou and Gill 1996), intrusive stress, and avoidance behaviors when compared with control communities. The personal, work, and community disruptions caused by the influx of cleanup activity also combined to suggest the beginning of chronic psychological stress for the most threatened subpopulations, i.e., subsistence users and fishers (Picou et al. 1992). Intra-community stressors were brought on because some residents, particularly boat owners, actually profited from the spill by getting contracts for cleanup work

(Russell et al. 1996). Friends and neighbors argued over the inequities in opportunity and over money lost and gained in the cleanup. The Exxon-sponsored cleanup undermined the spirit of voluntary cooperation, establishing instead a monetary basis for helping with the cleanup. An "environment of opportunism" prevailed (Russell et al. 1996) in which the morality of accepting money from Exxon became a bone of contention. Village social roles were altered, since nearly all able-bodied adults worked on the cleanup in one capacity or another, such as cleaning up oiled debris, rescuing oiled birds and other wildlife, collecting dead and dying animals, or assisting in sample collection for the subsistence studies.

The psychosocial effects of all of this were measured in terms of family and child relations, social relations and disruptions, subsistence activities, depression and anxiety, posttraumatic stress disorder, substance abuse, and domestic violence. All of these outcome measures were associated with the degree of exposure to the oil spill and cleanup (Russell et al. 1996). A study by Palinkas et al. (1993) one year after the spill documented the "profound impact that exposure to the oil spill had on the prevalence of psychiatric disorders in residents living in affected communities." In their study, women and Alaska Native residents of spill-area communities appeared to have been especially vulnerable to these negative effects.

In disaster situations, collective action is often co-opted by "collective trauma" during which the instincts for self-protection and security prevail. Although the OSHTF was dealing with "communities at risk," they were not initially able to provide the "therapeutics" needed to help the villagers deal constructively and cooperatively with the subsistence issues, such as early involvement in planning studies and formulating health advice. Also, the villagers were already embittered at the millions of dollars that were immediately poured into wildlife rescue while subsistence issues had to wait for attention.

Natural, technological, and social disasters

Picou and Gill (1996) have identified a pattern of chronic stressors set off by technological disasters that is rare for victims of natural disasters. Indeed, a paradigm shift has been occurring in disaster research based on studies that consistently document long-term negative mental health outcomes for victims of technological disasters. The "uncertainty" about the extent and consequences of biophysical contamination and the lack of finality associated with technological disasters are more corrosive to the social fabric of affected communities, particularly resource-based communities, than are natural disasters. Protracted litigation usually follows technological disasters, delaying not only an open exchange of information but also a timely resolution, and these factors contribute to chronic stress (Shaw and Bader 1996).

Perception of intangible, indefinable risks

Risk is a complex concept, and the public has a broad and multidimensional impression of it, encompassing far more than quantitative measures. In the case of the *Exxon Valdez*, the losses of the subsistence villagers were greater than the purely economic losses of the salmon fishermen or the aesthetic losses of conservationists, precisely because they were more complex. This complexity results from the strong economic and cultural importance of subsistence (see Chapter 2).

Risk communicators need to uncover the core beliefs, values, and perspectives that underlie the public's attitude toward a particular risk in order to focus their efforts on responding to the root of the public's concerns and sensitivities. Otherwise, the multiple qualitative characteristics of people's risk perceptions and attitudes will overwhelm any quantitative risk assessment.

Fears about long-term impacts

The concern about future effects of the spilled oil as it relates to future generations and potential future illness (especially cancer and genetic birth defects) was particularly significant in our discussions with the residents of these villages. The consistent and lasting questions were related to the long-term health consequences of low-dose exposure to hydrocarbons. "What should I tell my children about eating seafood?" was a key question raised repeatedly in communication with village residents.

Risk Communication Efforts

Following the spill, multiple approaches were used to communicate information to the subsistence communities about the potential health risks associated with consuming subsistence seafood resources in the path of the spill. This section reviews these varied attempts to provide food-safety advice and explanations of the basis for this advice. The primary methods of communication included advisory health bulletins issued by the Alaska Department of Health and Social Services (ADHSS) during the first year following the spill, OSHTF reports prepared by ADF&G, meetings in the villages with OSHTF representatives in the fall of 1989 and spring of 1992, and a video produced by ADF&G. In addition, a 1990 risk communication workshop in Anchorage solicited feedback from village representatives on the OSHTF risk communication efforts. The Subsistence Restoration project also sponsored several activities and reports from 1993 to 1996 that related to continuing subsistence concerns.

Health advisory bulletins, 1989 through 1990

During the first year of the spill, the ADHSS issued five bulletins, from May 1989 until February 1990. The first such bulletin, released on 5 May, focused on health effects from direct exposure to the oil, particularly by cleanup workers through skin contact, accidental ingestion, or inhalation. Under the heading "Potential Impact on the Food Chain," the bulletin advises that

> The best tests available at this time are the smell and taste of the fish (sensory test). If the fish smell or taste of petroleum, they should not be eaten. If they don't, they are almost certainly safe to eat . . . the same standard should be applied to clams, mussels, and shellfish . . . . We are unable to provide absolute assurances at this time and are working to have better information as our highest priority.

By prior agreement, the local nonprofit Native corporation, The North Pacific Rim, had agreed to use its villagers' mailing list to get this information into the hands of village subsistence users. However, at the 24 May OSHTF meeting, it became clear that the bulletin had not been distributed, since the villagers were still asserting that "no one was telling them anything." The fact was that The North Pacific Rim had not sent out the ADHSS advisory bulletin because of the advice regarding the sensory test. They believed that if they promoted what one of their leaders called the "scratch-and-sniff" test as a measure of food safety, they would lose all credibility. The villagers expected The North Pacific Rim to advocate rigorous testing of subsistence food. The "scratch-and-sniff" test simply was not the standard measure that the villagers would accept.

The July bulletin reported on the initiation of the pilot study by ADF&G, in collaboration with the Alaska Department of Environmental Conservation (ADEC) and the USFDA and the results of the organoleptic testing of more than 300 samples subsistence food items. The bulletin reported that these "findings reinforce our recommendation that living clams, mussels, and shellfish from intertidal areas and fish which do not smell or taste of oil are safe to eat."

The September bulletin highlighted the findings of the Toxicological Expert Committee, which met in September to review "all available information related to the potential impact of the oil spill on food safety," including the recently released analytical results from the ADF&G pilot study and the Exxon/NOAA subsistence study. Their conclusions were that 1) there was "powerful evidence that Alaskan finfish are and will continue to be safe to eat and 2) levels of aromatic hydrocarbons (AHs) found in contaminated finfish were similar to levels in uncontaminated fish." The bulletin was more cautious about crabs and mollusks, stating that "if mollusks *are* consumed, they should *not* be collected from areas that are obviously contaminated with oil." The bulletin added that "marine mammals not obviously contaminated with oil are probably also safe for consumption, but no tests on marine mammals have been done to date." The bulletin also reminded readers of advisories in place for many years that bivalve mollusks should not be collected from Alaskan beaches because of the danger of paralytic shellfish poisoning (PSP), although commercially collected clams and mussels that are routinely tested are safe for consumption.

The OSHTF was mentioned for the first time in the September bulletin, along with "many individuals, organizations, and agencies" who had become involved in answering the question "Are Alaskan seafoods and other subsistence foods safe for human consumption?"

The October bulletin provided an update on the second cycle of analyses of fish and shellfish that were collected in August as part of the "Exxon subsistence study." Mussels taken from a heavily oil-contaminated beach at Windy Bay showed "very high levels" of AHs and were not to be consumed, although they were so heavily oiled that no one would want to touch or taste them. Shellfish tested from "clean beaches" showed higher concentrations of AHs than those from uncontaminated areas, but at levels that did not represent a "serious health hazard."

Villagers were expected to combine their own observations with information provided by the OSHTF to determine the safety of consuming subsistence fish and shellfish. The ADHSS bulletin in February 1990 summarized the Toxicological Expert Committee's findings from their second February 1990 meeting in Seattle (see Appendix 2 for full text):

> Are there specific ways that concerned Alaskan villagers can reduce their potential risk? Any risk of adverse health effects as a result of the oil spill from consumption of Alaskan fish and shellfish is very small. Villagers should rely on common sense and their own judgment to avoid collecting foods from areas obviously impacted by oil. In addition, individuals should decide based on the appearance, smell, texture, and taste of subsistence foods. If food is of doubtful quality, it should not be consumed.

The bulletin carried the following caveats: it was "impossible to provide individual recommendations for specific beaches or harvest areas," but "general" recommendations for all areas impacted by the spill were based on results of samples collected and "available scientific knowledge." The bulletin also noted that "there are no established guidelines for acceptable levels of aromatic hydrocarbons in foods. Aromatic hydrocarbons are ubiquitous. They are present in many foods routinely consumed, including cooked and smoked meats and fish, grains and cereal products, and fruits and vegetables."

Reports of the Oil Spill Health Task Force, 1990 through 1991

From February 1990 to September 1991, a total of 4500 households in 18 communities received nine issues of the Oil Spill Health Task Force Reports illustrated with photographs of village meetings, sampling activities by state and federal employees and Native villagers, and the NOAA laboratory in Seattle. These newsletters attempted to address the villagers' questions in an easily understood form. They explained how the sampling was done and from where the samples were obtained, detailed how the tests were conducted, and explained the differences between fish and shellfish in their potential to accumulate hydrocarbons. Most significantly, the newsletters addressed the safety of subsistence foods based on the best-available expert opinions and analyses. The following sections review some of the key issues covered by these newsletters and the different approaches used to address the continuing concerns of the subsistence communities about the safety of subsistence food.

The first report (February 1990) introduces the OSHTF, which met bimonthly throughout the summer and fall of 1989 and monthly during the winter of 1989 to 1990. The report acknowledges the confusion that has resulted from "uninformed and erroneous reports" that "have received equal weight with reports that more accurately reflected realities." It also acknowledges the "immediate importance" of questions being raised by subsistence seafood users. The report states the OSHTF mission "to provide information to help subsistence users make informed choices." It goes on to say, "These residents must learn to contend with the effects of the oil spill on their resources" and "will have to make informed choices and adapt to the changed conditions, just as they have adapted to changing conditions for thousands of years" (OSHTF 1990a).

The report describes the ongoing subsistence studies and states two major messages from those studies in bold type:

> Results of studies to date, combined with available scientific information, provide powerful evidence that, except for shellfish taken from obviously contaminated shores, subsistence foods remain safe to eat.
>
> The best tests to determine the safety of subsistence foods are performed by those who gather the food. If the resources smell or taste of petroleum, they should not be eaten. If they appear clean by these methods, they are almost certainly safe to eat.

The March 1990 report highlights the findings of the 15-member Expert Toxicological Committee meeting in February 1990 at which the Exxon/NOAA subsistence study was reviewed. The full text of the Committee's review is found in Appendix 2. The OSHTF report states that the committee's findings "were generally good news to communities that rely on subsistence food resources. The study, which was paid for by Exxon, showed no or very low amounts of contamination in fish." The report went on to explain that "some contamination was found in shellfish, however, and the amounts found in shellfish in areas where the oil washed ashore were enough to raise questions about the safety of eating them" (OSHTF 1990b). The report explains the differences in the digestive systems of fish and shellfish: fish are well adapted to getting rid of oil, whereas shellfish tend to accumulate oil and other contaminants.

> Fish, the experts, concluded, are entirely safe to eat," whereas "if clams, mussels, bidarkies or snails are consumed, they should not be collected from areas that are heavily contaminated with oil. Contamination in shellfish from lightly oiled beaches was not considered to be a serious health hazard, the experts said.

The report compares different health risks between light or low-molecular-weight AHs and heavy or high-molecular-weight AHs. Light AHs are more volatile and thus more easily detectable by smell and taste, tend to cause acute sickness, and tend to disappear faster from the environment. In contrast, heavy AHs are less volatile and less readily detectable by the senses and can contribute to long-term health problems, including cancer. However, the report reiterates the importance of sensory testing as one of the determinants of seafood safety:

> Villagers should rely on common sense and their own judgment to avoid collecting foods from areas obviously impacted by oil. In addition, individuals should decide based on the appearance, smell, texture and taste of subsistence foods. If food is of doubtful quality, it should not be consumed.

This report also mentions other sources of AHs in food, such as grains, fruits, and vegetables. "Smoking of foods transmits many hydrocarbons. Cigarette smoking is also a significant source." To illustrate this, the report states that the study tested two samples of smoked fish taken from villages in the spill area: one "lightly smoked" and the other "hard smoked." The analysis of these samples was requested by village residents during the OSHTF first round of village meetings. The concentrations of total hydrocarbons were more than 20,000 ppb in the hard-smoked fish compared with "generally very low" (< 15 ppb) levels in finfish sampled in the spill area.

The report concludes with three disclaimers:

1) "It is impossible to provide individual recommendations for specific beaches or harvest areas,"
2) "There are no feasible tests available to test for or monitor human exposure to aromatic hydrocarbons or other components of crude oil," and
3) "There are no established guidelines for acceptable levels of aromatic hydrocarbons in foods."

The April 1990 report took a more human-interest approach to the subsistence food testing. The narrative brings the reader into the kitchen of a Port Graham household as an ADF&G employee and a volunteer from the village, wearing surgical gloves, dissect a gray cod caught off the mouth of Port Graham and collect bile from the gall bladder and a fillet for shipment to the NOAA laboratory in Seattle for analysis.

The report includes an article on the role of the ADEC laboratory in seafood studies and their organoleptic testing procedures. The article explains that shellfish are not taste-tested because of the possibility of PSP, which "presents a greater danger than any oil contamination" (OSHTF 1990c).

The report reiterates the Expert Committee's advice that "all fish are safe to eat" and that "shellfish taken from lightly to moderately oiled beaches showed some contamination but not enough to be considered a serious health threat." Subsistence gatherers were advised again to "rely on their own common sense and judgment in collecting foods," and to not consume any food of "doubtful quality" based on their own sensory testing.

The May 1990 report was primarily devoted to the NOAA National Marine Fisheries Service laboratory that had become "headquarters" for the subsistence testing. The front-page explains the laboratory's experience and expertise in analyzing effects of oil and other pollution on the marine environment. The two analytical processes used in the subsistence tests, GC/MS and HPLC, are explained in layman's terms. An illustrated primer on the vocabulary of hydrocarbons introduces the reader to AHs. The differences in health effects between low-molecular-weight AHs and high-molecular-weight AHs are explained. Heavier AHs persist in the environment, can cause long-term ill effects, including cancer, and are less detectable by smell. For these reasons, according to the report,

> Organoleptic testing—the sight, smell and taste test—will become less accurate for determining the presence of hydrocarbons as time goes on. . . . Chemical tests will be needed to detect high-ringed hydrocarbons after the lighter hydrocarbons are gone.

This is the first time that the limited efficacy of sensory testing over time is described in any of the OSHTF reports, although it was part of the information presented by the OSHTF at the village meetings in the fall of 1989. The next paragraph of the report acknowledges this: "The common-sense tests for oil-contaminated resources remain useful to a degree, however. To avoid contaminated shellfish, resource gatherers should stay away from areas that are or were heavily contaminated with oil" (OSHTF 1990d).

The cover story of the June 1990 report describes the test results from seven seals and one sea lion collected by subsistence marine mammal hunters earlier in the year. The samples were found to have "virtually no traces of oil contamination." These results were compared with the similar "very low readings" for six seals and nine sea lions collected in 1989 by ADF&G (OSHTF 1990e). The highest tissue readings for AHs (8 ppb) were contrasted with hydrocarbon levels of several thousand parts per billion for some shellfish from heavily oiled areas. However, the article reported that the Seattle laboratory was currently conducting tests on heavily oiled animals from 1989, as well as some seals from previously oiled areas of the Sound that were collected in the spring of 1990.

The July-August 1990 report focused primarily on those subsistence shellfish sites still showing significant oil contamination. The report explained that the types of hydrocarbons indicated possible sources of contamination other than the *Exxon Valdez* at three of the four sites (OSHTF 1990f).

Another article discussed the collection of samples from the reference site in Yakutat Bay in order to compare background hydrocarbon levels with those from the spill area. The report explained that all life in the sea is exposed to aromatic hydrocarbons and that levels up to 10 parts per billion may be considered background.

The report also discussed in detail the results of tests on the bile of 16 bottom-feeding fish collected during the winter in an article titled "Low Bile Levels Indicate Fish Flesh is Clean." The tests "found some exposure to oil contamination, but not enough to indicate that their flesh might be contaminated." The bile samples tested so low that the laboratory concluded that "tissue tests were not warranted" because detectable levels of contamination in their edible flesh was "very unlikely."

The lead article in the September-October 1990 report highlighted the results of the latest round of fish and shellfish studies under the heading "Latest Tests Show Less Oil Exposure." The results showed a "10-fold decrease in the level of oil-based compounds in the bile of pink salmon at Chenega Bay from the summer of 1989 to the summer of 1990" (OSHTF 1990g)

The report also presented the USFDA's advisory opinion on the safety of AHs in subsistence foods from areas affected by the *Exxon Valdez* oil spill (for full text, see Appendix 3). "The guidelines suggest that a person's risk of getting cancer from eating foods contaminated by the oil spill is considerably less than one in one million." The USFDA assessment came at the request of the OSHTF, in recognition that "no one could say what a safe level of contamination might be." The article goes on to describe the USFDA's risk assessment process, which was based on the following:

- polycyclic aromatic hydrocarbons (PAH) contaminant levels in fish and shellfish from one of the Exxon/NOAA sampling surveys,
- shellfish harvest data (lbs/household) for Chenega Bay from the ADF&G subsistence survey, and
- PAH doses from cancer studies of rats fed benzo[a]pyrene (B[a]P), a known animal carcinogen.

The June 1991 report highlighted the continuation of the subsistence food-safety testing program in 1991. The study would concentrate on shellfish, however, because 1) the two previous-years' testing had shown only non-detectable (or very low) contamination levels in the edible flesh of fish and the OSHTF felt that additional fish testing was unnecessary, and 2) clams and mussels had proven to be the most sensitive indicators of contamination (OSHTF 1991a).

The report also presented results of recent tests on shellfish. A shaded box in this section translated the expressions "one part per ten" through "one part per billion" into numerals in an attempt to clarify the units "parts per million" and "parts per billion" used in presenting the shellfish test results, which had been a source of confusion to the villagers trying to understand the results.

A "Questions and Answers" section addressed the following questions, which were based on questions posed to the Task Force at village meetings:

- How can people know if subsistence foods are safe to eat?
- What kinds of studies were done?
- How many fish were tested?
- Is that enough to know fish are safe?
- Where were the fish caught?
- Who collected the resources?
- Who did the tests?
- Who looked at the results?
- So, once again, are fish safe to eat?
- Does this mean that the oil didn't harm the fish?
- What about clams?
- What about other animals? Seals and sea lions? Ducks and deer?
- Does this mean that there is no need to be worried any more?
- What will be done next?
- How can we get more information?

The final, September 1991, report reconfirmed, based on the latest test results, that fish in the spill area are safe to eat (OSHTF 1991b). The latest test results on shellfish also reported less contamination from the oil spill. Finally, the report announced that NOAA had begun a shoreline monitoring program in the summer of 1990 to evaluate the recovery of intertidal and shallow subtidal marine communities impacted by the oil spill and then by cleanup operations.

Village visits

The OSHTF began its face-to-face communication of food safety information to spill-area villages in September through October 1989 with its first round of OSHTF-sponsored meetings in nine villages. The second and final round of OSHTF-sponsored village meetings was conducted three years later, in June 1992.

The OSHTF brought detailed maps to the meetings showing sampling locations and the results of the laboratory analyses (see Appendix 4) to illustrate where and when fish and shellfish were collected and specific levels of oil contamination in different resources at each site. They also brought larger sampling-area maps that were left with the villages. The response by the villagers to the meetings varied considerably among villages, from gratitude for the information to anger and mistrust of the advice.

Exxon had established its presence in the villages as early as April 1989 (see Chapter 5), hiring additional Native liaisons and conducting numerous meetings with community and village leaders and Native organizations. In addition to supervising the cleanup and dealing with commercial and subsistence fisheries issues, Exxon's liaisons were helping communities deal with the socioeconomic impacts of the cleanup. Exxon also had its own team of medical and toxicological experts who were holding village meetings of their own on subsistence food impacts, toxicity of oil to residents, and health threats to oil cleanup workers.

In the first series of OSHTF-sponsored village meetings, an Exxon toxicologist played an active role in the presentations along with state and federal and village representatives. Because villagers were already resentful of Exxon for its handling of some spill- and cleanup-related matters, their participation on the OSHTF left the audience wondering who was responsible for developing the health advice.

The June 1992 village visits, which took place several months after the final OSHTF report was published, were not formally summarized or reported to the public. Because of feedback from the earlier village visits, the OSHTF recognized the importance of making certain that Exxon was not "on stage" at these meetings. All transportation logistics were handled by the U.S. Coast Guard, and only Judy Meidinger, an Alaska Native well known in the villages who served as Exxon's community liaison, represented Exxon at the village meetings. However, it was clear that some villagers felt that the OSHTF was reporting on the "Exxon Subsistence Study."

The villagers were polite but still angry about the spill and the cleanup. In part, this anger was due to their lingering food-safety questions that the sampling studies simply could not answer. Villagers from Chenega Bay raised the issue of oil remaining on some beaches, making it clear that concerns about seafood safety would continue to exist as long as oil could still be found on the beaches.

Subsistence sampling brochures

The sampling areas and test results for the 1989 NOAA/Exxon sampling cycles were presented at the village meetings in Fall 1989 and for the Expert Committee in February 1990 on maps entitled "1989 Subsistence Fish & Shellfish Studies," one for each of the 12 sampling areas. The map of the sampling areas showed each sampling location, the species sampled and number of specimens tested, the number of analyses, and the resulting levels of aromatic contaminants.

In 1991, the OSHTF issued a second set of pamphlets, one for each of the sampling areas, entitled "Subsistence Food Safety." These flyers combined the sampling data from the 1989 sampling cycles with the data from the 1990 sampling cycle, one for each of 11 sampling areas. These tri-fold pamphlets, printed in color, were prepared for the OSHTF by Exxon. The maps show the sampling stations, and separate diagrams present the separate test results for fish (salmon and bottomfish) and shellfish (clams, mussels, and chitons). Median and range of test results, by species group, are shown separately for light and heavy aromatics. Results are presented on a consistent logarithmic scale from 0.1 to 10,000. No guideline is provided; thus, there is no visual basis for comparing test results against acceptable levels. For fish, the results for salmon and bottomfish from the 1989 reference area (Angoon) are shown for comparative purposes. The pamphlet briefly reiterates the general expert advice that, other than obviously contaminated mussels from oily beaches, subsistence foods were safe to eat and that, according to the USFDA report, "the risk of getting cancer from eating shellfish from even the most contaminated site . . . is extremely low."

The Oil Spill Health Task Force's educational video, June 1990

A half-hour video on the subsistence food testing program, "Oil Spill: Threat to Subsistence," was prepared by the ADF&G for the Oil Spill Health Task Force with assistance from the Office of the Governor. A film crew from the ADF&G Division of Subsistence and the Governor's Office visited four villages affected by the oil spill in Prince William Sound and Lower Cook Inlet. This was after the first year's sampling and testing program and after the Expert Toxicological Committee had reviewed the 1989 results and developed its recommendations. The crew interviewed villagers and people involved in the subsistence food studies and also visited the NOAA Northwest Fisheries Center laboratory in Seattle and the Alaska Department of Environmental Conservation laboratory in Palmer. The sensory test conducted at the Palmer and USFDA laboratories was demonstrated. Don Kompkoff of the village of Chenega Bay was interviewed. There were shots of village residents collecting samples around Port Graham, and of villagers preparing and eating cod in their kitchens. A meeting of the OSHTF was shown. The video conveyed the same health advisory that had been given from the start: an emphatic endorsement of the safety of fish, but with the warning about shellfish from heavily oiled areas. The video explained the ability of fish, mammals, and birds to rid themselves of hydrocarbons, in contrast to marine invertebrates that tend to accumulate PAHs as long as they are exposed to oil. The differences in detectability between light and heavy PAHs were explained, i.e., that heavy PAHs are more persistent and less discernible by smell or taste than are light PAHs. The video also noted the higher levels of PAHs in smoked fish and cigarettes.

The professionally written and directed video was distributed to village council offices, health clinics, schools, and other community centers. It was also shown on the state's Rural Alaska Television Network. Reportedly, few residents of the target communities viewed the video, although ADF&G did receive numerous requests for copies from scientists, agencies, schools, and village representatives.

Village feedback at the 1990 risk communication workshop

Within the first few months of the oil spill, the OSHTF members realized that communications with the village residents were not working as well as had been hoped. At the time of the spill, the fundamental differences in world view that were coming into play relative to the OSHTF's food-safety communication efforts were not fully appreciated by all members of the OSHTF.

In an attempt to critique and improve communication efforts for the subsistence food-safety program, the OSHTF brought representatives from the villages and from USFDA together at a Risk Communication Workshop in Anchorage in September 1990. At this workshop the Native participants made many forthright comments about our communication efforts, although initially they were reluctant to participate because of pending litigation.

The villagers told us that the official publications of the OSHTF summarizing results of the subsistence laboratory tests were ambiguous. Although many of the samples had insignificant levels of hydrocarbons, they were still present. The OSHTF was asked by the villagers, "How can food be absolutely safe and still contain hydrocarbons?" The notion of relative risk was never acceptable.

The testing of subsistence food samples was also considered suspect by the villagers because they believed that all the sample data were not being released. While this belief was not true for the samples collected as part of the OSHTF subsistence study, the villagers had seen a variety of samples taken from beaches, some of which were being collected for damage assessment and litigation. These damage assessment samples were being collected and tested by several different agencies and Exxon, and the results were considered to be litigation-sensitive and were not made public. The groups conducting these studies did not explain their purpose to the villages. Consequently, although these studies were not intended for public information, in the minds of villagers information was being gathered and withheld for unknown reasons. This was, of course, a problem over which the OSHTF had no control, although we could have explained the litigation-sensitive environment more clearly and explained that this evidence eventually would be used in the legal defense of the environment and the subsistence resources.

In the view of the villagers, the test results of the samples collected as part of the food-safety studies took too long to return and lacked information about various parts of fish, other than flesh, that they used for subsistence food. For example, fish heads are part of the subsistence diet, but only fish fillets were tested.

For many villagers, generalized statements about food safety were not as relevant as was specific information on levels of hydrocarbons in specific food resources on specific beaches. We now know that the idea of a scientific sampling design is difficult to reconcile with the Native science paradigm.

The direct mailing of the OSHTF reports to all village households seemed to the OSHTF to be an optimal means of communication. However, feedback from the villages indicated that much of the information in the newsletters was not basic enough for them to easily understand. Also, the use of print and broadcast media to communicate study findings and health advisories was not generally successful. Although these media were used frequently, the messages often were not heard or read by the villagers.

The Subsistence Restoration Project: Activities and Reports, 1993-1996

In 1993, a Subsistence Restoration Project funded by the *Exxon Valdez* Oil Spill Trustee Council allowed members of the OSHTF to continue their efforts to restore subsistence uses of fish and wildlife. The approaches to subsistence research, decision-making, and communication built on the lessons learned during the early post-spill years when the OSHTF was coordinating subsistence efforts.

This project was strongly community-based and was a clear signal that by 1993 the spill-area communities were interested in participating in subsistence-restoration activities. They brought their local knowledge and observations to help define research questions. For instance, sampling of subsistence foods for 1993 was designed to focus on the Native concerns expressed at the second series of OSHTF-sponsored village meetings in June 1992. As a result, seafood sampling and testing were planned for nine specific harvest areas. This activity was coordinated by the Pacific Rim Villages Coalition (a joint undertaking by the village corporations of Chenega Bay, Tatitlek, Port Graham, and Nanwalek and the Chugach Alaska Corporation) and was endorsed by the village councils of the Chugach region.

Four annual reports of this project were published between November 1993 and April 1996. These Subsistence Restoration Project reports provided test results on subsistence seafood sampling conducted by the Pacific Rim Villages Coalition and analyzed by the NOAA laboratory in Seattle.

Village representatives visit NOAA's Seattle laboratory

In August 1993, as part of the Subsistence Restoration Project, representatives of oil-impacted communities were invited to visit the Northwest Fisheries Center lab in Seattle to observe the testing procedures and to ask questions of the laboratory staff. Questions included, "Would the ingestion of oil lead to mutations?" and "Who signs off on the lab's expertise?" One village representative asked, "Do you get any money from Exxon?" Another asked "Has any of your staff worked for Exxon in the past?"

Oil Spill Health Task Force meeting with village representatives, August 1993

The February 1994 Subsistence Restoration Project Report described the meeting in late August 1993 to discuss continuing Alaska Native community concerns. In addition to representatives of the impacted communities, the Indian Health Service, the ADF&G, NOAA, and Exxon were also invited to the meeting at the Alaska Native Medical Center in Anchorage. Some of the statements made by village representatives include the following:

> Residents of the Native village of Tatitlek were concerned with the safety of consuming any of the subsistence resources in 1989; it has been more than four years since the oil was spilled and the residents are still concerned, and their concerns are growing with each failed commercial or subsistence fishing season. [Gary Kompkoff, President Tatitlek Village Council]

> The beaches around Chenega Bay continue to ooze oil, and no one even tries to harvest clams from near their community, because they are afraid to. [Larry Evanoff, Chenega Bay]

A resident from Nanwalek said that many people from his community "still don't trust the safety of the seafood, and tar balls are still found on the shores of the lower Kenai Peninsula." A villager from Old Harbor said that people in his community "still do not eat clams because they are afraid, and last summer four people got sick from eating clams." Although the issue here was PSP and not oil-spill contamination, people did not make the distinction.

Villagers expressed their frustrations about the scarcity of subsistence resources. Concerns were raised about the low herring returns to Prince William Sound: only one-third of the expected number of herring returned in spring 1993, and many that did return had lesions. Also, Tatitlek residents observed very little spawning. Herring and herring-spawn-on-kelp are food sources for villagers of Chenega Bay and Tatitlek. A state pathologist explained that the only pathogen identified in the herring was viral hemorrhagic septicemia virus (VHS), which has likely always been present in the herring population, but that "something has stressed the fish and weakened their resistance to the virus." The pathologist emphasized that the virus was not a human-health threat, although he acknowledged that the lesions were "not very appetizing."

When the community representatives were asked what could be done to convince them that their subsistence foods were safe to eat, Larry Evanoff of Chenega Bay replied, "Get the oil off the beaches." The village representatives also pointed out that "as long as people continue to see abnormalities, such as those observed in herring, they will be wary of consuming local wild foods."

This continued to be the position of some of the spokespeople. There were repeated requests for sampling of specific beaches. The state and federal on-scene coordinators had declared in June 1992 that the oil-spill cleanup was over. Exxon maintained that there was no point in testing beaches that were oiled because people were already being advised to stay away from those areas. The OSHTF explained that the Chenega Bay area got more sampling because its beaches were more heavily hit with oil. People continued to believe that "others" were still collecting samples but no information was forthcoming.

The scarcity and oil contamination of some subsistence resources had made it necessary for residents of Chenega Bay to travel long distances to harvest foods, at the cost of individual harvesters. Also, those relying on commercial fishing for their income were hurt by the failure of the herring and pink salmon runs in 1993. At the meeting, the funding for long harvesting trips and support for an exchange of resources among communities were identified as "urgent needs" in the Prince William Sound communities.

Resource abnormalities study

The August 1995 Subsistence Restoration Project Report announced that a "Resource Abnormalities Study" was underway. This study was in response to the loss of confidence by subsistence hunters and fishermen "in their own abilities to determine if their traditional foods are safe to eat." Residents of several impacted communities had "expressed the fear that animals which came in contact with the oil have been altered in some way that cannot be seen or detected in laboratory tests." Residents had also reported abnormalities in herring, sea lions, and chitons with lesions; apparently malnourished ducks; and abnormally small-sized herring, salmon, and clams. The report cites a "cultural proscription among Alutiiq peoples against the harvesting or eating of animals which appear sick or abnormal."

The last of the hydrocarbon testing was done in 1994, yet it was clear that the abnormalities people were observing reflected significant concern. Thus, the emphasis of the subsistence food-safety project would now shift to helping people understand the abnormalities they were seeing. The approach would be to continue and expand the dialogue between subsistence users and scientists. For example, under the Resource Abnormalities Study, the ADF&G Division of Subsistence set up a system whereby subsistence harvesters could send samples of abnormal resources for biologists and pathologists to examine.

At the same time, the consulting firm Dames & Moore began training village residents to use biological sampling kits. Training included identifying different kinds of abnormalities and their causes and sampling, preservation, and documentation techniques, all with funds provided by the EVOS Trustee Council. Village councils were contacted and asked to provide names of up to three residents of their community willing to participate in the training and volunteer their services. By April 1996, a total of 61 volunteers had been trained to take and preserve samples, fill out sampling forms, and package and ship the samples. A videotape version of the training and sampling kits and instructions were left in each community, and accounts were set up with air carriers for transport of samples. A resource abnormality hotline was established, and informational posters were placed in each participating community. Although the Trustee Council funded the project for only one year, continued funding was provided as part of the Community Involvement and Use of Traditional Knowledge Project.

The Community Involvement and Use of Traditional Knowledge Project

The August 1995 report of the Subsistence Restoration Project announced that the EVOS Trustee Council had begun funding a pilot Community Involvement and Use of Traditional Knowledge Project to facilitate communication among residents of impacted communities, the Trustee Council, and researchers working on oil-spill restoration projects. This project funded local residents, working for local village councils, to serve as facilitators in the communication of traditional knowledge and local interests among the community, the Trustee Council, and state and federal agency staff. The local facilitators strongly suggested that all the village council presidents in the oil-spill impact area meet to discuss community priorities for restoration.

What the Oil Spill Health Task Force Learned about Risk Communication

Better acknowledgment of Alaska Natives' ecological knowledge

The OSHTF did not convince all residents of the communities that subsistence resources were fit to eat. Their consistent findings, repeatedly conveyed to the villagers, were that all subsistence foods were safe to eat as long as they were not obviously tainted with oil or collected from areas that had been heavily oiled. However, Alaska Natives did not entirely trust this advice because it was in direct opposition to their holistic interpretation of the environment, which included concern about abnormal conditions and behaviors in fish, marine mammals, and birds. For example, the damage-assessment scientists detected metabolites of oil in the bile of harbor seals and traces of injury in the brain, which they suggested were worrisome for the long-term health of the seals. This analysis focused on seals that were visibly oiled in 1989 or collected from the same heavily oiled areas in 1990. The OSHTF subsistence study found that the concentrations of AHs in the tissues of most other harbor seals, including those collected by subsistence hunters, were so low as to be "virtually nondetectable." Because the damage-assessment study addressed the bile and brain and the OSHTF study addressed the tissues of liver, kidney, blubber, and muscle, the OSHTF tried to explain that the results were unconnected (i.e., that exposure to oil could adversely affect the health of the seals without resulting in accumulation of oil in the edible tissue). Yet some people in

Chenega Bay feared they would suffer brain damage themselves if they ate that meat. This fear reflects Hild's (1994) description of the holistic view of the Native community that "if any part is contaminated in any way then the entire system is out of balance [and] if any of the foods upon which they have always depended are identified as no longer being as they have been, then there is corruption in the entire system and it is out of balance."

If food-safety information provided to a subsistence community is to be both accurate and relevant to the affected people, both world-views must be recognized and integrated into the assessment and communication of risk. Both Native and Western systems of analysis and interpretation must be granted equal importance and validity. Had the OSHTF members fully acknowledged traditional knowledge, our efforts to communicate might have been more effective. For example, it would have been useful, as a standing agenda item at our OSHTF meetings, to invite representatives of Alaska Natives from the villages to present their observations—just as we presented our laboratory results—giving their local knowledge and bio-cultural concerns the same respect that our technical findings and advice received. We also could have included their observations in our official reports to demonstrate to them that we were taking their observations seriously and to present a more holistic overview of the impacts of the oil spill.

Direct public involvement in the risk-assessment process

The purpose of risk communication must be made clear at the outset of any program. Risk communication's purpose is not to allay public concerns, but to empower the community to participate in the risk assessment process and to ensure that the right risk decisions are reached (Hazen 1996). Although the OSHTF's stated goal was one of empowerment, communication efforts would have been enhanced by more public participation up-front in the OSHTF's overall planning process. It must be noted that, especially in 1989, community priorities focused on spill cleanup. The OSHTF relied on regional organizations to represent the local population. Nevertheless, the assessment methods and goals and the content and clarity of the OSHTF's risk communication would have benefited by including more public members in planning our subsistence testing and outreach strategies. Technical information, although edited, was still not clear enough to communicate well to the lay public. The model for effective community participation during later post-spill years is found in the Subsistence Restoration Project funded by the *Exxon Valdez* Oil Spill Trustee Council. This project brought the communities into the earliest stages of the planning, implementation, and evaluative process.

Our experience suggests that a large menu of communication methods must be explored and used for the risk communication effort, from face-to-face meetings to broad-scale television announcements. The measures of effective risk communication are multipronged, requiring many different kinds of skill. These measures (FAO/WHO 1998) include

- message content;
- mechanisms of delivery;
- timeliness of the communication;
- availability and use of supporting materials and information; and
- purpose, credibility, and meaningfulness of the communication.

First of all, risk communication is two-way. It is an interactive process by which information and opinions are exchanged among individuals, groups, and institutions. Those for whom the information is intended must be involved in the process: the public must be free to communicate their perceived risks, and the science community must provide an understandable analysis of the available scientific information that directly addresses the public's perceived risks. Therefore, a broad array of local, state, and community groups must be included early in the decision process to assess possible health effects resulting from events such as an oil spill (Hazen 1996).

Representatives from community groups do not necessarily represent the needs of the entire public, nor do they automatically take full information back to those they represent. It may have been advantageous to hold more community meetings in which individual villagers could have expressed their views directly to the OSHTF. In Alaska we could have taken advantage of telecommunication and other methods to include villagers in our frequent meetings in Anchorage. This would have broadened our community listening posts and given us more direct access to individuals' concerns. In retrospect, even though we thought we communicated well enough, more direct two-way information was needed.

The face-to-face village presentations by the OSHTF were effective for those who attended. However, the village meetings were somewhat lost in the swirl of other meetings and activities related to the cleanup, especially during the first spill year. Visits to the villages by reporters, investigators, researchers, lawyers, and oil-spill workers became so numerous that one village threatened to impound its runway and screen everyone who landed to determine their reasons for being in the village.

However, the fundamental concern about the initial round of village visits was Exxon's participation. Although Exxon was not specifically required by law to fund studies of subsistence food, there was considerable public and governmental pressure for them to do so, beginning with the National Response Team report in May 1989 (Skinner 1989). The report stated that "to ensure food safety properly over the long term, a system involving both organoleptic and chemical analytic testing needs to be developed." This statement was interpreted as being directed at Exxon as well as at the federal government. The presence of Exxon representatives in the villages and at the OSHTF meetings cast doubt on the motives behind the meetings and on the objectivity of the subsistence studies and their results, which raised the question of a conflict of interest. This suspicion made Exxon's association with the OSHTF problematic throughout the oil-spill activities, a problem that we were never able to resolve completely.

Access to complete and timely information

The goal of risk communication should be that reliable, frequent, consistent, and understandable messages are delivered at each village visit and through every print or electronic media that potentially can reach the vast majority of concerned individuals. A danger is flooding the community with too much information from too many different sources.

In the EVOS case, the situation was complicated by the separate collections and analyses conducted by Exxon, as the responsible party, and by the natural resource trustees in preparation for legal claims. Once the preparations for litigation began soon after the spill, by both commercial fishers and subsistence users, communication of the findings of these studies among the interested parties (i.e., Exxon, the trustees, the local populace, the OSHTF) came to an abrupt halt. Thus, the villagers saw damage-assessment investigators on their beaches and, with no information forthcoming from their studies, were suspicious that the "truth" about oil contamination and food safety was being kept from them (see Shaw and Bader 1996).

Getting timely information to the subsistence communities was a problem from the beginning of the spill. The initial food-safety pronouncements, which were based on organoleptic testing and the known ability of most vertebrates (e.g., fish and marine mammals) to rapidly metabolize and excrete aromatic hydrocarbons, were not well-accepted in the villages. By the time analytical data were available from the ADF&G pilot study and the Exxon/NOAA study, it was near the end of August, and the spring and summer harvest seasons were already past.

Organoleptic testing, which is a standard approach for detecting chemical taint or spoilage, has the advantage of a quick return of information. State officials began recommending in May 1989 that subsistence users conduct their own sensory testing by sight, smell, and taste. If there was no evidence of oiling, the seafood was considered safe to eat, although absolute assurances of purity could not be given. In essence, the Alaska Natives were being told to establish the cleanliness of a beach or other harvesting area by their own reconnaissance and to test the food according to their own common sense and sensory judgment. Oddly enough, the Alaska Natives, who traditionally rely heavily on their own acute senses, did not readily accept this advice; in fact, they were suspicious of it. It didn't make sense to them that these scientific experts were giving them such rudimentary advice. Instead, they insisted on hard science—on state-of-the-art, quantitative analyses of seafood samples.

The OSHTF's goal from the start was empowerment. They sought to deliver relevant and understandable information to people who already knew their environment well and whom the OSHTF presumed would readily interpret and use the information in the context of their own close contact with the environment. But the villagers turned out to be like any other local populace: they expected definite and unqualified answers based on all the state-of-the-art expertise and methods that science could muster.

The difficulty of communicating the risk assessment

Converting messages about hydrocarbon concentration levels in subsistence seafood samples (e.g., "low PAHs," "minimally contaminated") into the quantified risk of people getting sick from eating the foods was difficult. To explain the USFDA's risk assessment, the OSHTF held a Risk Communication Workshop in September 1990 in Anchorage. There, representatives of the OSHTF and the USFDA met with Native village representatives. A USFDA scientist gave a talk in which he stressed the gap between contamination and risk, referring to the then-recent Alar scare as a "grossly unreasonable" fear of Alar-sprayed apples. He told the group that the American diet in general posed a risk of dying of 1 in 15 compared with the one-in-one-million chance of getting cancer from eating seafood from oiled areas.

The village representatives openly expressed their lack of trust in the subsistence food testing results. Residents of Chenega Bay also reported a number of abnormalities and mortalities observed in animals found on land adjacent to areas sprayed with a fertilizer used to stimulate oil-degrading bacteria. They could not reconcile their observations of sick and dying animals with the risk information they were being given. The perception remains that any food with hydrocarbons is not completely safe. As long as oil can be found on the beaches, there will be concern about their food despite official agency announcements.

The OSHTF held a news conference in conjunction with the risk communication workshop. A headline in the *Valdez Vanguard* read "Scientists say contamination levels high but safe." A headline in the *Anchorage Daily News* said the seafood was found "OK" for subsistence. The lead paragraph of the article read, "Fish and shellfish samples in Prince William Sound and the Gulf of Alaska contain trace amounts of cancer-causing residues from the *Exxon Valdez* oil spill but are safe for subsistence users to eat, according to Food and Drug Administration guidelines issued Wednesday" (ADN 1990).

Sensitivity to the distinction between voluntary and involuntary risk

The OSHTF assembled the Expert Toxicological Committee (see Appendix 2) to analyze the subsistence seafood situation as well as to set guidelines on safety levels for hydrocarbons in seafood. The USFDA, who played a lead role on the Committee, chose the PAH benzo(a)pyrene (B[a]P) as their standard for the analysis, in part because B[a]P, found in high concentrations in smoked fish, was being investigated elsewhere as a possible link between a diet high in smoked fish and stomach cancer. The Alaska Natives eat much of their salmon smoked, because smoke curing has been a traditional way to preserve their salmon for generations. The USFDA used the data on hydrocarbon concentrations in several samples of smoked fish as part of their quantitative risk assessment, along with the data from subsistence samples. The concentration of AHs in the smoked salmon was nearly 10,000 times greater than that in wild salmon. Eating smoked salmon is a voluntary risk that Alaska Natives are willing to take. However, the involuntary risk associated with eating potentially contaminated shellfish is unacceptable. Ten years later we now know that it is counterproductive to make this voluntary and involuntary risk comparison in the public arena. In fact, one of USEPA's cardinal rules is to "be sensitive to the distinction between voluntary and involuntary risk, and avoid risk comparisons that equate the two" (Hazen 1996).

Exxon's participation in the subsistence study and risk communication

Trust and credibility are two of the most valuable assets in communicating risk information (Lowden 1997). It also must be remembered that society's definition of risk in the context of an oil spill has more to do with fairness and moral responsibility than with safety and actual risk. Exxon's direct and highly visible participation on the OSHTF created the perception of a conflict of interest because a class action suit against Exxon for loss of subsistence had been filed within weeks of the spill. In retrospect, Exxon's highly visible role in conducting the subsistence study, participating actively on the OSHTF and the Expert Toxicological Committee, and communicating the interpretation of the results cast doubt on the credibility of the OSHTF and its food-safety recommendations.

Conclusions

Communicating risk following a mega-disaster such as the EVOS is a major challenge for those organizations responsible for advising the public about the safety of using potentially contaminated natural resources as subsistence foods. The difficulties worsen the longer they go unaddressed as responding organizations struggle to define the problem, collect and analyze data, and develop a credible message. The degree of difficulty increases if there is a perception that the risk is being ignored or is not taken seriously and if the risk communication takes place in a cross-cultural setting. As shown in this chapter, the formation of the OSHTF and the evolution of its risk communication efforts illustrate one case of institutional changes in the context of disaster response. Federal and state agencies, Alaska Native groups, and Exxon conducted the subsistence study and developed and communicated health advice within the framework of the OSHTF as a response to changing perceptions of the nature of the problem.

After recognizing the need to form in the first place, the OSHTF then attempted to get information from outside experts on the potential risk to subsistence users; however, no guidelines were available, and information on the approach to seafood safety from other spills provided limited guidance. Consequently, the initial health advisories were based on organoleptic testing and the current scientific understanding that fish and other vertebrates would be safe to eat while shellfish from oiled areas should be avoided. While this proved to be reliable advice, the OSHTF learned that this message was not accepted in the villages. It recognized the need to have the best scientific information on the actual concentrations of AHs in subsistence resources from specific areas. With time, OSHTF members also realized that the expertise of the Alaska Native communities in observing and interpreting their environment needed to be included in the risk communication efforts.

As the OSHTF better understood its role, greater attention was paid to communication methods. The early health bulletins had unknown or limited distribution, to a great extent because they were developed without any community input or direct information from important subsistence harvest areas. The later bulletins, and especially the newsletters, received wider distribution as the collaborative studies were launched and more systematic health advice was developed. In addition, the OSHTF members traveled to the villages shortly after the first data returned from the laboratory to present the specific information and the interpretation provided by the expert committee. This visit provided an opportunity for direct communication and proved to be a valuable learning experience for the OSHTF members in terms of identifying key questions and concerns. It also became abundantly clear from the first round of village meetings that having Exxon, the party responsible for the spill, play a major role was a mistake that affected the credibility of both the OSHTF and its message.

In summary, the OSHTF used many different approaches to communicate the results of the scientific studies and the conclusions of the risk assessment, but it continued to recognize the need to better "take into account the knowledge and experience of the people" (Scott and Receveur 1995) and develop new ways to incorporate traditional knowledge. As the activities of the OSHTF came to a close, the Subsistence Restoration Projects funded by the Trustee Council built on our experiences to improve community involvement and collaborative study design. Community involvement and the application of traditional knowledge became key goals of the Trustee Council's oil spill restoration program.

References

[ADN] Anchorage Daily News. 1990. Study: Sound fish, shellfish safe for subsistence use. Anchorage Daily News 1990 Sep 27; Sect D:6.

Bolger MP. 1996. Hazard and risk assessment of crude oil contaminants in subsistence seafood samples from Prince William Sound. *Am Fish Soc Symp* 18:837–843.

Chess C, Hance, BJ, Sandman PM. 1994. Improving dialogue with communities: a short guide for government risk communication. New Brunswick NJ: State of New Jersey Department of Environmental Protection, Division of Science and Research and Environmental Communication Research Program, New Jersey Agricultural Experiment Station, Cook College, Rutgers University.

Covello VT, Sandman PM, Slovic P. 1988. Risk communication, risk statistics, and risk comparisons: a manual for plant managers. Washington DC: Chemical Manufacturers Association. 54 p.

[FAO/WHO]. Food and Agriculture Organization/World Health Organization. 1998. Joint FAO/WHO expert consultation on the application of risk communication to food standards and safety matters; 2-6 February 1998; Italian Ministry of Health; Rome.

Fessenden-Raden J, et al. 1987. Providing risk information on communities? Factors influencing what is heard and accepted. *Sci, Tech, Hum Val* 12: 3–4.

Hazen S. 1996. Communicating environmental risk. Washington DC: Environmental Assistance Division, USEPA.

Hild C. 1994. Cultural concerns regarding contaminants in Alaska local foods. Anchorage AK: Rural Alaska Community Action Program.

Johnson S. 1992. Public response to environmental health risks. *Natl Environ J* July/August:36–40.

Jones D, Hood C. 1996. Introduction. In: Hood C, Jones DKC, editors. Accident and design: contemporary debates in risk management. London: UCL Press.

Kuhnlein HV, Receveur O. 1996. Dietary change and traditional food systems of indigenous peoples. *Ann Rev Nutr* 16:417–442.

Lowden G. 1997. Identifying the factors that heighten public concern over oil spills. In: Proceedings, International Oil Spill Conference. Washington DC: American Petroleum Institute. p 747–751.

Lowry LF, Frost KJ, Pitcher KW. 1994. Observations of oiling of harbor seals in Prince William Sound. In: Loughlin TR, editor. Marine mammals and the *Exxon Valdez*. San Diego CA: Academic Press. p. 209–225.

Nisbett R, Fischhoff B. 1980. Human inference: strategies and shortcomings of social judgment. New York: Prentice-Hall.

[NRT] National Response Team. 1989. The *Exxon Valdez* Oil Spill. A Report to the President. Washington DC: National Response Team.

[OSHTF] Oil Spill Health Task Force. 1990a. February 1990 report. Anchorage AK: Division of Subsistence, Department of Fish and Game.

[OSHTF] Oil Spill Health Task Force. 1990b. March 1990 report. Anchorage AK: Division of Subsistence, Department of Fish and Game.

[OSHTF] Oil Spill Health Task Force. 1990c. April 1990 report. Anchorage AK: Division of Subsistence, Department of Fish and Game.

[OSHTF] Oil Spill Health Task Force. 1990d. May 1990 report. Anchorage AK: Division of Subsistence, Department of Fish and Game.

[OSHTF] Oil Spill Health Task Force. 1990e. June 1990 report. Anchorage AK: Division of Subsistence, Department of Fish and Game.

[OSHTF] Oil Spill Health Task Force. 1990f. July–August 1990 report. Anchorage AK: Division of Subsistence, Department of Fish and Game.

[OSHTF] Oil Spill Health Task Force. 1990g. September–October 1990 report. Anchorage AK: Division of Subsistence, Department of Fish and Game.

[OSHTF] Oil Spill Health Task Force. 1991a. June 1991 report. Anchorage AK: Division of Subsistence, Department of Fish and Game.

[OSHTF] Oil Spill Health Task Force. 1991b. September 1991 report. Anchorage AK: Division of Subsistence, Department of Fish and Game.

O'Riordan T. 1996. Exploring the role of civic science in risk management. In: Hood CH, Jones DKC, editors. Accident and design: contemporary debates in risk management. London: UCL Press.

Palinkas LA, Downs M, Petterson JS, Russell J. 1993. Social, cultural, and psychological impacts of the *Exxon Valdez* oil spill. *Human Organization* 52(1):1–13.

Patten S, Crowe T, Gustin R, Hunter R, Twait P, Hastings C. 1998. An assessment of injury to sea ducks from hydrocarbon uptake in Prince William Sound and the Kodiak Archipelago, Alaska, following the *Exxon Valdez* oil spill. *Exxon Valdez* Oil Spill Natural Resource Damage Assessment Final Report, Bird Study 11. Anchorage AK: Alaska Department of Fish and Game (ADF&G), Division of Wildlife Conservation.

Picou JS, Gill DA, Dyer CL, Curry EW. 1992. Stress and disruption in an Alaskan fishing community: initial and continuing impacts of the Exxon Valdez oil spill. *Industrial Crisis Quarterly* 6:235–257.

Picou JS, Gill DA. 1996. The *Exxon Valdez* oil spill and chronic psychological stress. *Am Fish Soc Symp* 18:879–893.

Rosenberg D, Petrula MJ. 1997. Distribution, abundance, and composition of harlequin ducks in Prince William Sound, Alaska, *Exxon Valdez* Oil Spill Restoration Project Annual Report. Anchorage AK: Alaska Department of Fish and Game (ADF&G), Division of Wildlife Conservation. Restoration Project 96427.

Russell JC, Downs MA, Petterson JS, Palinkas LA. 1996. Psychological and social impacts of the *Exxon Valdez* oil spill and cleanup. *Am Fish Soc Symp* 18:867–878.

Schraer CD, Adler AI, Mayer AM, Halderson KR, Trimble BA. 1997. Diabetes complications among Alaska Natives: eight years of observation. *Diabetes Care* 20:314–321.

Scott K, Receveur O. 1995. Ethics for working with communities of indigenous peoples. *Can J Physio Pharm* 73:751–753.

Shaw DG, Bader HR. 1996. Environmental science in a legal context: the *Exxon Valdez* experience. *Ambio* 25(7):430–434.

Sherry P, Mandregan Jr C, Schraer DJ, Boedeker B, Sealock E. 1999. Alaska Native mortality 1980–1997. Anchorage AK: Alaska Area Native Health Service; Alaska Native Tribal Health Consortium; and Division of Planning, Evaluation, and Health Statistics.

Spraker TR, LF Lowry, KJ Frost. 1994. Gross necropsy and histopathological lesions found in harbor seals. In: Loughlin TR, editor. Marine mammals and the *Exxon Valdez* oil spill. San Diego CA: Academic Press. p. 281–311.

Starr C. 1969. Social benefit versus technological risk. *Science* 165:1232–1238.

Stratton L, Chisum EB. 1986. Resource use patterns in Chenega, Western Prince William Sound: Chenega in the 1960s and Chenega Bay 1984-1986. Juneau AK: Alaska Department of Fish and Game, Division of Subsistence. Technical Paper 139.

CHAPTER 11

Overview of Lessons Learned from the *Exxon Valdez* Oil Spill: A 10-Year Retrospective

James A. Fall, L. Jay Field, Thomas S. Nighswander, John E. Stein, Michael Bolger

Crisis, Confusion, and Uncertainty Among Alaska Native Communities in the Oil-Spill Area

Grasping the cultural importance of subsistence resources

As in most rural areas of Alaska, subsistence harvests of fish, wildlife, and wild plants provide large amounts of high-quality foods in the communities of the area affected by the *Exxon Valdez* oil spill (EVOS). Because jobs are scarce and cash incomes are relatively low, subsistence harvesting is the most reliable sector of the local economies of these communities. Of at least equal or even greater importance, subsistence uses support central values of Alaska Native culture. These values include cooperation in the harvesting, processing, and sharing of subsistence foods; teaching fishing and hunting skills to young people; and an affinity to local places and traditional harvest areas. As a major environmental and social disaster, the oil spill placed this way of life at risk.

Over many generations, the Alutiiq people of Prince William Sound, Cook Inlet, the Kodiak archipelago, and the Alaska Peninsula have developed detailed knowledge of their natural environment through oral traditions and direct observation and practice. In addition to harvesting and processing methods, this knowledge includes the locations of subsistence resources and the seasonal cycles that influence the availability of fish and wildlife. Traditional knowledge and personal experience also inform people about the condition of subsistence foods. For example, particular animals that exhibit unusual behaviors or physical abnormalities may be ill and unfit for consumption. Further, Alutiiq traditions teach an ecological perspective that seeks connections between environmental conditions and natural and man-made events. Nevertheless, before the oil spill, the collective history and wisdom of

Evaluating and Communicating Subsistence Seafood Safety in a Cross-Cultural Context: Lessons Learned from the Exxon Valdez Oil Spill
L. Jay Field et al., editors. © 1999 Society of Environmental Toxicology and Chemistry (SETAC). ISBN 1-880611-29-5

each community taught that subsistence foods are wholesome, nutritious, safe, and reliable.

An important lesson of the *Exxon Valdez* experience is that in the aftermath of any oil spill, spill responders and public health professionals must be fully aware of the cultural importance of natural resources to the local populace, particularly to subsistence communities, as well as concerns about fishery closures and potential contamination. Only in this way can a response program be developed that is empathic and sensitive to the point of view of the affected human population.

Post-spill shock for subsistence communities

For the indigenous people and others who rely on subsistence foods, the oil spill introduced a new and unfamiliar element into the natural environment that was clearly dangerous and deadly. Not surprisingly, the primary issue for subsistence users became whether fish and wildlife were still safe to eat. While some plants and animals were obviously oiled and not edible, it was not clear to subsistence users whether those without signs of oiling might also cause acute or chronic health problems. Abnormal behaviors and conditions of wildlife also raised questions about the spill's effects for subsistence users. Because the spill had created such unfamiliar and unsettling conditions, people were no longer confident in their own abilities to understand and evaluate the natural environment. Their traditions advised them to be cautious. As a result, people discarded resources that they suspected had been tainted or did not use subsistence foods at all.

Adding to the difficulties was the nature of the oil spill and the subsequent cleanup as a technological or man-made disaster of a massive scale. Although the Native communities had suffered through epidemics, earthquakes, tsunamis, and volcanic eruptions, the oil spill was something new and very different. It was not possible, based on generations of accumulated traditional knowledge, to know what the long-term effects of the spill would be on the natural environment and the communities' way of life. Further, the Native communities had virtually no control or influence over the spill response and subsequent cleanup efforts (Piper 1993). Thousands of strangers flooded into the area to work on the cleanup; villages were overwhelmed by agency and corporate personnel, few of whom had any knowledge of Native culture and institutions. The psychological and social effects of these experiences during the year after the spill were widespread and profound (Palinkas et al. 1993; Rodin et al. 1997).

Technological disasters such as EVOS are caused by humans and generally are connected to industrial production activities. As noted by Picou et al. (1997:11),

> Assigning blame and responsibility is more likely for events of human culpability than for those seemingly attributable to divine or natural causes. Victims are angrier, more upset, and more distressed when fellow humans can be blamed for the disaster.

> More importantly, human culprits can be sued for damages in a court of law and publicly castigated for their transgressions. While people invariably stop blaming God a few days following a natural disaster, protracted litigation and fears of latent health impairments foster continuing reminders and mental anguish for victims of technological disasters.

In contrast to natural disasters that result in visible and measurable physical damage, technological disasters involve environmental contamination at levels that may not be detectable by the senses. As again noted by Picou et al. (1997:11),

> Technological disasters are of interest because of the tendency of these events to sever the relationship between the biosphere and the community. Once contamination occurs, people begin to doubt basic, taken-for-granted assumptions about the safety of their biophysical environment. In short, they begin to lose trust. Because contaminants and exposure are often undetectable, there remain lingering uncertainty and dread concerning the threats and potential outcomes from contamination. In this milieu of indeterminacy, rival interpretations of the situation often are advanced. Decisions are complicated by uncertainty over the amount of exposure, the possible danger of exposure, and the knowledge that exposure is not uniform.

In short, the experience of the Alaska Oil Spill Health Task Force (OSHTF) demonstrates that the complexities of the local public's perception and reactions to a technological disaster not only must be understood and anticipated—particularly in a cross-cultural setting—but also must help shape the overall response and communication efforts.

The institutional void in addressing subsistence issues

The situation created by the oil spill was one of crisis, confusion, and uncertainty. As noted in Chapter 3, there was no existing agency or group with a clear mandate to address the questions of subsistence food safety and develop an adequate response to people's concerns and fears. This void of responsibility initially resulted in the perception on the part of many in the Native community that no one took their concerns seriously. Another primary lesson of the oil spill is that this void must be filled quickly and decisively, preferably in contingency planning before a spill occurs, and in a manner that involves all the affected interests. In the case of the *Exxon Valdez* spill, the OSHTF was formed to fill this void. We hope that its successes and shortcomings will inform responses to future disasters such as the *Exxon Valdez* spill.

Difficulties Faced by the Alaska Oil Spill Health Task Force in Coordinating the Health Risk Assessment

The Oil Spill Health Task Force steps into a void

As described in Chapter 3, the OSHTF was formed under the chairmanship of the Federal Indian Health Service (Bureau of Indian Affairs) to respond to concerns about potential contamination of subsistence resources. The OSHTF coordinated and reviewed research on subsistence food safety, tried to develop a consensus on health issues, and communicated findings and advice to the villages. Regular participants in the OSHTF included

- Indian Health Service;
- Alaska Department of Fish and Game (ADF&G) Division of Subsistence;
- Alaska Department of Health and Social Services (ADHSS);
- Alaska Department of Environmental Conservation (ADEC);
- National Oceanic and Atmospheric Administration (NOAA);
- Exxon Corporation; and
- two Alaska Native regional organizations, the Kodiak Area Native Association (KANA) and The North Pacific Rim (later renamed "Chugachmiut").

The OSHTF met biweekly in 1989, regularly through 1990, and sporadically after that. Its last meeting was held in August 1993.

Until formation of the OSHTF in April 1989, there was no forum to discuss health issues related to the oil spill, to coordinate studies and responses, or to communicate health advice. The need for this forum became clear very early in the spill response, as the first efforts to provide food safety advice tended to raise suspicions rather than allay fears. These suspicions focused on the official advice by the ADHSS that the sensory or organoleptic test (appearance, odor, and taste) was sufficient to determine food safety. The Native communities rejected this advice because it contradicted their own observations of death, injury, and pollution. It was also inconsistent with their "holistic" view of the natural environment that there were potential interconnections between these observations of injuries and dangers that were unseen and undetectable by means of smell, taste, and sight.

In retrospect, the communities' rejection of sole reliance on the sensory test made sense. First, in the long term, polycyclic aromatic hydrocarbons (PAHs) with higher molecular weights are more likely to persist in the environment, are the most associated with long-term health risk, and are less susceptible to detection through human senses than are the more volatile, lower-molecular-weight PAHs. Second, there were no existing government guidelines on safe levels of PAH exposure. Finally, Alaska Native communities consume fish, marine invertebrates, and marine mammals at levels far above those of virtually any other population in the U.S.

The lesson here is that discussion and action on health issues must begin immediately in order to prevent fears and misunderstandings from taking hold among the local populace.

Obstacles facing the Oil Spill Health Task Force

Throughout its existence, the OSHTF remained "unofficial" and ad hoc. There was no statute mandating its formation or guiding its activities, nor was there any model to follow or database from which to draw. The OSHTF never received any direct funding and was dependent upon the participating agencies and Exxon to secure funds and assign staff. Many of these personnel had a multitude of other assignments, both related and unrelated to the oil spill. Exxon and some of the other groups collaborating on the OSHTF, as well as the villages, were adversaries in oil-spill litigation. Because of the remoteness of the villages and the large geographic area affected by the spill, logistics for travel were complicated and expensive. Direct, face-to-face communication between the OSHTF and the villages was infrequent and, partly as a consequence, took place in a cross-cultural setting full of distrust, anger, and despair.

In retrospect, another difficulty for the OSHTF was ambiguity concerning its mission. As stated in the first newsletter published for the OSHTF by ADF&G in February 1990, the mission was "to provide information to help subsistence users make informed choices." Thus, the OSHTF viewed its mission as one of empowering subsistence users by providing them the information to make their own decisions about if and when to use subsistence resources from the spill area. On the other hand, subsistence users often were asking for direct and definitive answers about the safety of specific resources on specific beaches. Thus, although the OSHTF members were confident that they were providing sound advice, their answers to the villagers' questions were stated in more general terms and with explanations that involved degrees of risk. Many villagers, rather than feeling empowered by this information, remained confused and skeptical, leaving the OSHTF often frustrated by villagers' persistent skepticism about the general safety of subsistence foods.

Because the response to Alaskan Native concerns about food safety had started so slowly, the OSHTF spent most of 1989 "playing catch-up." Even worse, the OSHTF had to try to make up for the general lack of understanding, or even acknowledgment, of Alaskan Native concerns that left deep and lasting scars. For example, in his final report for the State of Alaska on the oil spill, Piper (1993) relates an incident that he witnessed in May 1989 after Vice President Dan Quayle briefly visited an oiled beach on Smith Island in central Prince William Sound. When Quayle returned to Anchorage, he heard a Native woman from Cordova speak for five minutes about the importance of subsistence and how the oil spill threatened this way of life. The Vice President replied, "All the fishermen will be paid," completely missing the point that subsistence uses are not measured in dollar values but are the foundation of cultural survival as well as a vital source of food. Piper (1993:107) notes that,

> In the villages, during the early weeks of the spill the seeds of doubt and resentment were sown. As these problems grew, the subsistence issue came to be a focus for all the cynicism, anger, and fear. Communication stalled, even as efforts to open lines of communication and spread information intensified.

Additionally, Piper (1993) observed that "bitterness" developed in villages when people learned that millions of dollars were being spent to rescue and rehabilitate wildlife while humans struggled for any attention to the critical issues that they had raised. As noted by Picou et al. (1997:13), "Individuals impaired by technological disasters are often not recognized as victims and this denial of victimization by the larger society adds to the long-term nature of the trauma of these human-made catastrophes."

In summary, this experience illustrates the need to develop—preferably as part of regional contingency planning—a coordinated organizational structure that includes key agency and community representatives and a process for responding to questions of subsistence food safety in the earliest stages of an oil spill. The organization empowered with this responsibility must be given a clear mandate, official standing, and adequate funding.

Exxon's involvement and the perceived conflict of interest

As noted, Exxon, the party responsible for the spill, was a full participant in each component of the OSHTF program. This included representation at most of the OSHTF meetings; funding, organizing, and participating in sample collection; participation in both meetings of the Toxicological Expert Committee; staging OSHTF community meetings; and participating in the presentation of study results and health advice. Because the OSHTF was an open, public process, it would have been inappropriate to exclude Exxon from discussions of the study design or findings.

Early in April 1989, Exxon began a regular series of commercial food and fuel shipments to Tatitlek and Chenega. These shipments were supplemented by fish and subsistence foods donated by community organizations from outside Prince William Sound. Exxon made arrangements with Chugach Alaska Corporation for supplies of canned and frozen fish to go to Prince William Sound and Lower Cook Inlet villages. In total, Exxon provided more than 114,000 pounds of commercial food to Chenega and Tatitlek and distributed about 115,000 pounds of subsistence foods to all of the villages affected by the spill.

Exxon hired additional Native liaisons who were given the authority to make decisions, develop plans, and commit resources. Exxon set up a community liaison team in early April with one or two liaisons assigned to every community. With three Native consultants to respond to subsistence and commercial fishing issues, the liaisons held regular meetings with community and village leaders and Native organizations and advised Exxon on what financial and other support was needed. In addition to supervising the cleanup, Exxon's community liaisons dealt with impacts on communities from the influx of cleanup workers and operations, including serious housing shortages, interruption of normal tribal operations in villages, overcrowded harbors, and spill-related economic losses to local businesses. However, the initial delay in setting up these programs, in some cases two or three months, resulted in the general view that Exxon was difficult to work with and not responsive to communities. Despite Exxon's increasingly proactive role, this initial view persisted.

Exxon made subsistence food safety a priority and designed a sampling program to be conducted in all spill areas (except the Alaska Peninsula) over a period of weeks. Exxon hired the environmental consulting firm Dames & Moore to design and manage the program. In July 1989, NOAA and Exxon signed a Memorandum of Understanding (MOU) to cooperate fully in the sampling and analysis of subsistence food resources. The four major components of the MOU were that 1) NOAA would participate in the sampling program, 2) the National Marine Fisheries Service (NMFS) would conduct the chemical analyses, 3) all information would be released to the public immediately, and 4) Exxon would actively support and fund the program. During negotiation of the MOU with NOAA, Exxon raised concerns about the release of unedited test results to the public early in the testing phase. A class action lawsuit had been filed against Exxon on subsistence issues less than a month after the spill, and the idea of releasing test information to the public was perceived as risky by Exxon. Nevertheless, Exxon management agreed to the immediate release of all test results, good or bad, from the NOAA laboratory. This meant that Exxon received the results at the same time as the OSHTF.

Exxon representatives first attended an OSHTF meeting on 12 July, and a long relationship began. Although the OSHTF had the lead oversight role for the subsistence collection and testing program, including informing the villages of the test results, Exxon's primary coordinator and support to the OSHTF arranged meetings with Exxon and village leaders; provided transportation to coordinate sampling trips; coordinated with the Exxon Biomedical team; and kept Exxon's spill management team informed. On behalf of the OSHTF, Exxon also paid for high-quality brochures and fact sheets to be distributed to the villages.

At the same time, however, Exxon Command decided to form its own team, including a medical doctor and an industrial hygienist, to hold a series of meetings in all the spill-area villages and with Native organizations about subsistence food impacts, toxicity of oil to residents, and health threats to cleanup workers. These meetings were two months before the OSHTF-sponsored community meetings would begin. Exxon proceeded to arrange with the board of directors of The North Pacific Rim, the Native tribal organization for the Prince William Sound and Lower Cook Inlet villages, and the Kodiak Island Borough and the KANA to hold a series of village meetings. Exxon also wanted to present the early risk-assessment results from the USFDA and the sensory test results from the ADEC laboratory in Palmer. However, the downside of this initiative by Exxon was that these Exxon-sponsored meetings undermined the OSHTF's attempts to serve as a unified communication team while fueling the villagers' suspicions that they were being manipulated by competing parties.

Following negotiations with the Federal and State On-Scene Coordinator Team and after consulting with the chairman of the OSHTF, Exxon decided in October 1989 to fund a second year of comprehensive sampling and testing to begin in February 1990. However, Exxon did not participate in the final round of OSHTF-sponsored informational meetings in June 1992.

The level and visibility of Exxon's involvement on the OSHTF began to raise suspicions among villagers of a conflict of interest that muddied their relations with the OSHTF. Although Exxon had committed personnel and their Native consulting staff to the OSHTF's efforts, they were not trusted. The OSHTF needed the cooperation and support of Exxon; it certainly did not need any appearance of influence from the spiller. Trust and credibility among the villages were essential to the OSHTF's ongoing research and communication programs. No one needed the perception of being "in cahoots" with Exxon.

As Piper (1993:112) observed in his overview of the State of Alaska's spill response,

> The skepticism [of the health advice] was magnified by the fact that Exxon played a central and visible role in the operation [of the OSHTF]. The company not only funded the results, but it produced high-quality brochures and sent its company representatives to the villages with the scientists. Exxon can certainly claim credit for a vigorous effort to address the questions of villagers about subsistence food, but in hindsight, its involvement should have been limited to writing the checks. At town meetings in the fall and early winter of 1989–90, a number of villagers felt that Exxon-sponsored studies were not independent, since the company had a vested interest in positive news about safe seafood. This skepticism about Exxon's involvement brings us back to a basic structural and management problem that cropped up at nearly every stage of the response: people could not understand why Exxon was running a public health and public safety operation. Exxon was actually paying for it, not necessarily running it, but the perception was that the company was taking charge of the public interest. This, coupled with Exxon's public relations stance that tended to minimize the magnitude of the

problem, made people in the villages wary of Exxon's participation.

Ironically, the responsible party has more latitude in making decisions about spill-response issues than any government agency and therefore can be more proactive in developing its response strategies. But in terms of the subsistence seafood safety issue, Exxon could and should have taken a more neutral stance and simply provided the funds and expertise for the subsistence sampling, testing, and information program. In retrospect, Exxon's highly visible role cast doubt on the credibility of the OSHTF and its food-safety recommendations. Further, although the OSHTF process needed to be open and public, with full participation by all concerned (including the spiller), it is clear that Exxon should not have been on-stage alongside the OSHTF scientists at village meetings, nor should they have been producing glossy outreach materials. Prevention of actual or perceived conflict of interest problems that arise when the work of spill responders is funded by responsible parties needs to be thought out ahead of time, not when oil is hitting the beaches.

Conflicting cultural definitions of food safety and edibility

The OSHTF was formed to respond to the growing concern in the Alaskan Native communities about the potential contamination and safety of subsistence seafood. Nevertheless, as discussed in Chapters 3 and 10, the data and recommendations presented by the OSHTF were interpreted and evaluated by the subsistence communities within the context of their traditional culture. For many individuals and families, the continued sightings of sick and dead wildlife that were immediately blamed on spilled oil led many to question the health advice of the OSHTF. For example, how could the oil injure or kill wildlife and yet not pose a threat to humans? Given the strong cautions to cleanup workers about direct exposure to the oil through ingestion, skin contact, or inhalation, how could subsistence users trust the OSHTF's advice that a fish that had ingested oil could still be safe for humans to eat? Subsistence users continued to interpret the abnormal appearance or behavior of animals—such as the "lethargic" and "erratic" movement of herring schools or the "ugly" lesions on herring and sea lions (discussed in Chapter 4)—not only as oil-related, but also as symptomatic of the general unhealth of the ecosystem.

The OSHTF attempted to provide the subsistence communities with high-quality analytical data on the degree of contamination in subsistence resources and an evaluation of risk from consuming these resources based on current standard scientific methods of risk assessment. This information was provided along with what the OSHTF considered "common sense" advice, i.e., to avoid collecting shellfish from beaches that showed evidence of oil, even though the risk assessment concluded that these resources represented low long-term health risks. The OSHTF attempted to differentiate the results of the subsistence study from those evaluating ecological effects of the spill. However, the scientific sampling and analytical methods that formed the basis of the OSHTF's health advice needed to be informed by, and integrated with, traditional sensory evaluations and local ecological knowledge. This integration might have been facilitated through discussions with elders about how best to interpret and communicate the study results so as not to inadvertently diminish the integrity of Native observations and knowledge. Had the OSHTF drawn on the insight of the village elders, their messages may have been accepted more readily.

Withholding of litigation-sensitive information

Within a week of the grounding of the *Exxon Valdez*, scientific studies were planned to assess the damages from the spill on fish and wildlife, with the goal of recovering those damages from Exxon through settlement or litigation. Over 100 natural resource damage assessment studies were undertaken by a variety of government, university, and private-sector researchers. These studies were coordinated through the EVOS Trustee Council, with representation from three state (ADF&G, ADEC, and Department of Law) and three federal agencies (U.S. Forest Service, NOAA, and Department of the Interior). Because of the litigation-sensitive nature of these studies, their findings were deemed confidential and no results were made available to the public for nearly two years. It was not until March 1991 that the federal government released some of the preliminary results (USFWS 1991). The full results of these studies were finally made available for public review two years later in February 1993 at a four-day EVOS symposium in Anchorage (Rice et al. 1996).

The Exxon Corporation also conducted its own damage-assessment studies. As with the government-funded projects, these were considered litigation-sensitive. There was no coordination of the government and Exxon damage-assessment studies, and the results of the Exxon-funded research were not made available for public review until 1993. Although government and other scientists presented their damage-assessment findings at the February 1993 Oil Spill Symposium in Anchorage, Exxon's scientists and contractors chose instead to present their findings at the April 1993 meeting of the American Society of Testing and Materials in Atlanta, Georgia (Wells et al. 1995).

This embargo on the damage-assessment study designs and findings was a serious obstacle to effective health-risk communication. The unavailability of information from the various damage-assessment studies created the perception that the OSHTF did not have access to all the relevant data, and cast doubt on the comprehensiveness of their data and the reliability of their advice. The fact that there was no free flow of information among the various government and Exxon studies added to the view that important information was being hidden from the OSHTF, on whom the villagers were solely dependent for health advice.

The lesson here is very clear. There must be no doubt about public health officials' access to any and all data related to subsistence food safety. In future spills, the organization charged with responding to food safety concerns must be able to review all relevant data from all studies, including damage-assessment studies.

The "double standard" perceived by villagers

Alaska Native villagers perceived a double standard in the initial advice on subsistence food safety provided by the ADHSS and later by the OSHTF. While they were being advised that any resource that had no smell, taste, or appearance of oil was likely safe to eat, the ADF&G and ADEC established a "zero-tolerance policy" for commercial fisheries (Piper 1993). This meant that commercial fisheries were closed if oil was present in sufficient quantities to make fouling of gear or the harvest likely. In Prince William Sound, subsistence fisheries were also closed in heavily oiled areas. In other areas, such as Kodiak, subsistence fishing was left open even though commercial fishing was closed. The zero-tolerance policy for commercial fishing was established to protect the market for Alaskan salmon and was not based on concerns about consumer safety. The policy pertained to potential external contamination of fish from gear coming in contact with oil during the harvesting process. For example, if a boat unknowingly pulled its seine or net through an oily sheen or a patch of tarballs and delivered the fish to a processor who detected the oil, this could cast doubt on the entire Alaska commercial salmon catch. Although some villagers surmised from this precaution that ADF&G was concerned that fish from oiled areas were ingesting oil that would be undetectable, "the problem was with oiled gear, not oiled fish" (Piper 1993:107). ADF&G reasoned that subsistence fishermen, using smaller gear and having more maneuverability, could better avoid oiled areas and that those subsistence fishermen who chose to fish should have the opportunity to do so. The distinction was lost on some villagers, however, who concluded that "zero tolerance" meant that their health was less important than that of consumers of commercially harvested fish.

This perception of a "double standard" is an example of ways in which local victims of a man-made disaster may feel that their concerns are not being taken seriously. In the case of the *Exxon Valdez*, there was apparently insufficient effort on the part of the regulators and the OSHTF to respond to these allegations of a double standard, which in effect confirmed some villagers' perceptions. In future spills, resource management agencies must be aware of the potential for creating the perception that different user groups are being treated unequally. If fishery policies are not "across the board" for all user groups, as was the case here, resource agencies must openly and clearly justify their decisions.

The need for direct communication with village residents

The OSHTF made some assumptions about communication within the Alaska Native communities that in retrospect were overly optimistic. The OSHTF assumed that information would be widely shared among village residents through informal word-of-mouth channels and that community representatives would report back to their communities after attending OSHTF meetings or receiving written or oral communications. This was not always the case, however. This is one reason that village residents later reported that they were getting little or no information. In retrospect, the OSHTF's direct communications with community residents were too infrequent and irregular, especially during the first year (see Walker and Field 1991).

With the exception of the July 1989 meeting in Seattle, in conjunction with the first National Forum on the EVOS, the OSHTF held all its meetings in Anchorage. Village representation at these meetings consisted of the regional nonprofit groups—the KANA and The North Pacific Rim. There was no direct participation by community members themselves, except at the two rounds of village visits in September to October 1989 and June 1992, the Risk Communication Workshop in Anchorage in September 1990, and the very last OSHTF meeting in August 1993.

In retrospect, available technology such as teleconferencing could have been used to facilitate this direct involvement. Since the early post-spill years, teleconferencing, electronic mail, and Internet capabilities have evolved tremendously. Future responses to subsistence food safety issues should take advantage of these technologies to maximize direct community involvement in all phases of its activities. Equally important, community representatives and others who frequently visit the villages should be asked to play a more active role in transmitting information from the OSHTF to the communities and to provide feedback from the communities.

Lack of formal feedback mechanisms

The OSHTF had no formal method for evaluating its own program and gauging its effectiveness. Instead, it depended on feedback from regional Native organization representatives, other individuals who attended village meetings, and occasional written communications and phone calls. It was difficult for the OSHTF to assess how widely their health advice was being received by village residents, how well it was being understood, and how widely it was being followed. Long periods of time passed with little or no feedback from the communities. With the exception of the village meetings, the only evaluation of the program organized by the OSHTF itself took place in September 1990 at the Risk Communication Workshop in Anchorage. Even this was more of a retrospective evaluation, because by then most of the OSHTF efforts had ended.

Some of the responses to the social-effects survey conducted by the ADF&G Division of Subsistence in selected communities during 1992 to 1994 provide clues to the villagers' persistent fears about the effects of spilled oil on subsistence resources and the risks to human health of consuming traditional foods (Fall and Utermohle 1995; see also Chapter 4). During the last round of surveys in their communities (April 1992 in Chignik Bay, Chignik Lake, Karluk, and Old Harbor; April 1994 in Chenega Bay, Tatitlek, Nanwalek, Port Graham, Ouzinkie, and Larsen Bay), more than half of the households in spill-region villages indicated that they were not adequately informed about the safety of using subsistence foods. The most frequent (45.5% of those not adequately informed) reason for their negative assessment of food-safety information was simply a lack of trust in the information they received. Some respondents explained that they were uncomfortable with Exxon's involvement in providing the food safety assessments, while others said that the advice that fish, birds, and marine mammals were safe to eat contradicted their own observations of the natural environment. Almost as many respondents (41.9%) said that the information they received was inadequate because it was unclear or not definitive enough. Related responses included the belief that the information was incomplete (29.1%) or was based on an inadequate number of tests (16.4%). Other reasons included the suspicion that information was deliberately withheld (16.4%) and had not been provided in a timely manner (27.3%). Of those inadequately informed, 40% said that they had received no information at all. Had these evaluations been available while the OSHTF was active, the communication program could have been modified accordingly.

Responses to the social effects questionnaires in 1992 and 1994 (Fall and Utermohle 1995) also help gauge the continuing, but uneven, concerns among Alaska Natives about subsistence food safety. The question focused on whether villagers considered seals and clams safe for children to eat, since children would be using the resources over a much longer time than adults. Overall, a large majority (80.8%) of households in oil spill communities that used seals said they thought seals were safe for children, although, not surprisingly, the percentage was lower (73.1%) in the Prince William Sound and Lower Cook Inlet villages where the spill's effects were more persistent. Regarding clams, an overall 71.8% of households in spill-area communities that used clams said they believed clams were safe for children, although, again, the percentage was lower (59.2%) in Prince William Sound and Lower Cook Inlet. Those respondents who answered negatively, i.e., that the seals and clams were not safe for children, cited the *Exxon Valdez* contamination as the reason, although this varied by subregion.

Interestingly despite several deaths in southwest Alaska in the early 1990s caused by paralytic shellfish poisoning (PSP) in butter clams and annual health advisories from the state warning against eating clams from uncertified beaches, only 10.8% of households cited PSP as the reason for clams being unsafe for children. As noted in Chapter 4, subsistence harvests rebounded several years after the spill, indicating that some people were using the foods despite lingering suspicions about health risks.

In 1998, the EVOS Trustee Council sponsored an additional round of household interviews in eight spill-area communities conducted by the ADF&G Division of Subsistence in collaboration with the Chugach Regional Resources Commission, an Alaska Native organization concerned with natural resource issues (see Fall and Utermohle 1999 for an overview of the survey results). Among other things, the interviews collected updated information on subsistence food safety assessment. Confidence in the safety of using herring was relatively high (78.5%) in 1998, and confidence in the safety of eating seals increased to 86.1%. However, the confidence in clams declined due to a growing concern about PSP, especially in Lower Cook

Inlet and Kodiak area communities. Oil contamination no longer ranked high as a source of uncertainty about eating clams.

Communication lessons

The reasons for the growing level of confidence in subsistence food safety, and the decreasing suspicion of oil contamination, are uncertain and most likely complex. Despite the OSHTF's efforts to allay undue suspicion about subsistence seafood safety and to provide meaningful information to help Alaska Natives make sound decisions about their subsistence activities, time itself undoubtedly has played the largest role in restoring confidence, as have the villagers' own observations of their resources and overall environment (Piper 1993). Had a program been in place to monitor levels of confidence in subsistence foods, the reasons for the Alaska Natives' gradual return to subsistence uses would be better understood and could inform future programs. What all of this feedback suggests, however, is that although subsistence harvests rebounded gradually for several years after the spill, some people were using these foods perhaps with a sense of reluctance or resignation, but nevertheless despite lingering suspicions about the health risks.

There are several lessons here. One is that spill responders and public health officials cannot assume that health-safety information distributed to community representatives will necessarily be received by individual community members. The OSHTF lacked a system for monitoring how many people were actually getting the information and how many were finding it adequate for their needs. Future subsistence food safety programs need to develop formal mechanisms for soliciting feedback and evaluating how well their efforts are being received. Local community representatives, and others who frequently spend time in these communities, need to assist with a monitoring and evaluation program.

The Seafood Safety Study: Evaluating the Extent and Degree of Contamination in Subsistence Seafood

The investigation into the degree of contamination of subsistence resources began with the Pilot Study initiated by ADF&G in Prince William Sound and Lower Cook Inlet in May 1989. This included sensory testing in the field and in the laboratory of the ADEC, with chemical analysis provided by the USFDA laboratory in Washington, DC. Because the subsistence communities were skeptical of health-safety assurances based on sensory testing and because the results of the chemical analysis were slow in returning, their level of concern and anger about the perceived lack of response continued to increase.

NOAA, as Scientific Support Coordinator for the Coast Guard Federal On-Scene Coordinator, made two important decisions: 1) to work jointly with Exxon in a subsistence seafood study rather than initiating a separate investigation and 2) to conduct the study within the framework of the OSHTF. NOAA's decision to join forces with Exxon in conducting a study of the extent and degree of contamination in subsistence seafood was based, in part, on the fact that Exxon (in consultation with ADF&G and the villages) had already begun planning an evaluation of petroleum contamination in subsistence resources throughout the spill area. The work plan submitted by Exxon's contractor, Dames & Moore, covered 15 subsistence collection areas, including Kodiak Island as well as many of the same locations sampled in the ADF&G Pilot Study. The villages identified specific beach locations for collections of intertidal shellfish. The major deficiency in the initial work plan was the limited numbers of samples specified for each species at each location (in the beginning, sometimes only one sample per species was collected). At NOAA's recommendation, the number of samples of selected target species was increased to a minimum of three samples to allow minimal statistical analysis.

NOAA and other members of the OSHTF were concerned about the perceived credibility of an Exxon study to the spill-area communities. However, the consensus was that a joint comprehensive study—conducted with OSHTF participation and oversight and with the stipulation that all data collected would be released to the public immediately—offered the best possible means to conducting a comprehensive and credible study. It was also considered to be far preferable to the alternatives of a single study carried out by Exxon and their contractors or separate studies conducted by NOAA and Exxon.

The other major decision, which was incorporated into the formal agreement between NOAA and Exxon, was to have the chemical analysis conducted by the NOAA National Marine Fisheries Service laboratory in Seattle rather than by a laboratory under direct contract to Exxon. This enhanced the credibility of the study and meant that the data were delivered directly to the OSHTF for interpretation and communication to the communities.

Defining the study questions

Determining the appropriate study design to address seafood safety concerns requires careful definition of the questions that must be addressed, including the expected use of the data collected. The primary question that the subsistence seafood contamination study attempted to answer was whether specific subsistence resources were contaminated with oil following the EVOS. The study was designed with the expectation that other questions, such as the potential injury to biota and the recovery of contaminated resources over time, would be addressed by other programs. The principal need for the risk assessment was to determine the potential exposure concentrations in important subsistence resources that could be combined with information on consumption levels to assess risk. Therefore, it is important for the risk assessors to provide input into the sampling and analysis plan (SAP). For example, determining worst-case or reasonable average-exposure concentrations may mandate different sampling designs.

Assessing the persistence of oil contamination in subsistence resources and the potential duration of exposure (i.e., temporal trends) requires the regular sampling of biota from contaminated areas. Because the original sampling locations identified as important subsistence collection areas turned out, for the most part, to have only minimal contamination, evaluating temporal trends was possible at only a couple of locations. In addition, the lack of fixed transect locations and a statistical sampling design to specifically address temporal changes made it possible to conduct only a qualitative temporal trend analysis.

Developing a detailed sampling and analysis plan

After the important questions are identified, a detailed SAP should be developed. The SAP should address

- types and numbers of samples needed, including the need for individual or composited samples;
- sample-collection procedures and specific requirements for maintaining sample quality during transportation and storage;
- chain-of-custody procedures;
- analytical methods to be used and a list of analytes to be determined;
- quality-assurance (QA) procedures; and
- data-completion time requirements, data reporting format, and extent of data interpretation required.

Also, issues of statistical power (e.g., number of samples per sampling event, the frequency and duration of sampling) should be addressed during the study design stage.

Identifying priority subsistence harvest areas and resources

An essential step in designing a sampling program to assess the degree of petroleum contamination in subsistence foods is to identify primary subsistence resources and harvest areas, including the specific location and timing of collections for all of the subsistence communities within the spill area. Many of these areas and species already had been identified before the spill by ADF&G subsistence surveys. This information was supplemented by direct input from village representatives in the selection of specific sampling locations. While this approach provided information for many priority subsistence collection areas, the large geographic area and the large number of resources meant that not all subsistence collection locations or species could be sampled.

Although it is also important to establish the extent of contamination throughout the spill area, emphasizing priority areas that are most likely to be contaminated provides a greater amount of information in areas of the greatest risk and areas that can be used to assess temporal trends. Multiple target species were selected based on their importance to subsistence consumers. Invertebrate target species also represented different types of exposure (i.e., intertidal habitat or intertidal elevation). Other species were collected based on requests for information from the villagers.

Collecting background and/or pre-spill information

The collection and measurement of pre-spill concentrations of petroleum contaminants in key invertebrate and fish species in primary subsistence harvest locations provide important information needed to answer the question of whether subsistence resources were contaminated by the spill. Because of the laboratory's ability to measure very low concentrations of aromatic compounds (ACs), it is essential to provide some perspective for these measurements by comparing data on the same species from subsistence areas before the spill and/or background areas from outside the spill area. Sufficient numbers of samples must be collected from the target species to permit statistical comparisons. Background samples of the target species should be collected during the same time period as the test samples and should represent a comparable size range. If contamination is observed in pre-spill samples, full gas chromatography/mass spectroscopy (GC/MS) analysis can provide information that can be used to identify possible point-sources.

Addressing source-of-contamination issues

In the subsistence sampling conducted between 1989 and 1991, only four locations showed samples with highly elevated concentrations of ACs (> 1000 ppb wet weight) in shellfish. Two of these showed AC composition consistent with *Exxon Valdez* oil. Both of these areas showed rapid decline in concentrations over time. The other two locations (Port Ashton near the village of Chenega Bay and Near Island outside the Kodiak boat harbor) appeared to have other sources of contamination and showed little evidence of declining concentrations. The Port Ashton shellfish AC composition resembled the pattern found in creosote and had high concentrations of high-molecular weight ACs, which were identified in the risk assessment (see Chapter 9) as the contaminants of most concern for long-term health effects. Thus, if oil is observed during sampling, samples of the oil or oiled material should be collected for use in addressing source-of-contamination issues.

Residual oil contamination

A number of mussel beds with significant residual oil contamination were identified, primarily in Prince William Sound from areas that were heavily impacted by the spill, where oil appears to have been trapped in the sediment beneath dense mussel beds (Babcock et al. 1996; Harris et al. 1996). Although hydrocarbon concentrations in mussels and underlying sediment declined significantly in most of these beds between 1992 and 1995, a few of these beds showed no evidence of decline and a number continued to have concentrations above background six years after the spill (Babcock et al. 1998). These mussel beds remain a potential source of exposure to subsistence consumers. However, these highly oiled beds apparently are readily identified by sight and smell (Babcock et al. 1996; Babcock et al. 1998), which should make it easy for subsistence collectors to avoid them. Although the residual contamination in these areas may not represent a significant health concern to subsistence consumers, it serves as an unpleasant reminder that contamination from the spill may persist in some locations. Sampling to delineate these areas would provide useful information to subsistence gatherers and provide a means of monitoring their long-term recovery.

Assessing trends

In the aftermath of an oil spill, information on temporal and spatial trends in contaminant concentrations is important to managers for evaluating the risk to human health as well as affected biota and habitat. In the EVOS subsistence study, it was a challenge to establish a sampling design to meet the primary objective of determining the extent and degree of contamination in subsistence resources, considering the number of subsistence species and the large geographic area involved.

To assess temporal trends quantitatively along with other assessment objectives would have required a separate statistical sampling design. The sampling scheme for sites that will be monitored over time is critical to providing sufficient power of analysis to make statistically sound comparisons or biological inferences. For example, the need to analyze a wide range of subsistence species from a number of habitats compromised the ability to assess trends in contaminant exposure. Sufficient numbers of samples were not collected consistently for a single species from the same location over an adequate time frame to provide a robust time series of data for trend assessment. In addition, the relatively low degree of contamination found at most of the locations identified as important subsistence collection areas made it difficult to evaluate temporal trends quantitatively. Although it is difficult to be specific on the number of samples and number of independent sampling times, in general for the assessment of temporal trends, it is more important to have a larger number of independent sampling times than to have a higher number of tissue samples at each sampling interval. Because of the highly patchy distribution of oil following a spill and the potential high degree of variability in exposure associated with habitat type or tidal elevation, it is essential to identify fixed sampling locations in which sufficient samples of the species of concern can be collected over time.

The key to assessing temporal trends is to have enough data to adequately assess environmental variations in concentrations over time. Because tissue lipid content may be an important factor in seasonal variations in concentrations of contaminants such as ACs, analyzing for percent lipid may be useful in the interpretation of data for evaluating temporal trends. If the objective is to assess the range in AC concentration for a species within a particular area, then it is critical to sample sufficient numbers of individuals (n ≥ 10) from either 1) the range of specific habitat types or locales that could experience differential impact from the spill or 2) the full range of specific areas that are used extensively for harvest.

It is important to note that defining the variation in tissue concentrations of ACs in a species from the major harvest areas is critical for determining the risk of exposure of humans to ACs. Thus, the greater the number of individual analyses the greater the certainty in the variance of the mean tissue concentration for that population. There are practical sampling considerations, however; small species may require compositing to have sufficient sample, whereas for some species compositing also should be considered when limited samples may be available (e.g., seals). When compositing, it is important to balance compositing with the need to have sufficient numbers of independent samples. Furthermore, there are limitations on resources available for analyses. Moreover, "oversampling" in the initial field collection efforts can provide samples for archiving that can be of value to answer additional questions not foreseen in the planning stages. Oversampling may be cost-effective because the sampling takes place during the primary collection effort for which the major costs of getting personnel and equipment on-site have already been incurred. In summary, it is very important to define and prioritize objectives and not to "mix" incompatible objectives, e.g., assessing temporal trends in environmental contamination and assessing the range in concentration for an individual species over its range of habitat.

Protocols, Results, and Implications of the Laboratory Analyses

The experience gained from responding to the EVOS provides a unique perspective for guiding responses to future petroleum spills. Prior research, including both field and laboratory studies on the fate of oil in a range of marine species, was the foundation for the spill response on assessing exposure in subsistence and commercial species. Prior knowledge on the uptake and biotransformation of ACs in marine biota from laboratory studies also led to the development of an application of analytical techniques to assess exposure of invertebrates, fish, and marine mammals to ACs, a major toxic fraction of petroleum. The findings from detailed laboratory studies of the fate and biotransformation of ACs in fish and invertebrates were central to interpreting the data on tissue levels of ACs found in the wide range of subsistence species examined. From a scientific perspective, the EVOS also provided a large-scale field verification of previous laboratory findings and of the "real-world" applicability of recently developed analytical techniques to measure exposure of marine species to oil-related chemicals. The validation of the techniques and use of rapid analytical methods (e.g., high-pressure liquid chromatography [HPLC] analysis of fish bile for AC metabolites) made it possible to prioritize analyses of fish muscle for analysis with more complex and costly analytical methods (e.g.,

GC/MS). This experience provides the basis for employing these techniques and approaches in future spills. Several specific conclusions and recommendations follow that should be useful in guiding spill response to address human-health concerns, as well as being applicable to assessing ecological risks.

Power in the use of rapid analytical methods

A rapid, semi-quantitative method for analyzing fish bile for metabolites of ACs was developed from research-scale studies before the EVOS. The potential of this technique for use in a response to a spill was clear, but its utility had not been tested in a "real-world" situation. The method provides rapid analyses of large sample sets and the ability to assess exposure of fish and pinnipeds in a relatively short time at costs much lower than those of detailed analyses for parent ACs. In the EVOS response, the bile screening method was validated as a useful tool to prioritize individual fish and pinnipeds (e.g., seals and sea lions) for subsequent analysis by more detailed methods, such as GC/MS. The experience from the EVOS demonstrated the strengths of using rapid analytical methods to analyze large numbers of samples in a timely manner or to enhance our capacity to increase the spatial coverage of an environmental assessment. This validation of the effectiveness of rapid methods led to research in developing methods, comparable to the HPLC bile technique, for parent ACs in sediment and tissues of invertebrates. Researchers also studied ways to determine levels of other contaminant classes, such as polychlorinated biphenyl (PCB) in tissues and sediment (e.g., Krahn et al. 1994).

Practicality of a tiered approach

The findings from the EVOS showed that using a tiered approach consisting of a rapid method in Tier 1 (e.g., HPLC bile method) and more detailed, and costly, methods in Tier 2 is both scientifically sound and cost-effective in its application. For example, rapid screening methods can be used to identify the geographic extent of exposure of species of concern and as a substitute for costly GC/MS analyses when minimal exposure is observed. This tiered approach used in evaluating exposure of halibut to ACs led to the timely opening of the Gulf of Alaska fishery following the EVOS. Screening methods provide the ability to rapidly collect data on the scope and spatial extent of contamination of the habitat and biota in the spill area. Moreover, rapid screening techniques also can give both researchers and managers flexibility in their response to an oil spill. For example, results from a preliminary sampling can provide the necessary information needed by managers to design further sample collection or analysis. This tiered approach contributed to the rapid turnaround of samples so that the analytical data were available to be used in seafood safety decisions following the EVOS. To summarize, based on guidelines used in the EVOS subsistence study to categorize degree of contamination as high (> 1000 ng/g), medium (100 to 1000 ng/g), or low (< 10 ng/g), only about 10% of the shellfish samples collected (and < 5% of the fish tissue samples) would warrant detailed analyses of subsequent edible tissue using more costly, mass spectroscopy-based methods. This finding shows that screening can be very effective in minimizing the use of more costly methods on samples with low levels of contaminants.

Necessity of data quality assurance

A comprehensive QA plan is always essential. The central value of a QA plan is that it identifies the criteria that will determine if reported data are sufficiently complete, comparable, representative, unbiased, and precise, and thus, whether they should be used in decision-making. These criteria include specification of the analytes to be determined, the minimum sensitivity of the analytical methods, and, whenever possible, the use of certified calibration solutions and standard reference materials. With a QA plan in place, the performance of a laboratory's analytical results can be monitored and used to provide rapid corrective measures in the event that data quality is compromised. A comprehensive QA plan that involves repeated analyses of reference materials (a key component), replicate samples and laboratory method blanks and involves participation in refereed intercomparison laboratory exercises provides the assurance that the data generated fall within the specified limits that define high-quality data.

Validating laboratory studies on fate of aromatic compounds in marine biota

Before the EVOS, laboratory studies with fish and invertebrate species exposed to ACs through several different routes (e.g., water, food, sediment) demonstrated marked differential metabolism of ACs by fish and invertebrates (Varanasi 1989). In brief, fish readily take up and efficiently biotransform ACs to polar metabolites that are concentrated into the bile for excretion. This rapid biotransformation of ACs in fish limits the accumulation of parent compounds in edible tissues, such as muscle. In contrast, invertebrate species' less efficient metabolism allows them to bioaccumulate the parent-unchanged compounds in their tissues. These laboratory findings were corroborated by the results of the subsistence study, which showed a wide range of exposure of fish to ACs from the analysis of bile samples, but little or no accumulation of these compounds in fish muscle tissue. In contrast, parent ACs were accumulated to high levels in some invertebrate samples from the same areas. From a spill-response perspective, the corroboration of the laboratory findings on the fate of ACs increases confidence in the use of the information from laboratory studies to put into proper context the data on tissue levels of ACs measured in the field. Without the prior laboratory research, there would have been insufficient understanding of the fate of ACs in fish; for example, it would have been difficult to properly interpret the meaning of findings of very low concentrations of parent ACs in muscle tissue without the previous data. Conversely, there are laboratory findings on biotransformation and disposition of ACs in fish and invertebrates. The field data from the response to the EVOS corroborated the applicability of the laboratory findings to describe the fate of ACs in fish and invertebrates following a large spill.

For example, low levels of ACs in fish muscle cannot be interpreted as evidence of minimal or low exposure of a fish species to ACs.

Fate of aromatic compounds in marine mammals

Before the EVOS, there was scant information on the fate and effects of petroleum-related contaminants in marine mammals. The biochemical pathways of marine mammals for metabolizing ACs are similar to those of fish. However, unlike fish, marine mammals have large lipid reserves in their blubber in which ACs could potentially accumulate. Blubber is a subsistence food. However, the findings from the analysis of seal tissue samples showed very low accumulation of ACs in blubber, even in seals exposed to high levels of ACs, as demonstrated by the elevated concentrations of AC metabolites in bile and, in some cases, the visible presence of oil on the animals. The development of considerable data on seals and sea lions, therefore, confirmed that pinnipeds, and very likely other marine mammal species, efficiently metabolize ACs. This efficient biotransformation limits the accumulation of parent compounds in blubber, even though the blubber has a high lipid content, and has a high capacity to accumulate compounds such as parent ACs. This is evidenced by the findings of very high levels of PCBs in blubber of certain marine mammal species (e.g., Varanasi et al. 1992; Krahn et al. 1997). PCBs, in contrast to ACs in petroleum, accumulate to high levels because they are mostly resistant to metabolism. If analyses of seal tissue samples were not done following EVOS, it is very unlikely that this information on the fate of ACs in a marine mammal would have been collected, because of the limitations in conducting experiments with these protected species. This shows that there are opportunities to gain new knowledge during a response to an oil spill, while at the same time addressing important spill-related questions. It is important to take advantage of these opportunities to increase our knowledge base and our capacity to respond more effectively to future spills.

Database relevant to human health risk assessment

The potential for human health risk from consumption of contaminated seafood was of primary concern to Native Alaskans after EVOS. Before the EVOS, only limited information was available to those involved in assessing human risk from oil spills. The subsistence study generated scientific data on tissue concentrations of ACs in invertebrates, fish muscle, and pinnipeds (including muscle, blubber, liver, and kidney tissue) that contributed information on assessing human exposure in the human-health risk assessment (see Chapter 9). These data (Varanasi et al. 1993a, 1993b; Brown et al. 1996; Hom et al. 1996) are of value to others for future spills to augment the data they collect to assess human-health risk from ACs. Also, adding comparable data from future oil spills would expand the amount of available information on accumulation of ACs in edible tissues from additional species as well as from different petroleum types, making the information more robust in its applicability to future spills. Such an expanded database would be of greater value to scientists, managers, and others concerned with evaluating effects of spills on human health and would increase certainty in management decisions.

Response coordination

It is essential that there be a coordinated response in assessing the impact of a spill on food safety by all concerned groups (e.g., local residents, resource managers, regulators, scientists, responsible party). Those involved must collaborate to first identify and then answer key questions, which will define the type of investigation needed. Once the central questions are defined, an appropriate sampling and analysis plan can be determined. It is important that sufficient time and effort are committed to designing and implementing the best sampling and analysis schemes. Sampling schemes should provide enough samples to satisfy both power-of-analysis issues and archival of additional samples to avoid the expense of resampling when, for example, more data are needed to decrease the uncertainty of conclusions or to replace samples that were compromised or lost. The analysis scheme would benefit from the designation of a "central laboratory" where the majority of the samples will be analyzed or evaluated and the QA standards established. This would greatly assure consistency in the analytical analyses and QA, as well as maintain chain-of-custody criteria as needed. The central laboratory should have experience in analyzing oil in tissue samples, be well versed in QA, have demonstrated ability to produce high-quality data (documented participation in refereed interlaboratory comparison exercises), and have a responsibility for the resources at risk. These factors strongly suggest that a qualified government laboratory of a trustee agency is best suited to be the "central laboratory."

Frequency of analyses in future spills

In future oil spills, analyses of the oil and affected biota and habitat should always be considered because each situation has its own set of circumstances (i.e., type of oil spilled, and type of resources and habitat affected) that makes it unique from other spills. The other critical factor is that the community is likely unfamiliar with the impacts of an oil spill on both humans and the marine resources about which they are concerned. The infrequent occurrence of major oil spills limits the amount of information available to local communities affected by a spill. Analyses are needed because the perception of the affected community is that their seafood must be contaminated. The visual information is that a large amount of a "foreign substance" is harming their environment. As was the case with the EVOS, analyses of bile from fish can provide powerful information that clearly demonstrates exposure of fish to spilled oil. The bile data are important because they are generally consistent with the visual data of oil impacting marine habitats. The data on AC metabolites in bile also provide an important context for presenting and explaining contamination data on edible flesh that, on most occasions, will show very low levels of parent ACs. There have been rare occasions in which fish exposed to spilled oil have accumulated elevated levels (i.e., ppm range) in muscle tissue. Such a case was the *Braer* spill off the west coast of Scotland where penned Atlantic salmon accumulated elevated concentrations of ACs in muscle (Whittle et al. 1997). A contributing factor was certainly the fact that these fish could not avoid the contaminated water column. The occurrence of elevated concentrations of parent ACs in fish muscle appears to be rare. It is worth noting that salmon and other fish species sampled following the EVOS very rarely had concentrations of total parent ACs that exceeded 0.1 ppm, and, for the vast majority of fish muscle samples, the concentrations were less than 0.01 ppm.

To reiterate, however, each spill has its unique characteristics, and the affected human community will need to be convinced with data from chemical analyses of the degree of exposure of marine biota in the area and of the safety of potentially affected seafood species. In short, the effective communication of the findings from chemical analyses conducted as part of a spill response is an important component of outreach to the community. The low levels of ACs in edible tissue can be explained because of our knowledge of the fate of ACs in vertebrate species. For invertebrates, the range of necessary analyses will depend on the circumstances of the spill. If there are shellfish beds in the impacted area that are important to subsistence, recreational, or commercial fisheries, then analyses of tissue samples of shellfish from the beds will be needed to determine whether ACs have been accumulated and are affecting the quality of the seafood. Generating data from each successive oil spill would also continually expand and improve the amount of available information on oil spills and their effects, benefiting scientists, managers, and the public in responding to future spills.

Communication of analytical results

Communication of the results and the interpretation of chemical analyses to the communities in the spill area is a challenging task. It is important to present the results in context using the information now available on the fate and disposition of ACs in marine organisms and the marine environment. For example, the data from analyses of fish bile can be used to explain the lack of accumulation of ACs in fish muscle tissue compared with the results from shellfish because of the effective metabolism of those compounds and excretion into bile. In addition, it is important to explain the steps taken to ensure unbiased and high-quality data from chemical analyses to address skepticism on the reliability of quality of the data generated.

The types of outreach efforts that can work are

- timely progress reports to environmental managers to increase the sharing of information,
- timely progress reports written in a style appropriate for nontechnical people,
- written material on the past scientific record of the analytical laboratory that could demonstrate the soundness of the scientific data that are generated by the laboratory, and

- availability of key laboratory staff to interested groups so they can better understand the methods being used and the steps being taken to assure that high-quality data are being generated.

This can take the form of an "open house" and tour of the facility or meetings in which the sampling methods and information on the fate and effects of petroleum in the marine environment are discussed in a way that nontechnical people can understand. The goals should be to demonstrate the competence of the staff conducting the analyses, the quality of the data generated at the laboratory, and the steps being taken to assure high-quality data. These steps can go a long way toward building confidence and trust in the analytical techniques being used and in the impartiality and scientific soundness of the data being produced.

Research needs

The chemical, biochemical, and physiological techniques that can be used to assess the impact of spilled petroleum in marine ecosystems have greatly improved over the last 20 years. Analytical chemical methods are more reliable and sensitive; new rapid techniques have been developed; biochemical techniques (i.e., cytochrome P-450 induction) are available to detect exposure that is significant at the cellular level; and tools are available to detect effects of ACs on reproductive processes in fish (e.g., steroid hormone alterations, altered ovarian development) or changes in growth potential of mollusks (e.g., scope for growth assessments). The following items highlight some important research needs.

- Develop analytical screening methods for invertebrates that reduce the cost and time of analysis.
- Study higher trophic level mollusks (e.g., octopus). Since mollusks have minimal ability to metabolize oil, octopus and other higher-trophic-level mollusks may accumulate much higher concentrations of ACs than do most species of mollusks.
- Assess current non-biological methods to determine extent and magnitude of contamination. For example, semipermeable membrane devices have been used successfully to monitor the extent of contamination and the bioavailability (and thus potential exposure) of organic contaminants such as ACs (see Huckins et al. 1990; Prest et al. 1992; Roe et al. 1999).
- Assess potential for accumulation of ACs in edible tissues of fish under special circumstances (e.g., prolonged exposure, highly dispersed oil in water column, or high lipid-edible tissues such as liver, brain, blubber).
- Determine dose-response relationships in representative fish (e.g., benthic, pelagic species) and mollusk species. There is a lack of information on relationships between water/sediment/diet concentrations of complex petroleum and levels of ACs and their metabolites accumulated in tissues and fluid through these routes of exposure. This information can be used to estimate body burdens of ACs when analytical data on tissue levels are not

available or is not available for all species of concern. The tissue concentration data could be used in estimating health risks from consumption.

Health Risk Assessment

The advantage of baseline consumption information

The availability of specific consumption information on the affected subsistence population was a major asset in conducting the relative cancer risk assessment. It is rare that such precise consumption/exposure information is available for assessing the potential risk of exposure to environmental contaminants. In the vast majority of cases, inferences must be made of the potential exposure to a contaminant on the basis of consumption/exposure information that is not specific to the population of concern. Also, having distributional information on the range of consumption of individual foods and levels of oil contaminants is critical to reducing the uncertainty in the risk assessment. The survey design for obtaining specimens for analysis is also critical in reducing uncertainty in the risk estimates. Appropriate sampling should adequately reflect the likelihood of exposure and should not bias the sampling by overrepresenting certain affected areas. In assessing the potential exposure to polycyclic aromatic hydrocarbons (PAHs) from an oil spill, it is critical that the assessment be done in the context of overall PAH exposure, particularly from the diet of local communities.

Focus on long-term, PAH-induced cancer effects

Concern for the presence of contaminants from petroleum spills in marine organisms should be focused primarily on the potential carcinogenesis of certain petroleum components, specifically PAHs. While toxic effects other than cancer are associated with other crude oil components, particularly in the case of direct exposure to petroleum mixtures, the high levels required for these effects (e.g., worker or subsistence harvesters' exposure) will not occur from secondary exposure through the consumption of fish or shellfish without obvious effects on the marine organisms themselves. Also, because the methodology for relative cancer risk assessment is inherently more conservative than the methodologies used for noncancer endpoints, the focus on PAH-induced cancer effects is a prudent and appropriate public health focus.

Mollusks as a more sensitive index for exposure

PAHs were not present to any significant extent in the subsistence samples that were collected and analyzed as part of NOAA's subsistence survey. This is particularly the case for the numerous finfish samples in which no evidence was found of the presence of PAHs. With regard to fresh salmon, the 10^{-6} risk level is at or below the detection limit of PAHs. The risk associated with the consumption of unsmoked salmon is insignificant relative to that associated with consuming smoked salmon because smoking significantly increases the PAH level. Shellfish, particularly bivalves, deserve particular attention in any oil spill, because it has been shown consistently that components of petroleum accumulate to a much greater extent in bivalves than in finfish. Therefore, the contamination of mollusks is both a more sensitive index for exposure of a marine environment to petroleum and represents the most likely point of passage of aquatic oil spillage into human consumption. The data collected from the *Exxon Valdez* spill are consistent with the view that while finfish do not accumulate toxic petroleum hydrocarbons to any significant extent, mollusks may be a source of concern.

The risk estimate presented for molluskan bivalves was predicated on the initial conservative assumption that persons at risk would consume molluskan bivalves contaminated at the level of PAHs produced by the EVOS for a period of 10 years. Subsequent evidence gathered during the course of the study indicated that this was indeed a conservative assumption and that bivalves would not be expected to be contaminated with PAHs at this level for such an extended period of time. The lifetime carcinogenic risk is low for consumption of unsmoked salmon, other finfish, crustaceans, and even oil-contaminated molluskan bivalves.

Interpreting cancer risk estimates

In interpreting the relative cancer risk estimates, several points should be emphasized. First, because the equivalency approach to estimating the potencies of various PAHs was based on several assumptions, this approach cannot be assumed to produce exact potencies for the PAHs. Second, there are limitations in the available laboratory animal data used to estimate the potency of benzo(a)pyrene and other PAHs. Finally, as with most quantitative relative risk assessments for cancer, an upper-bound risk estimate has been produced with the knowledge that the actual risk is somewhere between the upper-bound estimate and zero and, in reality, is much closer to zero.

As with any assessment of risk associated with contaminated food, a greater degree of accuracy, or less uncertainty, could be achieved with additional information. In this assessment, the greatest contribution to uncertainty arose from the use of animal bioassay data to derive estimates of potency for the individual PAHs. This uncertainty derives from two major areas: the use and extrapolation of effects and dosages from laboratory animals to human exposure and the reliance on animal bioassays using non-oral routes of exposure. The consumption and exposure information contributed significantly less to uncertainty in the relative risk assessment than did the hazard information. This was because the consumption information was specific to the population of concern and precise analytical information on subsistence foods was available.

Use of the equivalency approach since the *Exxon Valdez*

The equivalency approach developed and used in this assessment has proven a useful framework for evaluating the potential effects of oil spills on food supplies in subsequent episodes. In March 1996, an oil spill occurred off the coast of Rhode Island that significantly impacted the substantial commercial fishery in the area. The state health officials responsible for assessing the public health impact of the spill contacted the USFDA for technical assistance. The equivalency approach was adopted and tailored by the state officials in assessing the impact of the spill. The primary adjustment made in the approach was the use of seafood-consumption information specific to the affected region.

Data gaps and research needs

There were major data gaps on the potential toxicity of components of crude oil at the time of the *Exxon Valdez* assessment, and these gaps still exist today. There are critical needs for a better animal bioassay database on crude oil constituents and, for the major crude-oil PAHs, a much better characterization of the potency estimates to serve as a basis for the assigned toxicity equivalents. A better characterization of the toxicity profile of the major classes of crude oil constituents is still needed. In their review of 1985, the National Research Council identified heterocyclic aliphatic hydrocarbons and non-hydrocarbons as compounds for which information is lacking on fate and distribution and/or toxicity (NRC 1985). High-molecular-weight isoalkanes also could be added to this list. Studies of different petroleum fractions show an imperfect correlation between PAH content and their degree of mutagenicity and/or carcinogenicity, which suggests that there are other crude-oil constituents with significant biological activity that remains undescribed.

Advice on Managing Subsistence Seafood Issues at Future Spills

What the Oil Spill Health Task Force did well

In retrospect, it is both easy and necessary to identify what the OSHTF did not do that should have been done and what could have been done better. But the key is to build upon the experience, both good and bad, so that those who respond to similar future situations may benefit from the successes and the failures of this effort. In sum, the model established by the OSHTF is one that could be useful in future responses to oil spills and other situations in which the safety of using subsistence foods is questioned. Among the strengths and accomplishments of the OSHTF approach were the following:

- Reliable, scientifically sound, and consistent health advice was provided based on multiple rounds of sample collection and on evaluation by some of the most prominent experts in the country.

- Consensus decisions were reached, and disparate agencies and organizations that were bitter antagonists on other oil-spill fronts spoke with a single voice in a genuine effort to respond to the concerns of a minority group (Alaska Natives) that is often ignored. Indeed, the OSHTF was one of the very few groups that actually responded to the needs of human beings during the first several years following the spill.
- The OSHTF communicated in a variety of formats, including health bulletins, newsletters, meetings in the communities, both by teams and individuals, biweekly meetings in Anchorage, an educational videotape, media interviews (radio, TV, newspapers), and maps, charts, and brochures.
- Subsistence harvests did rebound over time, at least in part due to the information provided through the OSHTF program and the programs later carried out by the Oil Spill Trustee Council. Over time, fewer and fewer people refrained from using subsistence foods because of oil contamination concerns; some said this was because they received health advice.
- Native people were represented at OSHTF meetings, were involved in collections (at least in part), and were consulted throughout the program, although not to the extent that would have been ideal.
- There were multiple rounds of sample collection and testing over a four-year period involving fish, marine invertebrates, mammals, and birds. After the first year, these studies examined trends in hydrocarbon levels from resources at particular sites, and also conducted "special assessments" of other sites at the request of the communities.

Recommendations for contingency planning

During an oil spill, the initial concern is containment and cleanup. Concerns about human health have usually related only to cleanup workers. Food safety issues, both subsistence and commercial, need to be directly incorporated into the contingency planning stage. In this final section, we provide an additional set of recommendations concerning contingency planning for future oil spills, based on the experience of the OSHTF. These supplement the recommendations that have appeared throughout this book.

- Develop a clearinghouse of available literature and data gathered during the response

The efforts of the OSHTF were hampered by the lack of historical information about oil contamination and human health. There was no central resource for finding this information. A resource library needs to be maintained that contains appropriate historical information about oil and human health and that serves as a repository of the rich database on subsistence foods and other human-health documents that have been written as a result of the EVOS. It is suggested that this be located at NOAA in Seattle.

Baseline consumption data: In community contingency planning for future oil spills, baseline food-consumption information is needed where any oil spill might damage a major food source. Without this information, an accurate health risk analysis cannot be done.

Baseline hydrocarbon concentration levels (*benchmark data*): We learned that oil contaminants are ubiquitous in the environment. We found evidence of low levels of contamination in seafood in non-oiled spilled areas at great distance from the oil spill area. If there is risk of an oil spill to a food source, baseline levels should be obtained as part of the contingency planning efforts.

- Seek out nontraditional alliances

The strength of the OSHTF was the diversity of interests and expertise found among its members. The members of this group had no prior experience in working together and, in the context of a normal working environment, would have few occasions to do so. When the focus became subsistence food safety evaluations, it was necessary to bring together groups as diverse as village health and social service corporations, the USFDA, and the ADF&G.

- Tap into disaster-psychology knowledge

We did not take advantage of the available knowledge base in the social sciences that could have given us a basic understanding of how to manage the complex human dimensions of a man-made disaster (versus a natural disaster) and to guide us in developing strategies for effective communication with the communities in the spill area. The literature base in the sociology of disasters and in risk communication has greatly expanded since the *Exxon Valdez* and clearly should be utilized in contingency planning.

- Identify in advance the experts you will need

In the aftermath of the EVOS, Alaska's health and science community did not have the range of expertise to evaluate the toxicological data that were being returned from the sampling program or to respond effectively to the post-spill social, psychological, and communication challenges. Had the OSHTF realized this in advance, we could have identified the levels and kinds of expertise that would meet our needs, and potential sources of this expertise, and lined them up sooner.

- Be prepared to find information that is incidental but important

During the course of our sampling for oil contamination we found non-oil-spill contamination in the harbor at Kodiak from boats and at Chenega Bay from creosote seeping out of pilings. Both of these findings were unexpected and had to be communicated to the public. Additionally, to point out the fact that aromatic hydrocarbons occur in other foods, we sent two samples of their traditional smoked fish to the NOAA laboratory in Seattle for analysis. These samples contained levels of hydrocarbons far higher than any samples from the subsistence harvest areas. Smoked fish are an important part of the subsistence diet and are deeply rooted in the Alaska Native culture. However, in retrospect, making an analogy between the safety of traditional smoked fish and fish sampled for oil-spill contamination was ill-advised, only adding to the contention between the OSHTF and the villagers.

Concluding Remarks

Part of the legacy of the EVOS are the images of fouled beaches and wildlife, armies of cleanup workers, and an uncertain future for the natural environment and human communities. But this legacy also includes a better understanding of ecological relationships and an enhanced preparedness to prevent and respond to future spills. The intent of this book has been to contribute to the lessons learned from the EVOS by focusing on an important aspect of environmental disaster response that is often ignored or neglected: the human dimension. And while the nutritional and cultural significance of subsistence uses of fish and wildlife is especially noteworthy in Alaska, these lessons apply to any human population that uses local natural resources for food.

The contributors to this book have recognized that we must learn from the successes and shortcomings of the OSHTF and the program it guided. From the standpoint of technical program development, the procedures for collecting, testing, and evaluating samples of subsistence resources for contamination and food safety may serve as modest models, both in future disaster response and environmental monitoring. From the perspective of risk communication, two key themes stand out. The first is the importance of a collaborative, multidisciplinary approach from the earliest stages of response. The second is the necessity of an effective, interactive communication process that develops a credible message and delivers it well and is flexible and reflexive enough to adapt as its audience responds. Crosscutting both of these themes is the importance of sound science, local knowledge and observations, a public process above suspicion, and a sensitivity to the cultural context in which the issues are defined and the message is received. These lessons must be applied to each stage of the process, from contingency planning, to spill response, to long-term restoration.

Addressing an issue so fundamental, and yet so complex, as the wholesomeness of a food supply upon which a way of life depends in the midst of a major environmental and technological disaster will never be straightforward, especially in a cross-cultural setting. The experience of the *Exxon Valdez* spill provides guidance that may assist future development of reliable evaluations of subsistence resources and effective communication of study findings and health advice. The essential goals of any response must be to help people to cope with injuries to the natural resources upon which their communities depend and to promote both biological and social healing.

References

Babcock MM, Irvine G, Harris PM, Cusick JA, Rice SD. 1996. Persistence of oiling in mussel beds three and four years after the *Exxon Valdez* oil spill. In: Proceedings of the EVOS Symposium. Anchorage AK: EVOS Trustee Council.

Brown, DW, Burrows DG, Sloan CA, Pearce RA, Pierce SM, Bolton JL, Tilbury KL, Dana KL, Chan S-L, Varanasi U. 1996. Survey of Alaskan subsistence invertebrate seafoods collected in 1989–1991 to determine exposure to oil spilled from the *Exxon Valdez. Trans Am Fish Soc Symp* 18:844–855.

Fall JA, Utermohle CJ, editors. 1999. Subsistence service update, Exxon Valdez Oil Spill Restoration Project Final Report (Restoration Project 99471). Juneau AK: Division of Subsistence, Alaska Department of Fish and Game. Technical Paper No. 252.

Harris PM, Rice SD, Babcock MM, Brodersen CC. 1996. Within-bed distribution of *Exxon Valdez* crude oil in Prince William Sound blue mussels and underlying sediments. In: EVOS Symposium Proceedings. Anchorage AK: EVOS Trustee Council.

Hom, T, Varanasi U, Stein JE, Sloan CA, Tilbury KL, Chan S-L. 1996. Assessment of the exposure of subsistence fish to aromatic compounds following the *Exxon Valdez* oil spill. *Trans Am Fish Soc Symp* 18:856–866.

Huckins JN, Manuweera GK, Petty JD, Mackay D, Lebo JA. 1993. Lipid-containing semipermeable membrane devices for monitoring organic contaminants in water. *Environ Sci Technol* 27:489–2496.

Krahn, MM, Becker PR, Tilbury KL, Stein JE. 1997. Organochlorine contaminants in blubber of four seal species: integrating biomonitoring and specimen banking. *Chemosphere* 34:2109–2121.

Krahn MM, Stein JE. 1998. Assessing exposure of marine biota and habitats to petroleum compounds. *Anal Chem* 70:186–192.

Krahn, MM, Ylitalo GM, Buzitis J, Sloan CA, Boyd DT, Chan S-L, Varanasi U. 1994. Screening for planar chlorobiphenyls in tissues of marine biota by high-performance liquid chromatography with photodiode array detection. *Chemosphere* 29:117–139.

[NRC] National Research Council. 1985. Oil in the seas. Inputs, fates and effects. Washington DC: National Academy Press.

Palinkas LA, Downs M, Petterson JS, Russell J. 1993. Social, cultural, and psychological impacts of the *Exxon Valdez* oil spill. *Hum Org* 52(1):1–13.

Picou JS, Gill DA, Cohen MJ. 1997. The *Exxon Valdez* oil spill as a technological disaster: conceptualizing a social problem. In: Picou JS, Gill DA, Cohen MJ, editors. The *Exxon Valdez* disaster: Readings on a modern social problem. Dubuque IA: Kendall/Hunt Publishing p 3–21.

Prest HF, Jacobson LA, Wilson M. 1997. Passive water sampling for polynuclear aromatic hydrocarbons using lipid-containing semipermeable membrane devices (SPMDs): application to contaminant residence times. *Chemosphere* 35:3047–3063.

Rodin M, Downs M, Petterson J, Russell J. 1997. Community impacts of the *Exxon Valdez* oil spill. In: Picou JS, Gill DA, Cohen MJ, editors. The *Exxon Valdez* disaster: readings on a modern social problem. Dubuque IA: Kendall/Hunt Publishing. p 193–205.

Roe TJ, Johnsen S. 1999. Bioavailability of polycyclic aromatic hydrocarbons in the North Sea. *Environ Sci Technol* 33:1963–1969.

[USFWS] U.S. Fish and Wildlife Service. 1991. Summary of effects of the *Exxon Valdez* oil spill on natural resources and archaeological sites. Anchorage AK: Division of Subsistence, Alaska Department of Fish and Game.

Usher PJ, Baikie M, Demmer M, Nakashima D, Stevenson MG, Stiles M. 1995. Communicating about contaminants in country food: The experience in aboriginal communities. Ottawa: Inuit Tapirisat of Canada.

Varanasi U, editor. 1989. Metabolism of polycyclic aromatic hydrocarbons in the aquatic environment. Boca Raton FL: CRC Press. 341 p.

Varanasi, U, Stein JE, Reichert WL, Tilbury KL, Chan S-L. 1992. Chlorinated and aromatic hydrocarbons in bottom sediments, fish and mammals in U.S. coastal waters: laboratory and field studies of metabolism and accumulation. In: Walker CH, Livingstone DR, editors. Persistent pollutants in marine environment ecosystems. Oxford UK: Pergamon Press. p 83–115.

Varanasi, U., Brown DW, Hom T, Burrows DG, Sloan CA, Field LJ, Stein JE, Tilbury KE, McCain BB, Chan S-L. 1993a. Vol. I. Survey of Alaska subsistence fish, marine mammal, and invertebrate samples collected 1989–91 for exposure to oil spilled from the *Exxon Valdez.* U.S. Dept. of Comm., NOAA Tech. Memo. NMFS-NWFSC-12. 110p.

Varanasi, U., Brown DW, Hom T, Burrows DG, Sloan CA, Field LJ, Stein JE, Tilbury KL, McCain BB, Chan S-L. 1993b. Vol. II. Supplemental information concerning a survey of Alaska subsistence fish, marine mammal, and invertebrate samples collected 1989–91 for exposure to oil spilled from the *Exxon Valdez.* U.S. Dept. of Comm., NOAA Tech. Memo. NMFS-NWFSC-13. 173p.

Wells PG, Butler JN, Hughes JS, editors. 1995. *Exxon Valdez* oil spill: fate and effects in Alaskan waters. Philadelphia PA: American Society for Testing and Materials.

Whittle, et al. 1997. The impact of the *Braer* oil on caged salmon. In: Davies JM, Topping G, editors. The impact of an oil spill in turbulent waters: The *Braer*. Proceedings of a symposium held at the Royal Society of Edinburgh; 7–8 Sep 1995; Edinburgh, Scotland. Edinburgh, Scotland: Stationary Office.

APPENDIX 1

Analytical Protocols for Aromatic Contaminants in Alaskan Subsistence Seafood*

Catherine A. Sloan, Donald W. Brown, Ronald W. Pearce, Gina M. Ylitalo, Douglas G. Burrows, Margaret M. Krahn

Samples of subsistence fish, marine mammals, and invertebrates from sites near Native Alaskan villages and from reference areas were analyzed for selected aromatic contaminants (ACs) found in petroleum. Crude oils, such as Prudhoe Bay crude oil (PBCO), contain many hundreds of organic compounds generally classified into groups including aliphatic and polycyclic aromatic hydrocarbons and compounds that contain sulfur, oxygen, and nitrogen. Among these compounds are dibenzothiophenes and alkyl-substituted dibenzothiophenes, which are significant components of PBCO and are often useful in differentiating PBCO from other crude oils and petroleum-related products (Clark and Brown 1977; Sauer and Boehm 1991). Aromatic hydrocarbons comprise the group of ACs that are known for their toxicity and can be monitored in biota as indicators of exposure to, and possible effects from, petroleum-related ACs.

Previous laboratory studies have shown that fish and mammals efficiently metabolize ACs to polar derivatives, which are concentrated in their bile for excretion (Statham et al. 1976; Varanasi et al. 1989). As a result of this biotransformation, ACs may not readily accumulate in the edible flesh of fish or marine mammals (Varanasi and Gmur 1981; Stein et al. 1984). Therefore, exposure of fish and marine mammals to ACs was measured using a rapid, sensitive method that screens bile for the presence of polar derivatives of petroleum ACs, referred to as fluorescent aromatic contaminants (FACs). This semi-quantitative procedure for measuring FACs utilizes high-performance liquid chromatography (HPLC) with fluorescence detection (Krahn et al. 1984) and has been employed previously to evaluate exposure of fish to ACs from an oil spill on the Columbia River (Krahn, Kittle et al. 1986). The results of biliary FAC analyses were used to determine the extent of exposure to PBCO and to

*NOAA and participating laboratories do not approve, recommend, or endorse any proprietary product or proprietary material mentioned in this publication.

prioritize corresponding samples of fish muscle and marine mammal tissues for analyses of individual ACs by gas chromatography/mass spectrometry (GC/MS).

Other laboratory studies have shown that invertebrates readily bioaccumulate ACc (Varanasi et al. 1985; James 1989), in part because of their limited ability to metabolize these compounds. All samples of invertebrate tissues, therefore, were analyzed for individual ACs and were not screened for FACs.

The concentrations of individual ACs in fish, marine mammal, invertebrate, and other tissues (e.g., kelp and roe on kelp) were determined by GC/MS following extraction and isolation of the ACs. This quantitative procedure is much more costly and time-consuming than is the measurement of FACs in bile. Nevertheless, several important improvements in the procedure have been made, including automation of the extract cleanup procedure for isolating the ACs and use of a special sequenced selected-ion monitoring (SSIM) GC/MS program (Sloan et al. 1993). These advancements enabled us to provide high-quality analytical data for ng/g concentrations of ACs in the tissue samples more quickly and with less labor than previously. To evaluate the performance of the instruments and protocols, the quality-assurance program for this study incorporated measurements of the accuracy and precision of the analyses. Method blanks, replicate samples, and instrument calibration solutions, as well as spiked blanks and either matrix spikes or a standard reference material, were analyzed with the samples. Demonstration of the reliability and validity of the analytical measurements allowed confident use of the data.

Selection of Analytes

Petroleum contains a wide variety of hydrocarbons and their derivatives, including a large number of ACs. The relative abundance of these compounds varies among different petroleums (Clark and Brown 1977); thus, the spilled PBCO was analyzed at the beginning of the study to determine the composition of the ACs in this oil. GC/MS analysis of the PBCO showed the presence of a large number of ACs. The availability of several substitution sites on parent ACs can result in many different isomers having substituted alkyl groups of one or more carbon atoms. For example, the C2-substituted naphthalenes (C2NPH) consist of 12 individual isomers. Thus, the total concentration of C2NPH in PBCO is composed of the sum of the concentrations of the 12 individual C2NPH isomers. Accordingly, the 35 non-substituted and alkyl-substituted ACs listed in Table A1-1 include about 270 individual components.

For discussion purposes, it is convenient to divide the ACs into the low-molecular-weight ACs (LACs), composed of two to three benzene rings, and the high-molecular-weight ACs (HACs), composed of four to six rings (Table A1-1). This has the convenience of dividing the AC approximately into 1) the water-soluble and acutely toxic compounds (LACs) and 2) the less water-soluble and chronically toxic compounds (HACs). The LACs are prone to dissolution, evaporation, and bacterial

Table A1-1 Aromatic contaminants determined in edible tissue in the Alaskan subsistence fish, marine mammal, and shellfish studies[1]

2- and 3-ring aromatic contaminants (LAC)	4- to 6-ring aromatic contaminants (HAC)
naphthalene (NPH)	fluoranthene (FLA)
C1-naphthalenes (C1NPH)	pyrene (PYR)
C2-naphthalenes (C2NPH)	C1-fluoranthenes/pyrenes (C1FLA)
C3-naphthalenes (C3NPH)	benz[a]anthracene (BaA)
C4-naphthalenes (C4NPH)	chrysene (CHR)
acenaphthylene (ACY)	C1-benz[a]anthracenes/chrysenes (C1CHR)
acenaphthene (ACE)	C2-benz[a]anthracenes/chrysenes (C2CHR)
fluorene (FLU)	C3-benz[a]anthracenes/chrysenes (C3CHR)
C1-fluorenes (C1FLU)	C4-benz[a]anthracenes/chrysenes (C4CHR)
C2-fluorenes (C2FLU)	benzo[b]fluoranthene (BbF)
C3-fluorenes (C3FLU)	benzo[k]fluoranthene (BkF)
phenanthrene (PHN)	benzo[a]pyrene (BaP)
C1-phenanthrenes/anthracenes (C1PHN)	indeno[1,2,3-cd]pyrene (IDP)
C2-phenanthrenes/anthracenes (C2PHN)	dibenz[a,h]anthracene (DBA)
C3-phenanthrenes/anthracenes (C3PHN)	benzo[ghi]perylene (BZP)
C4-phenanthrenes/anthracenes (C4PHN)	
dibenzothiophene (DBT)	
C1-dibenzothiophenes (C1DBT)	
C2-dibenzothiophenes (C2DBT)	
C3-dibenzothiophenes (C3DBT)	

[1]C1, C2, etc., are abbreviations for methyl-, dimethyl/ethyl-, etc., respectively.

degradation; hence, their levels in the environment would generally decline as spilled oil weathers. The HACs, on the other hand, are resistant to weathering and therefore tend to persist in the environment. Although about 97% of the ACs in fresh PBCO are LACs, this percentage gradually declines over time as the oil weathers (Atlas et al. 1981; Boehm et al. 1981).

Protocols

Analyses of fluorescent aromatic contaminants in fish bile

Samples of fish bile were analyzed for FACs by the HPLC screening method of Krahn et al. (1984) described below (see Figure A1-1). Reverse-phase chromatography with fluorescence detection was used to separate and semi-quantitatively measure the

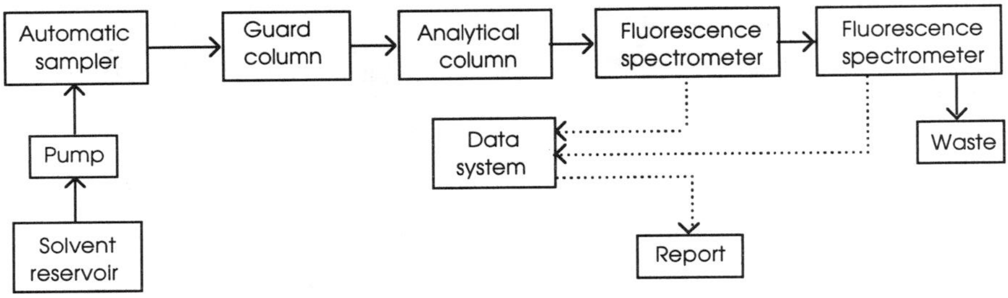

Figure A1-1 High-performance liquid chromatography system for analyses of bile for FACs (arrows indicate flow of mobile phase; dashed lines indicate electrical connections.)

FACs in bile at the maximum fluorescence wavelength pairs of napthalene (NPH) and phenanthrene (PHN), where many petroleum-related ACs also fluoresce.

Fish bile samples were chilled after collection in the field, then frozen as soon as possible. Samples were shipped frozen and stored at –80°C at the laboratory until analyzed. Quality-assurance measures were incorporated into the protocol for each sample set (25 bile samples per set). Previous captivity studies (Collier and Varanasi 1991) have shown that the levels of FACs and protein in fish bile vary, depending on feeding status (i.e., increased levels of FACs and protein were observed in non-feeding fish compared with fish that had been feeding). Therefore, the protein levels of the bile samples were measured to correct for varying FAC levels in fish captured at different feeding stages. The concentrations of biliary protein were determined by the method of Lowry et al. (1951), which measures the absorptance at 660 nm of the protein-phenol complex formed, using bovine serum albumin as the standard.

Determination of fluorescent aromatic

The FACs in bile were analyzed on a Waters (Milford, MA) model 6000A HPLC equipped with a Waters WISP™ model 715 automatic injector and two Perkin Elmer (Norwalk, CT) model 40 fluorescence detectors connected in series and interfaced to a Waters Maxima data system. A 0.20 x 2.0-cm guard column containing Perisorb™ 30 to 44 µm reverse-phase C_{18} packing (Upchurch Scientific, Oak Harbor, WA) was used in series with a 0.26 x 25.0-cm analytical column containing Perkin Elmer HC-ODS/PAH 10-µm reverse-phase C_{18} packing

For each sample, 5 µL of thawed, untreated bile was injected directly into the HPLC and eluted through the reverse-phase column. The FACs were eluted with a linear gradient running from 100% solvent A (water containing 5 ppm acetic acid) to 100% solvent B (methanol) at a flow rate of 1.0 mL/min during a period of 15 min. After holding the mobile phase at 100% solvent B for 10 min, it was returned to 100% solvent A during a period of 3 min. The system was then allowed to equilibrate for 10 min at 100% solvent A before the next sample was injected. The total run time, including running of the linear gradient and re-equilibration of the system, was 38 min. All solvents were degassed with helium and the column temperature was held at 50 °C.

As the samples eluted through the column, chromatograms were recorded at two fluorescence wavelength pairs where many ACs fluoresce: NPH and dibenzothiophenes at excitation/emission wavelengths 290/335 nm and PHN at excitation/emission wavelengths 260/380 nm. HPLC/fluorescence chromatograms, e.g., Figure A1-2, were acquired and analyzed using the above data system. The analyte responses were measured as the areas of their peaks in the chromatograms. If the concentration of FACs in a sample was sufficiently high that a detector response reached its maximum, the sample was reanalyzed using a smaller injection volume.

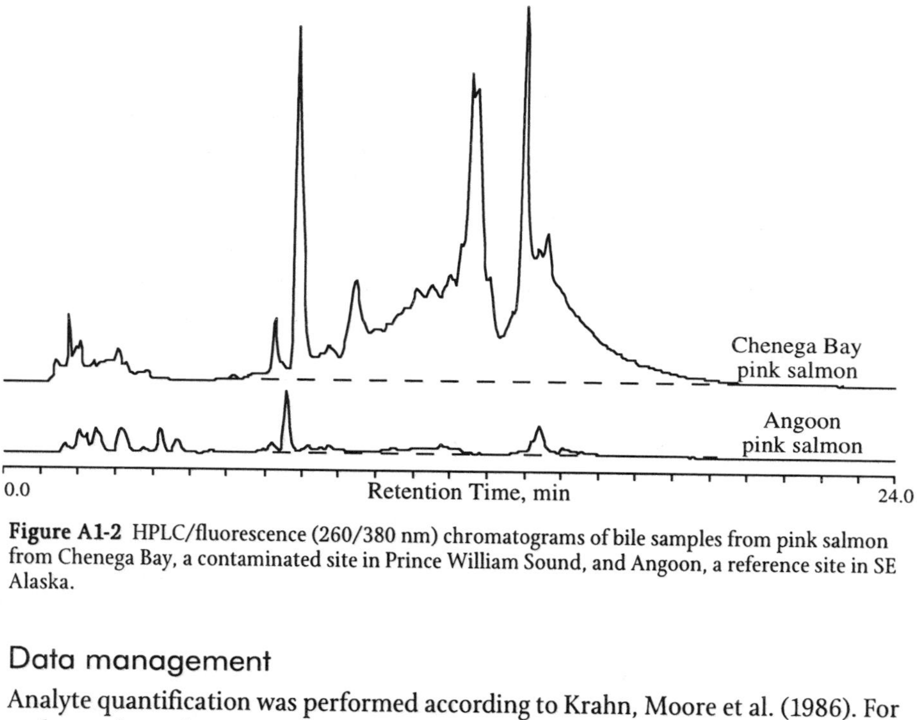

Figure A1-2 HPLC/fluorescence (260/380 nm) chromatograms of bile samples from pink salmon from Chenega Bay, a contaminated site in Prince William Sound, and Angoon, a reference site in SE Alaska.

Data management

Analyte quantification was performed according to Krahn, Moore et al. (1986). For each set of samples, an HPLC calibration solution (HPLC CS) containing NPH and PHN was analyzed at the beginning of the set and after every six or seven samples. For the analyses of the HPLC CS and the samples, the total area for all peaks in the region of the chromatogram where FACs are known to elute (> 6 min) was integrated for each wavelength pair. The concentrations of FAC (ng equivalents/g of bile, wet weight) in the analyses of the samples were calculated by relating their responses to the responses of the reference compounds (RC) in the respective analyses of the

HPLC CS. Similarly, the concentrations of FACs were also calculated in terms of ng RC equivalents/mg protein.

Quality assurance

The quality-assurance program included analyses of HPLC CS, method blanks, replicates, and the bile-pool reference materials described below. Before analyzing samples, the stability of the HPLC performance was verified by replicate analysis of an HPLC CS (three or more times, as necessary), then comparing the area of each compound in the CS from analysis to analysis. Before and during analyses of sample sets, the HPLC performance was considered stable when the mean response for each compound in the HPLC CS had a relative standard deviation (RSD) within 5%. If the RSD for any compound was > 5% during a sample set, corrective maintenance was performed and the bile samples were reanalyzed.

One method blank was analyzed at the beginning of each set of samples. If FACs were seen in a blank, column maintenance was performed before proceeding with analyses of samples. Two bile-pool reference materials were analyzed with each set of samples, at least one being analyzed near the beginning of the set. A sample of pooled harbor seal bile (collected by the Alaska Department of Fish and Game) that contained high concentrations of FACs was analyzed daily as part of an interlaboratory quality-assurance exercise by the Environmental Conservation Division's laboratory and a Texas A & M (Krahn et al. 1991) laboratory. The other reference sample was taken from a pool of flatfish bile (collected by the Environmental Conservation Division from a contaminated urban waterway) that contained moderate levels of FACs. The concentrations of FACs from each analysis of the reference materials were compared with the results from analysis of the materials in the previous sample sets. If the concentrations varied > 1 SD, corrective action was taken, including instrument maintenance or repair and reanalysis of samples.

Statistical methods

Results of FAC analyses of samples of fish and marine mammals from each sampling area were compared using GT2 comparison interval graphs. The GT2 comparison interval for each mean is calculated based on the number of samples for that mean, the variability about that mean, and the number of means being compared (Gabriel 1978; Sokal and Rohlf 1981). The FAC results and the statistical analyses of those results are presented and discussed in Chapter 8.

Analyses of Aromatic Contaminants in Tissue

Since detailed analysis for ACs in tissue samples by GC/MS is time-consuming and expensive, a selection process was established to choose samples for analysis based on the likelihood of ACs being present. The ranking of exposure based on the FAC results was used to select samples of edible fish tissue and marine mammal organs for analysis for ACs from PBCO by the GC/MS technique. Edible flesh samples from the same fish species from a sampling area were analyzed as individual samples or as composites of individual samples that had similarly high FAC levels in their bile. Samples of flesh from fish with relatively low levels of bile FACs were generally analyzed as composites. A small number of marine mammal samples were available for analysis and, with only limited historical data, all marine mammal blubber samples collected were analyzed for ACs, whereas only selected liver and kidney samples were analyzed based on their exposure rankings. Tissue samples from marine mammals were not composited for analysis. All samples of invertebrates collected were analyzed for ACs. For each species of invertebrates, the edible tissue from two or more animals was composited for analysis.

Tissue samples were stored in the laboratory at –80 °C until analyzed. Edible flesh of fish, marine mammals, and invertebrates was analyzed for the ACs listed in Table A1-1, using the procedures, slightly modified, from Sloan et al. (1993). The three major components of the protocols are extraction, HPLC cleanup, and analyte determination by GC/MS. Quality-assurance measures were incorporated into each of these components for each set of approximately 10 samples. In addition to tissues collected in the field, samples of smoked salmon from Native Alaskan communities were analyzed for ACs. Petroleum and related products, which contain ACs, were also analyzed, beginning with the HPLC step below, after being weighed and dissolved in methylene chloride.

Extraction of aromatic contaminants

The edible tissues of invertebrates that comprised a sample were homogenized, and a portion (~ 5 g) of the homogenized tissue was analyzed for ACs. For fish and marine mammal tissue samples, the surface layer of tissue was cut back, and ~ 5 g of tissue that had not been in contact with the foil wrapping was taken for analysis. When tissue samples from more than one fish were to be composited for analysis, the individual 5-g samples were combined and homogenized; a 5-g portion of the homogenized composite then was analyzed for ACs. For smoked salmon samples, 2 g of individual samples were taken for analysis.

The tissue was weighed into a centrifuge tube containing sodium sulfate and methylene chloride. The surrogate standard (S-Std), a solution containing NPH-d_8, ACE-d_{10} and BaP-d_{12} also used as an internal standard, for ACs was quantitatively added for a concentration of ~ 500 ng of each compound per sample. The mixture was then macerated with a Tekmar Tissumizer™. The resulting extract was filtered through a 22-mm i.d. x 25-cm gravity-flow chromatography column containing 10 cc of alumina and 20 cc of silica. The filtered extract was concentrated to 1 mL, then an HPLC internal standard (HPLC I-Std), PHN-d_{10}, was quantitatively added for a concentration of ~ 5000 ng per sample.

Fractionation of the extract to isolate aromatic contaminants

The ACs were isolated from the concentrated sample extract using a Spectra-Physics (Mountain View, CA) model 8800 HPLC equipped with a Spectra-Physics model 8450 UV/VIS detector (254 nm), and a Gilson (Middleton, WI) model 231 automatic injector and model 201 fraction collector. Two 22.5 x 250.0 mm stainless-steel preparatory-size columns containing Phenogel™ 100-Å size-exclusion packing (Phenomenex, Inc., Torrance, CA) were used in series with a 2-µm Rheodyne (Cotati, CA) model 7302 in-line filter and a 7.8 x 50.0 mm guard column containing the same Phenogel™ packing. The guard column and preparatory columns were connected to a six-port valve that allowed the guard column to be backflushed, which removes extraneous materials after cleanup of a set of samples (Figure A1-3).

For each sample, a 250-µL portion of the concentrated extract was injected into the HPLC and eluted through the columns. The mobile phase, 100% methylene chloride, degassed with helium, was pumped at a flow rate of 7 mL/min for 20 min at ambient temperature. The helium was delivered through a regulator equipped with a stainless-steel diaphragm and was passed through an in-line charcoal filter (200-cc hydrocarbon trap, Alltech Assoc., Deerfield, IL) to eliminate contaminants that could be transferred to the HPLC.

As the samples eluted through the column, the fraction containing the ACs was collected. The fraction collection time (~ 15 to 19 min) was initially determined by calibrating the HPLC system for the beginning and end of analyte elution relative to the retention times of biphenyl and perylene, respectively. An HPLC CS containing biphenyl and perylene was analyzed at the beginning, middle, and end of each sample set to adjust the fraction collection time and monitor the stability of the retention times.

The methylene chloride solvent in the HPLC fraction was exchanged into hexane as the volume was reduced by evaporation to approximately 1 mL. Further evaporation, followed by the quantitative addition of a GC internal standard (GC I-Std), hexamethylbenzene for a concentration of ~ 1600 ng per fraction, brought the final volume of the fraction to 120 µL for quantification by GC/MS.

Determination of aromatic contaminants by GC/MS SSIM

The ACs were determined by GC/MS using a 30-m x 0.25-mm DB-5 capillary column with a 0.25-µm film thickness (J & W Scientific, Rancho Cordova, CA) in a Hewlett-Packard (HP), (Avondale, PA) model 5890 GC interfaced to either a Finnigan (Sunnyvale, CA) INCOS™ model 50B mass spectrometer with a Data General model DG-10 data system or an HP model 5970B MSD mass spectrometer with an HP UNIX Chemstation data system, and an HP model 7673 autosampler. A 3-µL portion of the concentrated fraction from HPLC was injected splitless, and the split valve was opened after 30 sec (split ratio 20:1). The transfer line and injector temperatures were held at 300 °C. The oven temperature was programmed to hold

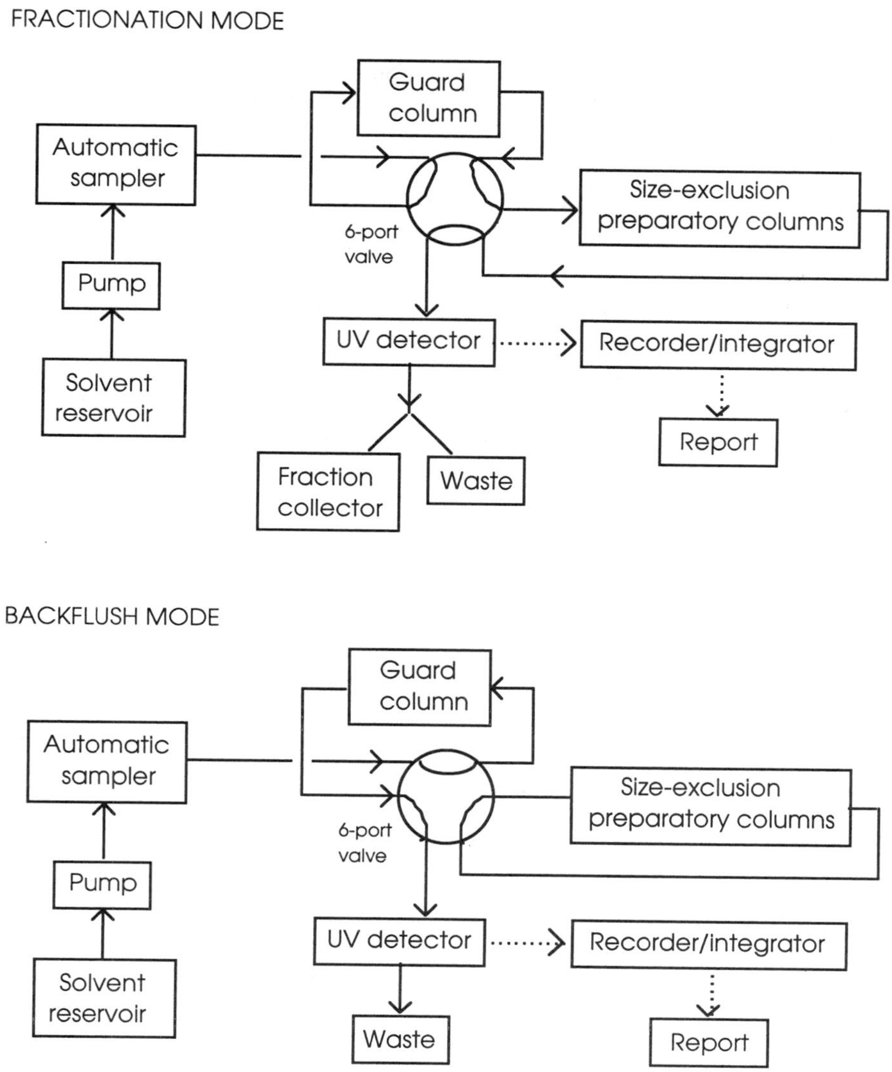

Figure A1-3 High-performance liquid chromatograph system for isolation of aromatic contaminants (arrows indicate flow of the mobile phase; dashed lines indicate electrical connections).

at 50 °C for 1 min, then increased at 4 °C/min to 300 °C, where the temperature was held for 10 min. The linear velocity of the He carrier gas was set to 33 cm/sec at an oven temperature of 300 °C. A SSIM scan descriptor that included 10 groups of 5 to 22 ions each was used (Table A1-2). The SSIM mass spectral chromatograms from either GC/MS system were acquired and interpreted using their respective data systems and software. The analyte and surrogate responses were measured as the areas of their major-ion peaks in the chromatograms.

Data management

Quality-control measurements and analyte quantification were performed according to Sloan et al. (1993). A GC calibration solution (GC CS) containing selected analytes plus the surrogates and internal standards (Table A1-3) was analyzed at the beginning, middle, and end of each set of samples. The analytes in the samples were identified by matching their retention times with the retention times of the analytes from the analyses of the GC CS and a sample of PBCO (Figures A1-4a and A1-4b). The analyte identities were confirmed by verifying the appropriate ratio of the target ions in the SSIM spectra (Table A1-2).

The percent recoveries of the surrogates and the concentrations of the analytes (wet-weight basis) in the samples were calculated by relating their responses in the analyses of the samples to their responses in the analyses of the GC CS. For quantifying the alkylated-AC analytes that were not present in the GC CS, the response factor for an isomer present or for the corresponding unsubstituted AC were used in the

Table A1-2 Selected-ion monitoring sequences for aromatic contaminants

Approximate time range	Compounds	Major ion	Confirming ion(s)
10–18 min	Naphthalene	128	127
	Naphthalene-d_8	136	
	C1-naphthalenes	142	141, 127
18–23 min	Hexamethylbenzene	147	162
	Acenaphthylene	152	151
	Acenaphthene	154	153, 152
	C2-naphthalenes	156	141
	Acenaphthene-d_{10}	170	155
23–32 min	Hexamethylbenzene	147	162
	Acenaphthylene	152	151
	Acenaphthene	154	153, 152
	Acenaphthene-d_{10}	164	162
	Fluorene	166	165
	C3-naphthalene	170	155
	Phenanthrene	178	176
	C1-fluorenes	180	165
	C4-naphthalenes	184	169
	Dibenzothiophene	184	139
	Phenanthrene-d_{10}	188	
	C2-fluorenes	194	179, 165
32–32 min	Phenanthrene	178	176
	Dibenzothiophene	184	139
	Phenanthrene-d_{10}	188	
	C2-fluorenes	194	179, 165
	C1-dibenzothiophenes	198	197
33–36 min	C1-phenanthrenes/anthracenes	192	191
	C2-fluorenes	194	179, 165
	C1-dibenzothiophenes	198	197
	C3-fluorenes	208	193,179
	C2-dibenzothiophenes	212	211

Table A1-2 continued

Approximate time range	Compounds	Major ion	Confirming ion(s)
36–43 min	C1-phenanthrenes/anthracenes	192	191
	Fluoranthene	202	101
	Pyrene	202	101
	C2-phenanthrenes/anthracenes	206	191
	C3-fluorenes	208	193, 179
	C2-dibenzothiophenes	212	211
	C1-fluoranthenes/pyrenes	216	215
	C3-phenanthrenes/anthracenes	220	205, 191
	C4-phenanthrenes/anthracenes	234	219
43–47 min	C1-fluoranthenes/pyrenes	216	215
	C3-phenanthrenes/anthracenes	220	205, 191
	C3-dibenzothiophenes	226	211
	Benz[a]anthracene	228	226
	Chrysene	228	226
	C4-phenanthrenes/anthracenes	234	219
47–51 min	Benz[a[anthracene	228	226
	chrysene	228	226
	C4-phenanthrenes/anthracenes	234	219
	C1-benz[a]anthracenes/chrysenes	242	239
	C2-benz[a]anthracenes/chrysenes	256	239
51–59 min	C1-benz[a]anthracenes/chrysenes	242	239
	Benzo[b]fluoranthene	252	250
	Benzo[k]fluoranthene	252	250
	Benzo[a]pyrene	252	250
	C2-benz[a]anthracenes/chrysenes	256	239
	Benzo[a]pyrene-d_{12}	264	260
	C3-benz[a]anthracenes/chrysenes	270	255
	C4-benz[a]anthracenes/chrysenes	284	269
59–72 min	C3-benz[a]anthracenes/chrysenes	270	255
	Indeno[1,2,3-cd]pyrene	276	138
	Benzo[ghi]perylene	276	138
	Dibenz[a,h]anthracene	278	139
	C4-benz[a]anthracenes/chrysenes	284	269

Table A1-3 Aromatic contaminants and standards contained in the GC CS

Compound	Concentration (ng/µL)	Compound	Concentration (ng/µL)
Naphthalene	0.3	Naphthalene-d_8	0.5
2-methylnaphthalene	0.3	1-methylnaphthalene	0.3
Hexamethylbenzene	16	Acenaphthylene	0.3
Acenaphthene	0.3	Acenaphthene-d_{10}	0.5
2, 6-dimethylnaphthalene	0.3	Fluorene	0.3
2, 3, 5-trimethylnaphthalene	0.3	Phenanthrene	0.3
Phenanthrene-d_{10}	6	Dibenzothiophene	0.6
1-methylphenanthrene	0.2	Fluoranthene	0.3
Pyrene	0.3	Benz[a]anthracene	0.3
Chrysene	0.3	Benzo[b]fluoranthene	0.3
Benzo[k]fluoranthene	0.3	Benzo[a]pyrene	0.3
Benzo[a]pyrene-d_{12}	0.5	Indeno[1,2,3-cd]pyrene	0.3
Benzo[ghi]perylene	0.3	Dibenz[a, h]anthracene	0.2

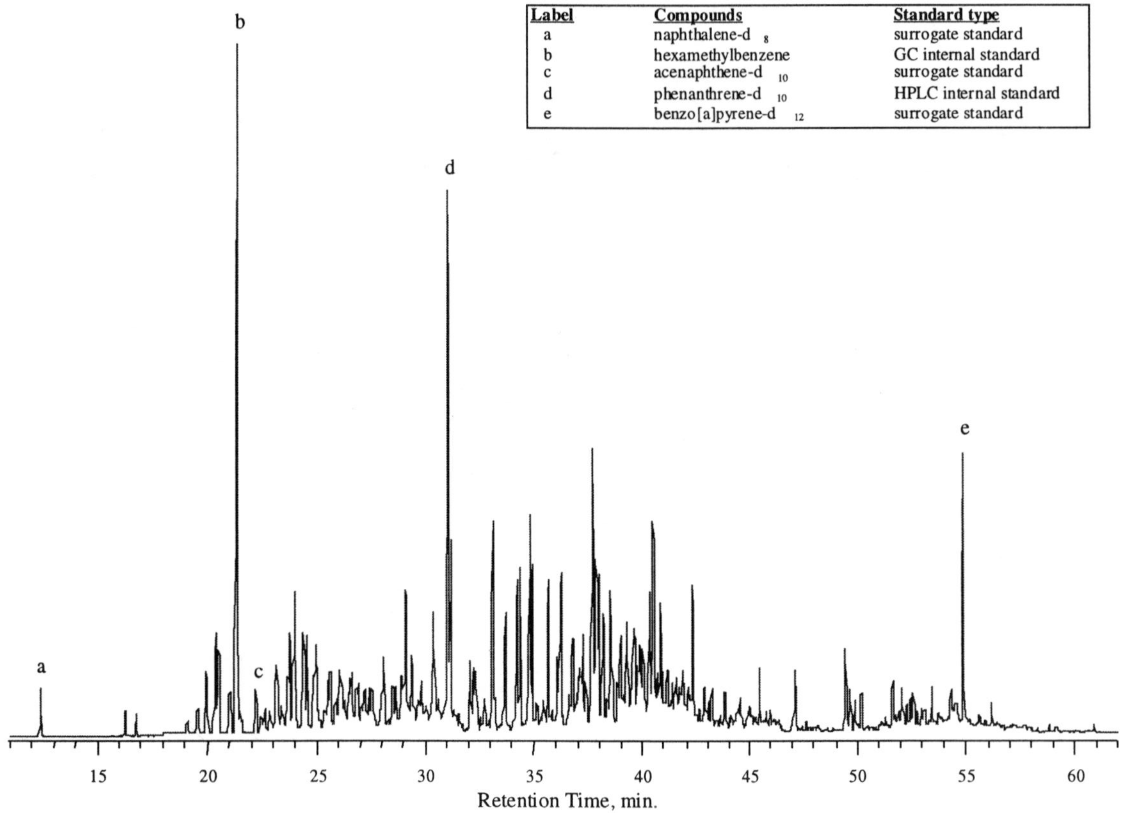

Figure A1-4a Chromatogram of aromatic contaminants in Prudhoe Bay crude oil using gas chromatography–mass spectrometry with sequenced selected-ion monitoring

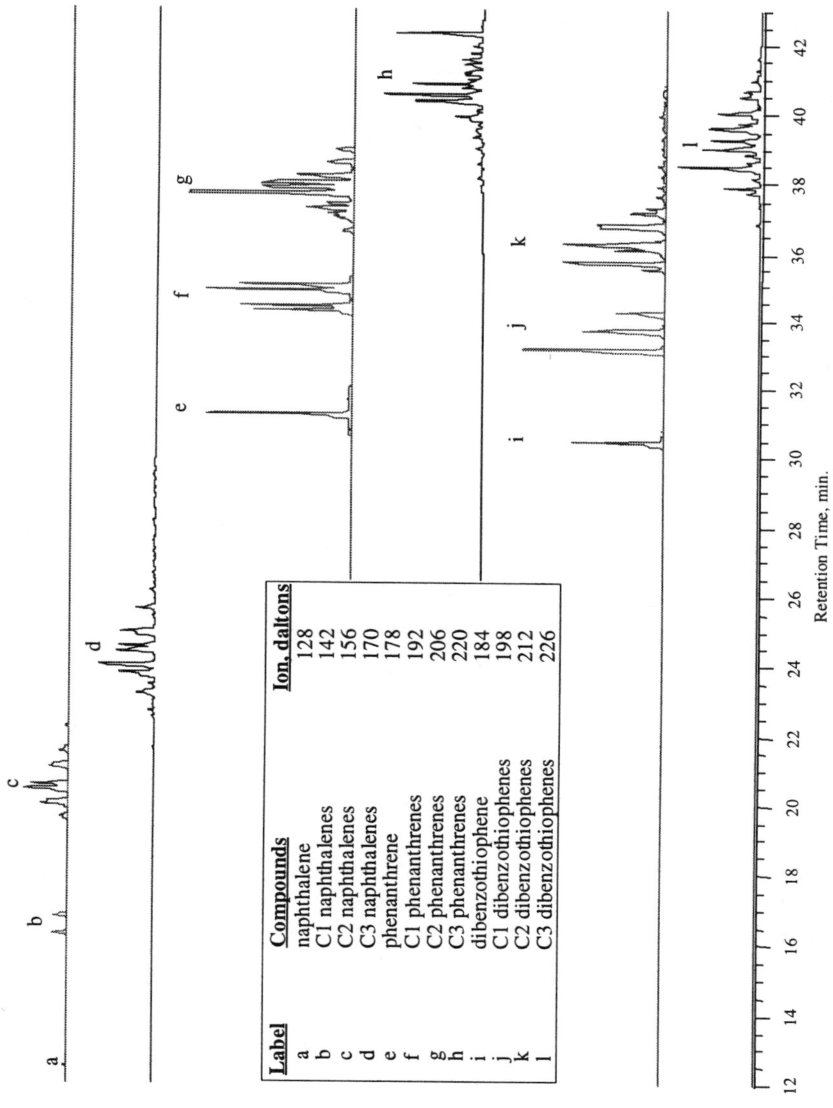

Label	Compounds	Ion, daltons
a	naphthalene	128
b	C1 naphthalenes	142
c	C2 naphthalenes	156
d	C3 naphthalenes	170
e	phenanthrene	178
f	C1 phenanthrenes	192
g	C2 phenanthrenes	206
h	C3 phenanthrenes	220
i	dibenzothiophene	184
j	C1 dibenzothiophenes	198
k	C2 dibenzothiophenes	212
l	C3 dibenzothiophenes	226

Figure A1-4b Chromatograms of prominent aromatic contaminant groups in Prudhoe Bay crude oil using gas chromatography–mass spectrometry with sequenced selected-ion monitoring calculations. The surrogates in the S-Std added to the sample at the beginning of the extraction were used as internal standards to adjust for losses of analytes during sample preparation. The surrogate that elutes in the same region of the chromatogram as do the analytes was used as the internal standard for those analytes, i.e., NPH-d_8 for NPH through C4NPH (Table A1-1), ACE-d_{10} for ACY through C1FLA, and BaP-d_{12} for BaA through BZP.

Similarly, the percent recovery of each surrogate was calculated using the HPLC I-Std to adjust for the percent of the sample extract injected onto the HPLC column. The GC I-Std was used to normalize the amount injected on the GC/MS for each sample analysis.

Quality assurance

The quality-assurance program included analysis of instrument calibration solutions, method blanks, replicates, spiked blanks, matrix spikes, and NIST Standard Reference Material 1974 (SRM 1974) Organics in Mussel Tissue *Mytilus edulis.* The recoveries of the surrogates added at the beginning of sample extraction were also reported as quality-control information.

Analyses of GC CS containing graduated concentrations of the AC (multilevel standards) were used for determining the linearity of detector response versus concentration and the instrument detection limit. Before analyzing samples, the stability of GC performance was verified by repeated analysis of a GC CS (four to six times), then comparing the responses of each analyte and surrogate from analysis to analysis. Before and during analyses of sample sets, the GC/MS performance was considered stable when the response for each AC in the GC CS was reproducible within ± 10%. A deviation > 10% was considered indicative of a problem with the GC system, and corrective maintenance was performed before proceeding with analyses of samples.

One method blank was analyzed with each set of samples. Ideally, the ACs (except NPH) in the blanks would not be present above the detection limit. The method detection limit is usually defined by a combination of factors, including instrument signal-to-noise ratio, the concentration of analytes in the lowest multilevel standard that can be reliably measured, the original sample weight, the final volume of the sample extract, etc. Based on the results for field blanks and method blanks analyzed with each set of samples, detection limits ranged from ~ 0.1 ng/g to ~ 1 ng/g.

NPH was present in the solvents in detectable amounts and contributed ~ 1 ng NPH/g of tissue. Generally, the other analytes were not found in the method blanks above the stated detection limit.

The percent recoveries of the surrogates provide a measure of losses incurred for each sample during the extraction and cleanup steps. Ideally, recoveries would be near 100%, but realistically, recoveries of ~ 90% are considered quite good because the procedures involve many sample-handling steps. The criterion for the recovery of each surrogate standard was between 50% and 130%, and the RSDs for recoveries of surrogates in a set of samples were < 25%. When the recovery of any surrogate was outside these limits, corrective action was taken and another subsample of the unused portion of the tissue sample was extracted and analyzed. The mean percent recovery of the surrogates (NPH-d_8, ACE-d_{10}, and BaP-d_{12}) was 92% ± 15%, and was within our guidelines.

Duplicates or triplicates of ~ 5% of the samples were analyzed for ACs. The results of the analyses of the replicate samples were reported as quality-control information.

For samples collected during the first year of the study (1989), a spiked blank (40 to 70 ng each of selected analytes added to a method blank) or a matrix spike (50 to 80 ng each of selected analytes added to a tissue sample) was analyzed with each set of samples. Although the results were used to show that the analytes would be found by the method and to show any losses due to sample handling, they would not provide any information on extraction efficiency. The criterion for the recovery of each AC was between 50% and 130%. When the recovery of any AC was outside these limits, corrective action was taken. The recoveries for the analytes in spiked blanks and in matrix spikes ranged from 75% to 130%. As soon as SRM 1974 tissue was available, a sample of it was analyzed with every set of samples in place of a spiked blank or a matrix spike. The SRM is considered a homogeneous material and 11 analyte values are certified or noted. Because its use afforded a way to monitor extraction efficiency as well as losses due to sample handling, the SRM was far more useful for quality control. Also, SRM 1974 contained all of the analytes being monitored in the subsistence samples, thus enabling the reproducibility of quantification for all of the analytes to be monitored. The results of the analyses of the SRM were reported as quality-control information.

Statistical methods

Results of chemical analyses of samples of fish and invertebrates from stations within each sampling area and of selected petroleum and related products were compared using GT2 comparison interval graphs (Gabriel 1978; Sokal and Rohlf 1981). The comparison intervals provided a graphic method of observing significant differences between means. The AC results and the statistical analyses of those results are presented and discussed in Chapter 7.

Summary

Crude petroleums, including PBCO, contain many hundreds of individual chemicals that are generally divided into classes such as aliphatic hydrocarbons, aromatic hydrocarbons, and other constituents including dibenzothiophenes. Of these chemicals, the aromatic hydrocarbons are considered the most toxic and are commonly selected for chemical analysis and toxicological evaluation.

Benthic fish efficiently metabolize ACs to polar derivatives, which are concentrated in bile for excretion. Therefore, the bioaccumulation of ACs in fish tissues, such as edible flesh, is greatly limited. Because ACs are readily metabolized, the presence of AC polar derivatives in bile would indicate relatively recent exposure. Unlike fish, molluscs have little ability to metabolize ACs, which are accumulated in their tissues.

Whereas bile from fish and marine mammals was analyzed for FACs to assess exposure to ACs from petroleum and to prioritize the analyses of the corresponding samples of edible flesh for ACs, invertebrates were not analyzed for FACs. For each species of fish and marine mammals, edible flesh samples were analyzed for ACs as individual samples or as composite samples according to the concentrations of FACs in bile. For each species of invertebrates, composite samples of the edible tissue were analyzed for ACs. By using these sample-selection and compositing schemes, it was possible to maximize laboratory effectiveness in analyzing large numbers of samples. The quality-assurance program provided measurement and control of the performance of the analytical methods. Statistical methods were used for evaluating the results of the analyses for FACs and ACs.

Acknowledgments—We appreciate the expert contributions from a number of EC Division scientists to the development of the methods used in this study. In particular, we thank Jennie Bolton, Deborah Holstad, Tom Hom, Susan Pierce, and Karen Tilbury. We also thank Katherine Dana for assistance with graphics and typing, and Drs. Cheryl Krone and Dave Herman for reviewing the manuscript. We also appreciate the encouragement and support from Dr. Charles Ehler, John Robinson, and Dr. Richard Berry for this study. We also thank numerous other staff in several segments of NOAA. Dr. James Fall, Rita Miraglia, and other staff of the Alaska Department of Fish and Game also provided valuable assistance.

References

Atlas RM, Boehm PD, Calder JA. 1981. Chemical and biological weathering of oil, from the *Amoco Cadiz* spillage, within the littoral zone. *Estuarine Coast Shelf Sci* 12:589–608.

Boehm PD, Fiest DL, Elskus A. 1981. Comparative weathering patterns of hydrocarbons from the *Amoco Cadiz* oil spill observed at a variety of coastal environments. Proceedings, International Symposium on the *Amoco Cadiz*: Fates and effects of the oil spill. Paris, France: Centre National pour l'Exploitation des Oceans. p 159–173.

Clark Jr RC, Brown DW. 1977. Petroleum: Properties and analyses in biotic and abiotic systems. In: Malins DC, editor. Volume I. Effects of petroleum on arctic and subarctic marine environments and organisms. New York: Academic Press. p 1–89.

Collier TK, Varanasi U. 1991. Hepatic activities of xenobiotic metabolizing enzymes and biliary levels of xenobiotics in English sole (*Parophrys vetulus*) exposed to environmental contaminants. *Arch Environ Contam Toxicol* 20:462–473.

Gabriel KR. 1978. A simple method of multiple comparisons of means. *J Am Stat Assoc* 73:724–729.

James MO. 1989. Biotransformation and disposition of polycyclic aromatic hydrocarbons (PAH) in aquatic invertebrates. In: Varanasi U, editor. Metabolism of polycyclic aromatic hydrocarbons in the aquatic environment. Boca Raton FL: CRC Press. p 69–91.

Krahn MM, Myers MS, Burrows DG, Malins DC. 1984. Determination of metabolites of xenobiotics in the bile of fish from polluted waterways. *Xenobiotica* 14:633–646.

Krahn MM, Kittle Jr LJ, MacLeod Jr WD. 1986. Evidence for exposure of fish to oil spilled into the Columbia River. *Mar Environ Res* 20:291–298.

Krahn MM, Moore LK, MacLeod Jr WD. 1986. Metabolites of aromatic compounds in fish bile. NOAA Tech. Memo. NMFS/NWC-102. 25 p.

Krahn MM, Hom T, Ylitalo GM, Chan S-L, Varanasi U. 1991. Report on quality assurance for bile measurements. Alaska Oil Spill Damage Assessment Program. Seattle WA: Environmental Conservation Div., Northwest Fisheries Science Center, National Marine Fisheries Service, NOAA.

Lowry OH, Rosebrough WJ, Farr AL, Randall RS. 1951. Protein measurement with the folin phenol reagent. *J Biol Chem* 193:265–275.

Sauer TC, Boehm PD. 1991. The use of defensible analytical chemical measurements for oil spill natural resource damage assessment. Proceedings, 1991 International Oil Spill Conference. Washington DC: American Petroleum Institute. p 363–369.

Sloan CA, Adams NG, Pearce RW, Brown DW, Chan S-L. 1993. Northwest Fisheries Science Center organic analytical procedures. In: Lauenstein GG, Cantillo AY, editors. Sampling and analytical methods of the National Status and Trends Program National Benthic Surveillance and Mussel Watch Projects 1984–1992. Volume IV, Comprehensive descriptions of trace organic analytical methods. NOAA Tech. Memo. NOS ORCA 71. p 53–97.

Sokal R, Rohlf F. 1981. Biometry, second edition. San Francisco CA: W. H. Freeman. 854 p.

Statham CN, Melancon Jr MJ, Lech JJ. 1976. Bioconcentration of xenobiotics in trout bile: A proposed monitoring aid for some waterborne chemicals. *Science* 193:680–681.

Stein JE, Hom T, Varanasi U. 1984. Simultaneous exposure of English sole (*Parophrys vetulus*) to sediment-associated xenobiotics: I. Uptake and disposition of [^{14}C]-polychlorinated biphenyls and [^{3}H]-benzo[a]pyrene. *Mar Environ Res* 13:97–119.

Varanasi U, Gmur DJ. 1981. Hydrocarbons and metabolites in English sole (*Parophrys vetulus*) exposed simultaneously to ^{3}H-B(a)P and ^{14}C-naphthalene in sediment. *Aquat Toxicol* 1:49–67.

Varanasi U, Reichert WL, Stein JE, Brown DW, Sanborn HR. 1985. Bioavailability and biotransformation of aromatic hydrocarbons in benthic organisms exposed to sediment from an urban estuary. *Environ Sci Tech* 19:836–841.

Varanasi U, Stein JE, Nishimoto M. 1989. Biotransformation and disposition of polycyclic aromatic hydrocarbons (PAH) in fish. In: Varanasi U, editor. Metabolism of polycyclic aromatic hydrocarbons in the aquatic environment. Boca Raton FL: CRC Press. p 93–149.

Appendix 2

Summary of Findings of Toxicological Expert Committee for Evaluating Data Related to the Consumption of Marine Subsistence Foods (*Exxon Valdez* Oil Spill) Seattle, Washington 21–22 February 1990

Based on all available knowledge of crude oil, sampling results, toxicology, biochemistry, and epidemiology, are Alaskan subsistence foods safe for human consumption?

A total of 365 analyses from 548 samples of Alaskan fish and shellfish have been completed by the National Marine Fisheries Service, Environmental Conservation Division. Based upon available data and cumulative scientific knowledge, and consistent with the conclusions reached earlier, finfish are safe for human consumption. Levels of aromatic hydrocarbons found in finfish are very low and are similar to levels in fish from areas unaffected by the oil spill.

Specimens of mollusks taken from heavily oil-contaminated beaches (for example, Windy Bay) showed high levels of aromatic hydrocarbons. Shellfish tested from less impacted beaches, such as Chenega Bay and Old Harbor, showed the presence of aromatic hydrocarbons in higher concentrations than that found in uncontaminated areas, but these levels are not considered to represent a serious health hazard. If mollusks are consumed, they should not be collected from areas that are obviously contaminated with oil.*

Will components of weathered crude oil persist or bioaccumulate?

Because finfish metabolize crude oil contaminants more rapidly than do bivalves, they do not accumulate significant aromatic hydrocarbons in their muscle tissue. Bivalve mollusks (e.g., clams and mussels) metabolize the crude oil contaminants at a much slower rate than do fish and are therefore much more likely to bioaccumulate these contaminants.

Are there any restrictions on amounts that can be eaten?

There are no restrictions for fish and none for mollusks taken from beaches that have not been obviously contaminated with oil.

---

*The Alaska Division of Public Health and Alaska Department of Environmental Conservation for many years have advised that bivalve mollusks should not be collected from Alaskan beaches because of the dangers from paralytic shellfish poisoning. Paralytic shellfish poisoning represents the greatest danger from eating bivalve mollusks. Commercially collected clams and mussels are routinely tested for paralytic shellfish poisoning and are safe for consumption.

Can we expect to see any acute or chronic illness in those eating subsistence foods?

No acute effects have been seen in the eleven months since the spill. Risk of chronic illness from exposure to aromatic hydrocarbons in food resulting from the oil spill cannot be said to be zero, but the contribution to levels of aromatic hydrocarbons in food not obviously contaminated with oil are so low as to constitute no basis for public health concern.

Are aromatic hydrocarbons an adequate marker to reflect exposure and contamination of marine foods?

Yes, aromatic hydrocarbons are a good indicator of the presence of crude oil. Dibenzothiophenes are characteristic of crude oils.

How do levels of polycyclic aromatic hydrocarbons compare to other finfish tested?

Two samples of subsistence smoked salmon prepared in a traditional manner contained 8170 and 22,400 ppb of total aromatic hydrocarbons, respectively. By comparison, levels of total aromatic hydrocarbons found in finfish thus far are generally very low (< 15 ppb) and are not significantly greater than in the unpolluted areas tested. Less than 1% of fish tested had levels of total aromatic hydrocarbons slightly in excess of 100 ppb.

What do we believe will be the long-term fate of crude oil?

The oil will be biodegraded eventually; however, pockets of oil in various forms exist throughout the area. As finfish move into shallow areas, water turbulence and their exposure may increase, resulting in higher levels in bile and tissue. Therefore, continued monitoring of these fish is necessary to document levels of contamination.

Can recommendations be made only for areas sampled or can they apply to all areas?

It is impossible to provide individual recommendations for specific beaches or harvest areas. Results available from samples collected combined with available scientific knowledge provide the best information upon which to base general recommendations that apply to all areas affected by the oil spill.

Are there levels of aromatic hydrocarbons that are considered to be safe for human consumption?

There are no established guidelines for acceptable levels of aromatic hydrocarbons in foods. Aromatic hydrocarbons are ubiquitous. They are present in many foods routinely consumed, including cooked and smoked meats and fish, grains and cereal products, and fruits and vegetables.

Is there any way to test for human exposure?

There are no feasible tests that are available to test for or to monitor human exposure to aromatic hydrocarbons or other components of crude oil.

Are there specific ways that concerned Alaskan villagers can reduce their potential risk?

Any risk of adverse health effects as a result of the oil spill from consumption of Alaskan fish and shellfish is very small. Villagers should rely on common sense and their own judgment to avoid collecting foods from areas obviously impacted by oil. In addition, individuals should decide based on the appearance, smell, texture, and taste of subsistence foods. If food is of doubtful quality, it should not be consumed.

What additional studies need to be done?

- Monitoring studies of mollusks from heavily impacted areas such as Windy Bay and less heavily impacted areas such as Chenega Bay, Kodiak Harbor, and Old Harbor are needed. In addition, fish should be monitored to document that levels have not increased over time. Appropriate control specimens should be included.
- Two smoked salmon samples have thus far been tested and more samples are needed.
- Testing of mollusks from oiled areas for heavy metals and polar organic compounds is needed.
- Testing of hepatopancreas and corresponding edible tissue of crab for aromatic hydrocarbons is needed.
- Sampling and testing of marine mammals that are part of the subsistence diet are needed.

The Need for a Clearinghouse

Because of the lack of historical information on oil spills and human health, a clearinghouse should be established to serve as a repository for datasets, clinical and epidemiological studies, and information on food safety related to petroleum and its impact on human health. The committee recommends that National Oceanic and Atmospheric Administration (NOAA) resources be used to implement this recommendation.

Need for a Workshop

Based upon experiences garnered from the Alaska oil spill, a workshop should be held to identify 1) continuing gaps in scientific data, 2) the issues related to human-health concerns, and 3) strategies to respond to future oil spills. The committee recommends that NOAA resources be used to implement this recommendation.

Role of the Toxicologic Expert Committee

The Prince William Sound oil spill raised many immediate and long-term issues about human health and the safety of subsistence foods for human consumption. To address these concerns, the Oil Spill Health Task Force (OSHTF) was organized to provide reliable information to persons in the areas involved.

Because information on health was needed rapidly, many sources were tapped in order to draw on available scientific knowledge. To improve the quality and reliability of health information, a group of experts was convened by NOAA at the request of the Alaska Division of Public Health (ADPH) and the OSHTF.

The role of this group was to review all available existing scientific information and the results of laboratory tests on Alaska subsistence foods in order to provide consultation to the ADPH and OSHTF about the safety of subsistence foods, to identify gaps in information, and to recommend additional studies needed to improve the quality of public health advice.

The Toxicological Expert Committee has reviewed available data and has drawn heavily on the considerable expertise of its members to formulate its recommendations. The committee was not asked to (and does not) assume responsibility for making final interpretations of ongoing studies. This responsibility rests with the primary investigators.

The Committee is providing valuable advice to local, state, and federal agencies and to the OSHTF to assist these agencies and organizations in formulating the best possible policies for the protection of the health of individuals affected by the oil spill.

The Oil Spill Health Task Force consists of the following members:

- The North Pacific Rim,
- Kodiak Area Native Association,
- The Alaska Area Native Health Service,
- Exxon Company, USA,
- The State of Alaska Department of Health and Social Services,
- The State of Alaska Department of Fish and Game, Subsistence Division,
- The State of Alaska Department of Environmental Conservation, Division of Environmental Health, and
- National Oceanic and Atmospheric Administration.

The Toxicological Expert Committee consists of the following members:

Dr. Mike Bolger
U.S. Food and Drug Administration

Dr. Larry Curceo
Exxon Company, USA

L. Jay Field
NOAA/HAZMAT

Dr. John French
University of Alaska

Dr. Richard Griesemer
National Institutes of Environmental Health Services

Dr. A.M. Guarino
U.S. Food and Drug Administration

Dr. Steve Lewis
Exxon Biomedical Research Sciences, Inc.

Dr. John Middaugh
Alaska Department of Health and Social Services

Dr. Tom Nighswander, Chair
Alaska Native Medical Center

Dr. Ken Orloff
Agency for Toxic Substances and Disease Registry

Dr. Bill Thar
Exxon Biomedical Research Sciences, Inc.

Dr. Usha Varanasi
National Marine Fisheries Service, NOAA

Ann Hayward Walker
NOAA Scientific Support Coordinator

Dr. Gary Winston
Louisiana State University

Appendix 3

Report of the Quantitative Risk Assessment Committee, Center for Food Safety and Applied Nutrition, U.S. Food and Drug Administration, 9 August 1990*

Estimation of Risk Associated with Consumption of Oil-Contaminated Fish and Shellfish by Alaskan Subsistence Fishermen using a Benzo[a]pyrene Equivalency Approach

In this report, the Quantitative Risk Assessment Committee (QRAC) is responding to a request to the U.S. Food and Drug Administration (USFDA) Commissioner by the Alaska Oil Spill Health Task Force (OSHTF). This task force is an interagency advisory group charged with assessing the effects of the oil spill on health and human resources. The OSHTF has been tasked with providing guidance for the sampling studies of subsistence foods that were affected by the *Exxon Valdez* oil spill and for interpreting the results of these studies to the public. Lack of safety guidelines for aromatic hydrocarbon contamination in foods, particularly seafood, has hampered the OSHTF's work; hence the request to the USFDA was made.

Two surveys of fish consumption were submitted to USFDA. One report surveyed the fish consumption patterns of the village of Chenega Bay on Evans Island in Prince William Sound that was conducted by the Alaska Department of Fish and Game, Division of Subsistence in 1984 and 1986 (Stratton and Chisum 1986). This survey was particularly appropriate for QRAC's purposes since this is an area in which fish and shellfish recently were exposed to oil after the *Exxon Valdez* incident. In a second report, food consumption on Kodiak Island, Alaska, was surveyed by the Kodiak Area Native Association (KANA) and the State of Alaska in 1983 (KANA 1983).

*Reprinted with permission

L. Jay Field et al., editors. © 1999 Society of Environmental Toxicology and Chemistry (SETAC). ISBN 1-880611-29-5

Use of the Equivalency Approach in Estimating Risk Associated with Polycyclic Aromatic Hydrocarbon Content

The equivalency approach for polycyclic aromatic hydrocarbons (PAHs) has been discussed in a memorandum to the QRAC (memo from C. Carrington, Standards and Monitoring Branch, USFDA, to S. Henry, QRAC, 26 June 1990). The equivalency approach is a technique for assessing the risk from a number of different compounds that are present in a single exposure source. Instead of calculating individual risks for each component, one component of known potency is used as a standard and the concentration of each of the other components is adjusted on the basis of its estimated, comparative potency to calculate a concentration equivalent to the standard. Summation of the equivalent concentrations produces a single number from which the risk may be estimated.

Two rationales for using the equivalency approach in the case of a risk assessment for PAH are applicable. First, there may not be fully adequate data for assessing risk for all of the individual components of the mixture, nor is it feasible to obtain such data. However, there may be data from in vitro systems or short-term in vivo exposures that measure a parameter thought to be relevant to the carcinogenic mechanism of the compounds allowing the potency of a data-deficient component to be quantitatively related to a compound for which a long-term study is available. Second, the data available for estimating risk may be much better for some of the components than for others. In such cases, the potencies of the components for which there are relatively little data are highly subject to revision, whereas the potency number for a well-studied compound may be expected to be stable. Calculation of an acceptable intake based on the concentration of the component with the best-available data will be the least likely to require revision.

The risk calculated by this procedure is only an estimate, although it is invariably more reasonable than the estimates obtained either by ignoring all but a few well-described contaminants or by assuming that all the congeners have equivalent potencies. The available toxicology data for benzo[a]pyrene (B[a]P) are much better than those data available for any of the other compounds detected in the fish. Short-term studies for most of the compounds are available that allow potencies relative to B[a]P to be approximated. These studies include 1) comparison of the initiating potency of individual PAHs after a single dermal application, followed by promotion; 2) comparison of the carcinogenic potency of individual PAHs after intraperitoneal injection in dimethyl sulfoxide in newborn CD-1 and Swiss Webster mice; 3) comparison of the carcinogenic effects after implantation in the lungs of female Osborne-Mendel rats (Deutsch-Wenzel et al. 1985) and; 4) comparison of the carcinogenic potency of individual PAHs after long-term dermal application (Slooff et al. 1989; Clement International Corp. 1990). Therefore, the equivalency approach is desirable because it emphasizes the data considered to be the most sound and facilitates the incorporation of anticipated future revisions in the relative potencies of the PAHs other than B[a]P.

Estimation of the Benzo[a]pyrene Equivalents of Other Polycyclic Aromatic Hydrocarbons

Two recent documents have dealt with the relative potency of PAHs, one produced by the National Institute of Public Health and Environmental Protection of the Netherlands (Slooff et al. 1989) and the other produced by Clement International Corporation (1990) under a contract with the U.S. Environmental Protection Agency (USEPA). Both reports review a total of 19 studies with five common to both documents. The Netherlands report used a linear model for calculating potency, while the USEPA report used either a two-stage (Moolgavkar and Knudson 1981) or a linear multi stage model. The potencies from neither report are entirely suitable for QRAC's purposes. However, because the Clement report provided estimates for more of the compounds in question and because it systematically selected the best study for each compound, the analysis below used the equivalencies derived with the multi stage model. This model more closely resembles the risk-estimate procedure typically used by the QRAC than does the two-stage model.

The Clement report did not provide multi stage estimates for either pyrene or fluoranthene. However, the best available study was selected for pyrene (Wislocki et al. 1986). Fluoranthene was not considered in the Clement report. The one study listed in the Dutch report (Slooff et al. 1989) in which a clear tumorigenic response was observed was therefore used to calculate a potency number for fluoranthene (Busby et al. 1984).

Table A3-1 lists the potency numbers relative to B[a]P judged to be the best available for the nine PAHs measured in the Alaskan marine samples. The B[a]P equivalency (B[a]PE) values are positively correlated with carcinogenic potency. For the purposes of B[a]PE, all the compounds in Table A3-1 are assumed to be probable human carcinogens, despite the conservatism in this approach implied by the IARC Classification (IARC 1989).

For the alkylated PAHs, the addition of the side chains was assumed to have no effect on carcinogenic potency. Since the alkylated compounds were reported as either mixtures of fluoranthenes and pyrenes or chrysenes and benz[a]anthracenes, the assumption was made that the relative proportions of the alkylated mixtures were the same as the unsubstituted compounds that were measured separately. The alkylated PAHs were not placed in any IARC category because there are no data.

Table A3-1 B[a]P equivalencies for PAHs

PAH	B[a]P equivalency	IARC Class[1]
Fluoranthene[2]	0.02	3
Pyrene[2]	0.13	3
Benz[a]anthracene	0.014	2A
Chrysene	0.013	3
Benzo[b]fluoranthene	0.11	2B
Benzo[k]fluoranthene	0.07	2B
Benzo[a]pyrene	1.00	2A
Indeno[1,2,3-cd]pyrene	0.25	2B
Dibenz[a,h]anthracene	1.05	2A
Benzo[g,h,i]perylene	0.03	3

[1]IARC classification: 2A = probable human carcinogen; 2B = possible human carcinogen; 3 = unclassifiable.
[2]All values are from Clement Int. Corp. (1990), except for pyrene and fluoranthene which were calculated by Janet Springer (memo. J. Springer, Division of Mathematics, USFDA, to C. Carrington, 19 June 1990).

Levels of Benzo[a]pyrene Equivalents in Alaskan Fish and Shellfish Samples

The spreading of oil spilled from the *Exxon Valdez* on 24 March 1989 led to concern among native Alaskans that their seafood could be contaminated by petroleum hydrocarbons. In response, the National Oceanic and Atmospheric Administration (NOAA) entered into a Memorandum of Understanding with Exxon to analyze several hundred subsistence fish and shellfish from 13 subsistence fishing grounds used by native Alaskans in or near Prince William Sound for aromatic contaminants, including aromatic hydrocarbons and dibenzothiophenes. Uncontaminated fish and shellfish samples were collected near the village of Angoon in southeast Alaska to serve as a reference. Results of analyses of samples collected from July through September 1989 are reflected in this QRAC report as taken from a NOAA report (Varanasi et al. 1990).

The NOAA study indicated that the pattern of aromatic contaminants in the fish samples is consistent with the known extensive metabolism of aromatic hydrocarbons by fish. In mollusks, which have little ability to metabolize aromatic contaminants, both alkylated and unsubstituted aromatic contaminants were present.

Using the equivalency values in Table A3-1, the B[a]P equivalencies in the Alaskan fish and shellfish samples are shown in Table A3-2. In Table A3-2, it is seen that levels of B[a]PE are higher in the smoked salmon. PAHs in smoked foods are known to be generated by pyrolysis of the smoke constituents during preparation; searing or smoking food commonly results in a considerable increase in PAH levels (Fazio and Howard 1983).

Table A3-2 Number of Alaskan fish and shellfish samples collected in 1989

Source	B[a]P Equivalencies (ppb)				
	<0.5	1	2–5	8–17	>49
Fish (incl. salmon)	>100	0	0	0	0
Molluskan bivalves (except Windy Bay)	139	11	4	1	0
Windy Bay molluskan bivalves	1	0	2	2	2
Smoked salmon	0	0	0	0	4

Individual values (ppb) for Windy Bay molluskan bivalves and smoked salmon:
Windy Bay molluskan bivalves: 0, 3, 4, 11, 17, 71, 107 (mean = 30)
Smoked salmon: 49, 52, 133, 215 (mean = 112)

Fish Consumption Estimate for Alaskan Subsistence Fishermen

The Food and Color Additives Review Section (memo M.A. Adams, USFDA, to Mike Bolger, Contaminants Team) has evaluated for QRAC the two Alaskan subsistence fish consumption surveys previously mentioned.

Fish consumption patterns were surveyed for the village of Chenega Bay by the Alaska Department of Fish and Game, Division of Subsistence between 1984 and 1986 (Stratton and Chisum 1986). Chenega Bay is accessible only by air or water. The residents, 77% of whom are Alaska Native, use traditional hunting and fishing practices to obtain a major portion of their food. Food consumption on Kodiak Island, Alaska, was surveyed by KANA and the State of Alaska in 1983 (KANA 1983).

The Food and Color Additives Review Section also recently estimated freshwater fish consumption among subsistence fishermen in the contiguous U.S. (memo G. Cramer, USFDA, to S. Henry, 13 Nov. 1989). Consumption estimates from these three sources are tabulated for comparison in Table A3-3.

The residents of Chenega Bay are more dependent on food obtained directly from nature than are subsistence fishermen of the contiguous U.S. who have access to alternate food sources such as supermarkets or farms. In addition, the rigors of living in a cold climate may increase the caloric demand of the body, requiring a higher food intake to maintain normal body function. Thus, it is not surprising that total per-capita fish consumption is higher among the Alaskans than among subsistence fishermen in the contiguous U.S. Fish and shellfish consumption in the isolated Alaskan communities depends on resources available, prevailing customs and tradition, and access to alternate food sources from outside the community. Average fish and shellfish consumption values may vary somewhat from community to community, but all are of the same order of magnitude, as is illustrated by the Kodiak Island study when compared with the Chenega Bay study. Isolated Kodiak Islanders apparently make much greater use of the naturally occurring food resources.

Table A3-3 Fish and shellfish consumption for subsistence fishermen in Alaska and contiguous U.S.

Resource	g/person/day
Chenega Bay survey (per capita data)	
Salmon[1]	89
All other fish[2]	52
Subtotal	141
Bivalve mollusks[3]	2
Crabs[4]	8
Shrimp	11
Subtotal	21
Kodiak Island, Alaska (per capita data)	
Most isolated population	
Fish (excluding shellfish)	369
Butter clams	27
Less isolated population	
Fish (excluding shellfish)[5]	124
Butter clams	10
Contiguous U.S. (estimate for subsistence fisherman and family—USFDA)	
Freshwater fish	69 (mean) 116 (90th percentile)

[1]Includes king, red, pink, chum, and silver salmon
[2]Includes halibut, herring, herring roe, gray and black cod, red and black rockfish, smelt/eulachon, shark, eel, Dolly Varden, and trout
[3]Includes razor and other clam species, cockles, and mussels
[4]Includes Dungeness, king, and tanner crabs
[5]Mostly red and pink salmon

Risk Assessment for Cancer

An approach to estimating the carcinogenic risk from contamination of food with many PAHs is to design a scheme whereby the total PAH contamination is expressed as B[a]P potency equivalents. This approach has been taken above with the levels of PAHs found in the Alaskan fish and shellfish samples.

After evaluating the available data, the Cancer Assessment Committee of the Center for Food Safety and Applied Nutrition concluded that the most suitable chronic cancer bioassay for B[a]P, although less than ideal, is the one reported by Brune et al. (1981). In this study, there was one dose group of rats which were administered B[a]P alone for their lifetime, a feature which was not available in the small number of other studies that might even be considered for this purpose. The fact that there is only one dosage level administered makes a dose-response evaluation somewhat limited. However, the existence of a low incidence of treatment-related tumors, which were mostly benign, indicates that the response is at the lower end of the observable dose-response curve. The response, therefore, is where QRAC would initiate a linear extrapolation to a zero dose, even if there were more data points.

The administered dose in this study was 0.15 mg/kg bw/day, five days per week, to Sprague-Dawley rats for 131 weeks. The males were more sensitive with eight out of 32 having either a benign forestomach tumor or esophageal tumor. The control group had an incidence of two out of 32 rats with benign forestomach tumors after 129 weeks. The time-averaged daily dose was

$$0.15 \text{ mg/kg bw/day} \times 5/7 \qquad 0.107 \text{ mg/kg/bw/day}$$

Unit risk (potency)

$$8/32\text{-}2/32 \qquad 1.75 \text{ (mg/kg bw/day)}^{-1} \qquad 0.107 \text{ mg/kg bw/day}$$

QRAC has chosen to use the Chenega Bay fish and shellfish data as presented in Table A3-3 for the estimation of upper-bound lifetime risks presented in Table A3-4. It is believed that the Chenega Bay residents are among the most likely consumers of fish and shellfish that might have come in contact with spilled oil, making the Chenega Bay data most useful and relevant for risk assessment.

Table A3-4 Risk for Alaskan subsistence fishermen consuming PAH-contaminated fish and shellfish

Source	Intake (g/person/d)[a]	B[a]PE (mg/person/d)[b]	Upper-bound lifetime risk[c]
Salmon[d]	89	ND[e]	NQ[e]
All other fish[d]	52	ND[e]	NQ[e]
Smoked salmon[f]	45	5.0×10^{-3}	1.5×10^{-4}
Bivalve mollusks[g]	2	6.0×10^{-3}	1.8×10^{-6}[h]

[a]Taken from Table A3-3

[b]From Table A3-2, the mean concentration of B[a]PE for smoked salmon is 112 ppb B[a]PE x 44.5 g (5.0×10^{-3} mg/p/d).

[c]For smoked salmon: 5.0×10^{-3} B[a]PE x 60 kg person unit risk of 1.75 = 1.5×10^{-4}

[d]Includes halibut, herring and herring roe, gray and black cod, red and black rockfish, smelt/eulachon, shark, eel, Dolly Varden, and trout. Salmon is mostly red and pink salmon.

[e]ND = not detectable; NQ =- not quantifiable.

[f]Alaskan subsistence fishermen are estimated to consume about 50% of their salmon catch smoked (personal communication, Robert Wolfe, Div. of Subsistence, Alaska Dept. Fish and Game, Juneau).

[g]Using the mean Windy Bay value of 30 ppb for molluskan bivalves from Table A3-3.

[h]This assumes that persons are exposed to B[a]PE for their entire lifetime from this oil spill. It can be assumed that exposure would be at most no more than 10 years at this level. Therefore, at a minimum, the upper-bound lifetime risk can be adjusted by a factor of 1/7 of a lifetime (i.e., 1/7 x 70 years = 10 years) to provide an adjusted upper-bound risk of 2.5×10^{-7}. The dose corresponding to a 10^{-6} lifetime upper-bound risk would be: $10^{-6}/1.75$ (mg/kg bw/d)$^{-1}$ 0.57 ng/kg bw/d. For a 60-kg person, the dose corresponding to a 10^{-6} lifetime upper-bound risk would be: 0.57 ng/kg bw/d x 60-kg person 34 ng B[a]PE/person/day

For the purpose of estimating levels of concern for B[a]PE from the *Exxon Valdez* oil spill in subsistence fishery resources, it will be assumed that the impact of the spill will occur for no more than 10 years. This assumption is based on data accumulated from prior spills in which the environmental status of an affected area generally returns to that existing prior to the spill within several years (Gundlach et al. 1983). The evidence from these spills indicates that oiled environments do cleanse themselves and that there are environmental mechanisms of oil degradation and biological recovery (NRC 1985). Therefore, the duration of exposure would not be for a 70-year lifetime, but rather for 10 years or less. Table A3-5 presents advisory levels for various subsistence fishery resources.

Table A3-5 USFDA advisory levels for Alaskan subsistence fishery resources

Resource	Intake g/person/day	B[a]PE Levels (ppb) for 10^{-6} Risk	
		Lifetime	10 years[1]
Salmon	89	0.4	3
Other finfish	52	0.7	5
Bivalve mollusks	2	17.0	120
Crustaceans	21	1.6	

[1]Advisory level corresponding to a 10^{-6} risk and a period of exposure of 10 years (1/7 of a 70-year lifetime): Advisory level (ppb or ng/g) 34 ng B[a]PE/person/day x 7 g of fishery resource/ person/day, where 34 ng B[a]PE = dose corresponding to a 10^{-6} lifetime upper-bound risk, and 7 = correction factor for less than lifetime exposure of 10 years.

If a 10^{-5} upper-bound risk standard were used rather than a 10^{-6} upper-bound standard, then the corresponding advisory levels would be 10-fold greater than those presented in Table A3-5. In the case of the dioxin advisory opinion, a 10^{-6} upper-bound risk standard was used. Other governmental institutions (e.g., USEPA and various states) have often based their risk-assessment decisions on a 10^{-5} risk standard. The issue of an acceptable risk standard for a consideration such as subsistence fishing is one that resides with the state.

These advisory levels can be interpreted as concentrations that, if not exceeded for the given conditions of exposure (lifetime or 10 years consumption at 7-fold higher levels), will conservatively limit any carcinogenic risk from ingested B[a]PE to less than 10^{-6}*. Although PAHs produced by smoking fish are unrelated to the oil spill, an advisory level of 0.8 ppb could be established for smoked salmon (0.8 ppb = 34 ng B[a]PE/45 g salmon). The fact that the mean concentration of B[a]PE in smoked salmon was reported to be 112 ppb (see Table A3-2) illustrates the importance of this method of food preparation as a source of PAHs.

Generally the procedures used to estimate low levels of carcinogenic risk provide exposure levels that are well below those that elicit other toxicological endpoints. Therefore, any advisory level based on carcinogenic activity of a toxicant is a conservative estimate of risk that virtually always would subsume the risk from other potential toxicological endpoints.

*The actual risk may be lower than these figures suggest.

Conclusions

The PAHs reported in the subsistence survey account for the majority of the aromatic residues that are measurable by current available analytical methodology. The risk assessment is therefore confined to these measurable PAHs.

In interpreting the risk estimates and advisory levels presented in Tables A3-4 and A3-5, several points should be emphasized. First, the equivalency approach to estimating the potencies of various PAHs taken in this report is based on several assumptions pointed out earlier. This approach cannot be assumed to produce exact potencies for the PAHs. Second, there are limitations in the laboratory animal data used to estimate the potency of B[a]P and other PAHs. Third, as with all QRAC quantitative risk assessments, an upper-bound risk estimate has been produced with the knowledge that the true risk is somewhere between the upper-bound number presented and zero.

With regard to fresh salmon, the dose level corresponding to the lifetime 10^{-6} upper-bound risk level is at or below the detection limit of the PAHs. The risk associated with the consumption of salmon that is not smoked is insignificant relative to that associated with consuming smoked salmon because smoking significantly increases PAH levels.

Analyses of molluskan bivalves from areas unaffected by the oil spill have indicated that PAH levels are negligible (Varanasi et al. 1990). The risk estimate presented for molluskan bivalves in Table A3-4 is predicated on the conservative assumption that persons at risk would consume molluskan bivalves contaminated at the level of PAHs produced by the *Exxon Valdez* oil spill for a lifetime; molluskan bivalves would not be expected to be contaminated with PAHs at this level for such a long time period.

Therefore, QRAC concludes that the lifetime upper-bound risk of consumption is low for unsmoked salmon, other finfish, crustaceans, and oil-contaminated molluskan bivalves.

References

Brune H, Deutsch-Wenzel RP, Habs M, Ivankovic S, and Schmahl D. 1981. Investigation of the tumorigenic response to benzo(a)pyrene in aqueous caffeine solution applied orally to Sprague-Dawley rats. *J Cancer Res Clin Oncol* 102:153–157.

Busby Jr WF, Goldman ME, Newberne PM, Wogan GN. 1984. Tumorigenicity of fluoranthene in a newborn mouse lung adenoma bioassay. *Carcinogenesis* 5:1311–1316.

Clement International Corporation. 1990. Development of relative potency estimates for PAHs and hydrocarbon combustion product fractions compared to benzo[a]pyrene and their use in carcinogenic risk assessments. Fairfax VA: Clement International Corporation. 30 September 1990.

Deutsch-Wenzel RP, Brune H, Bond JA, Hesseltine GR. 1985. Experimental studies in rat lungs on the carcinogenicity and dose-response relationships of eight frequently occurring environmental polycyclic aromatic hydrocarbons. *J Natl Cancer Inst* 71:539–544.

Fazio T, Howard JW. 1983. Polycyclic aromatic hydrocarbons in foods. In: Bjorseth A, editor. Handbook of polycyclic aromatic hydrocarbons. New York: Marcel Dekker. p 461–505.

Gundlach E, Boehm P, Marchand M, Atlas R, Ward D, Wolfe D. 1983. The fate of *Amoco Cadiz* oil. *Science* 221:122–129.

[IARC] International Agency for Research on Cancer. 1989. Crude oil. In: IARC monographs on the evaluation of carcinogenic risks to humans. Volume 45, Occupational exposures in petroleum refining: Crude oil and major petroleum fields. Lyons, France: International Agency for Research on Cancer, World Health Organization. p 119–158.

[KANA] Kodiak Area Native Association. 1983. Kodiak Island area local fish and game resource guide. December 1993. Prepared for the Alaska Dept. of Fish and Game.

Moolgavkar SH, Knudson AG. 1981. Mutation and cancer: A model for human carcinogenesis. *J Natl Cancer Inst* 66:1037–1052.

[NRC] National Research Council. 1985. Oil in the sea: Inputs, fates, and effects. Washington DC: National Academy Press p 549–582.

Slooff W, Janus JA, Matthijen AJCM, Montizaan GK, Ros JPM. 1989. Integrated criteria document PAHs. The Netherlands: National Institute of Public Health and Environmental Protection. Report No. 758474011

Stratton L, Chisum EB. 1986. Resource use patterns in Chenega, Western Prince William Sound: Chenega in the 1960s and Chenega Bay 1984–1986. Juneau AK: Division of Subsistence, Alaska Department of Fish and Game. Technical Paper 139.

Varanasi U, Chan S-L, MacLeod WD, Stein JE, Brown DW, Burrows DG, Tilbury KL, Landahl JL, Wigren CA, Hom T, Pierce SM. 1990. Survey of subsistence shellfish for exposure to oil spilled from the *Exxon Valdez*. Summary. Cycles I-III. Seattle WA: Environmental Conservation Division, Northwest Fisheries Science Center, National Marine Fisheries Service, NOAA.

Wislocki PG, Bagan ES, Lu AYH, Dooley KL, Fu PP, Han-Hsu H, Beland FA, Kadlubar FF. 1986. Tumorigenicity of nitrated derivatives of pyrene, benz[a]anthracene, chrysene, and benzo[a]pyrene in the newborn mouse assay. *Carcinogenesis* 7:1317–1322.

Appendix 4

Results of 1989 Exxon/NOAA Subsistence Fish and Shellfish Studies for 12 Sampling Areas

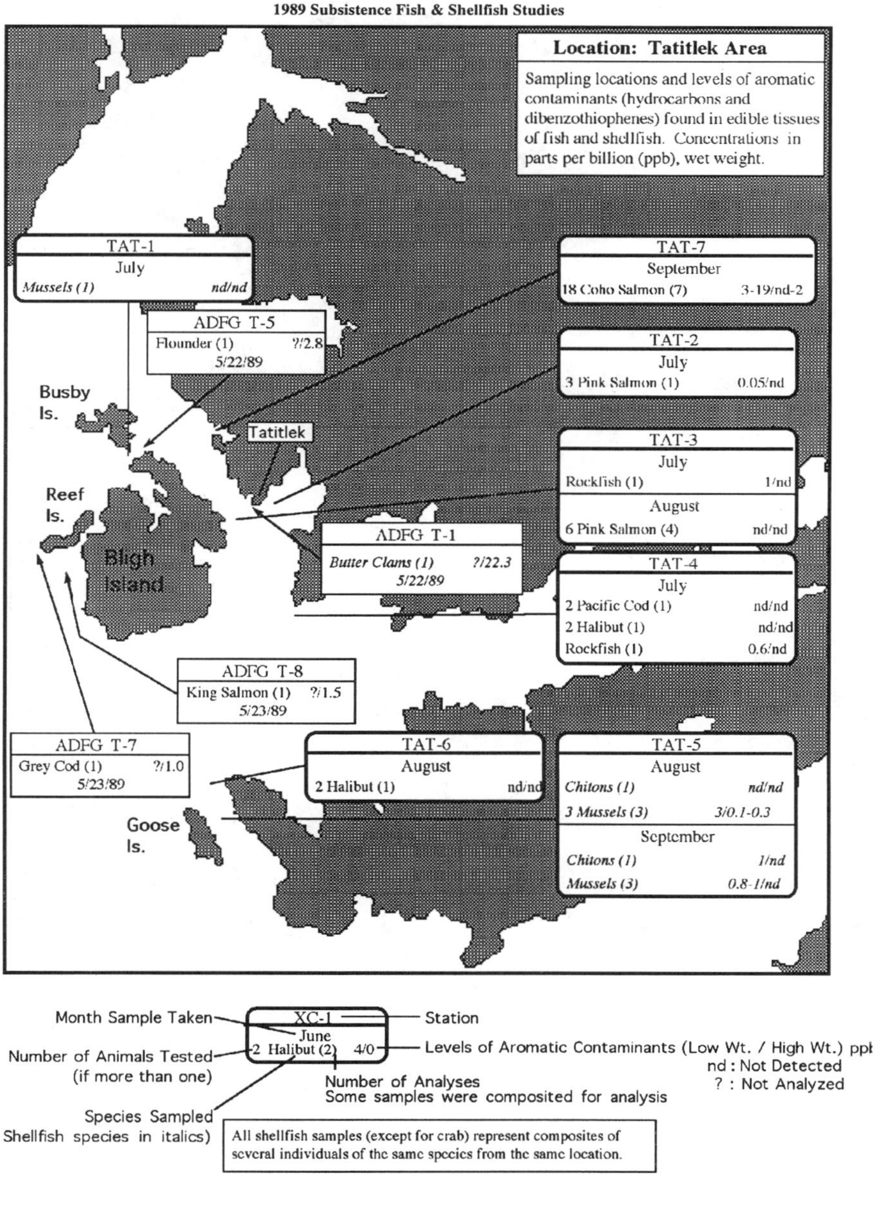

1989 Subsistence Fish & Shellfish Studies

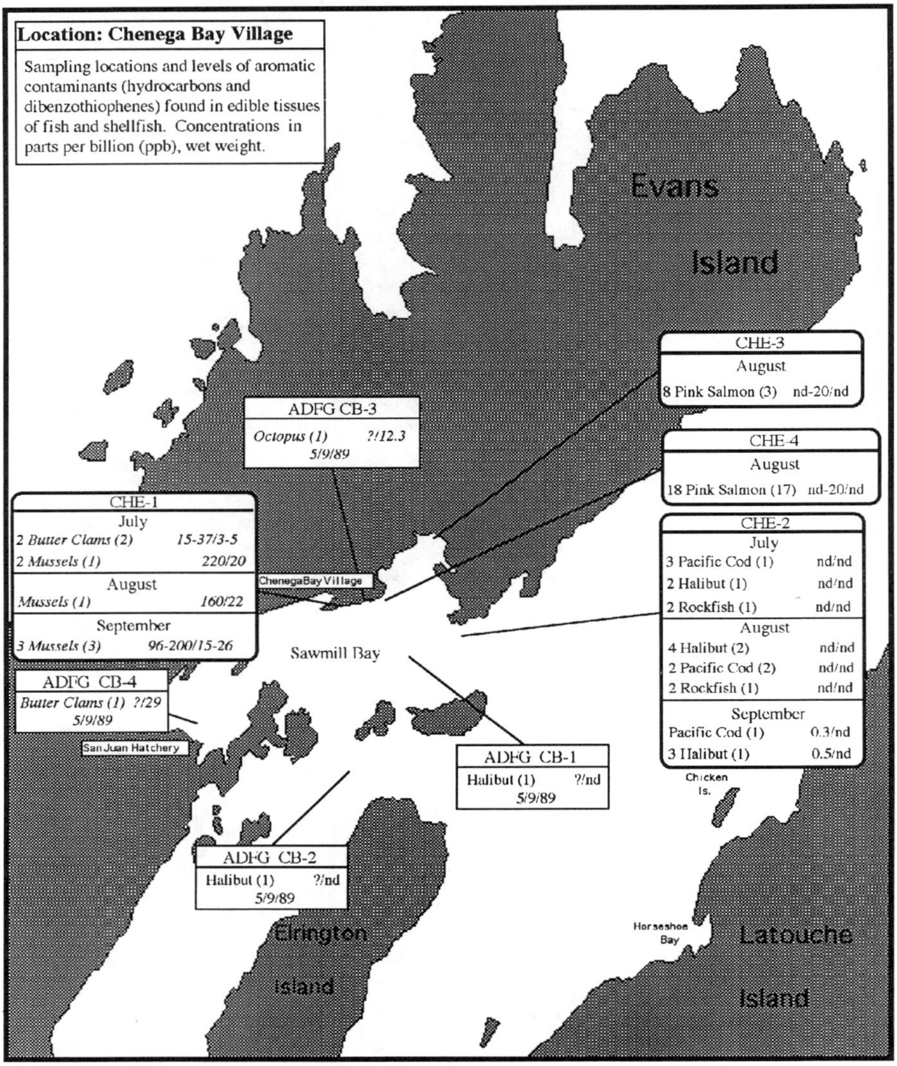

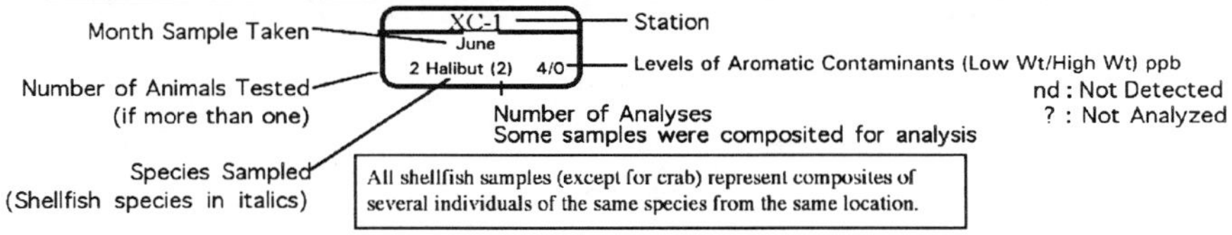

1989 Subsistence Fish & Shellfish Studies

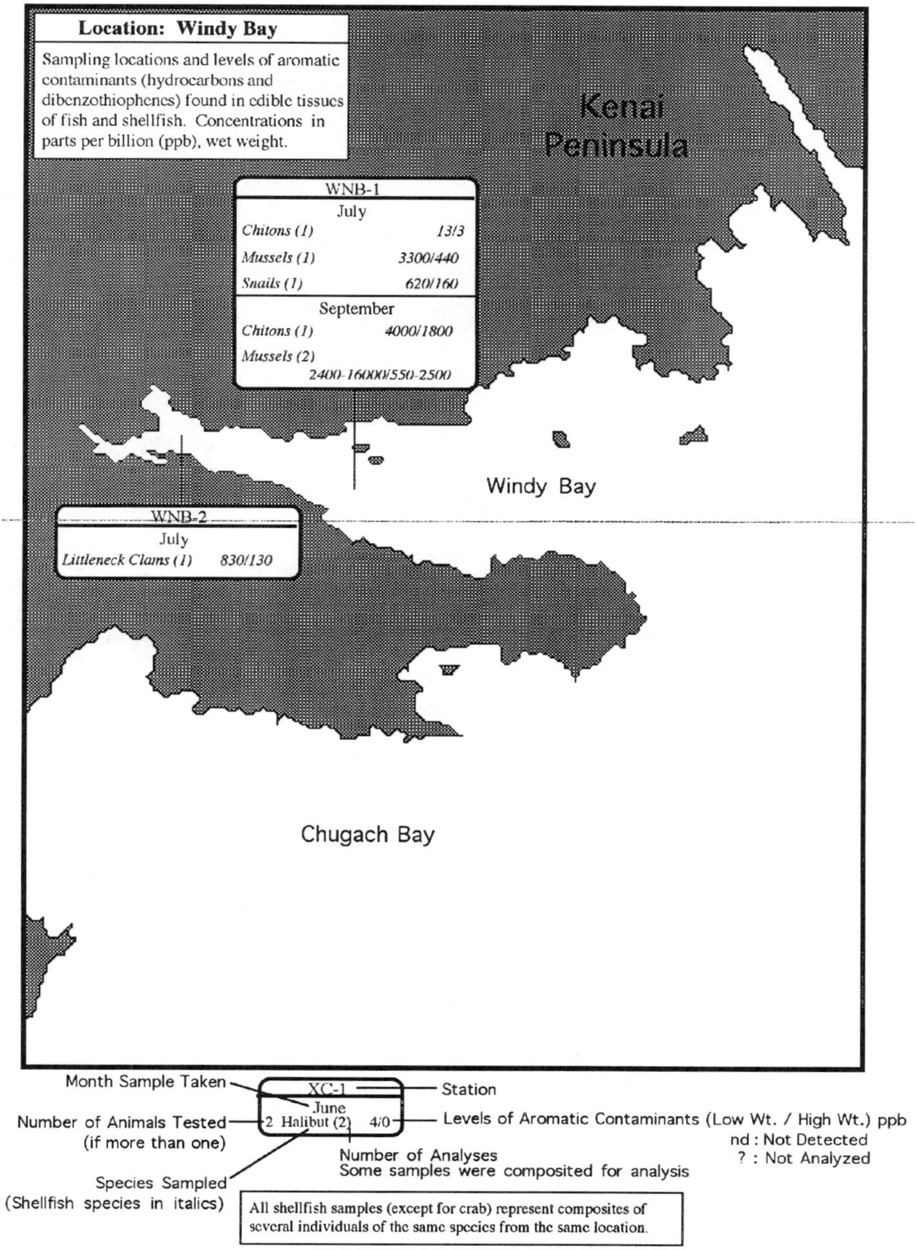

1989 Subsistence Fish & Shellfish Studies

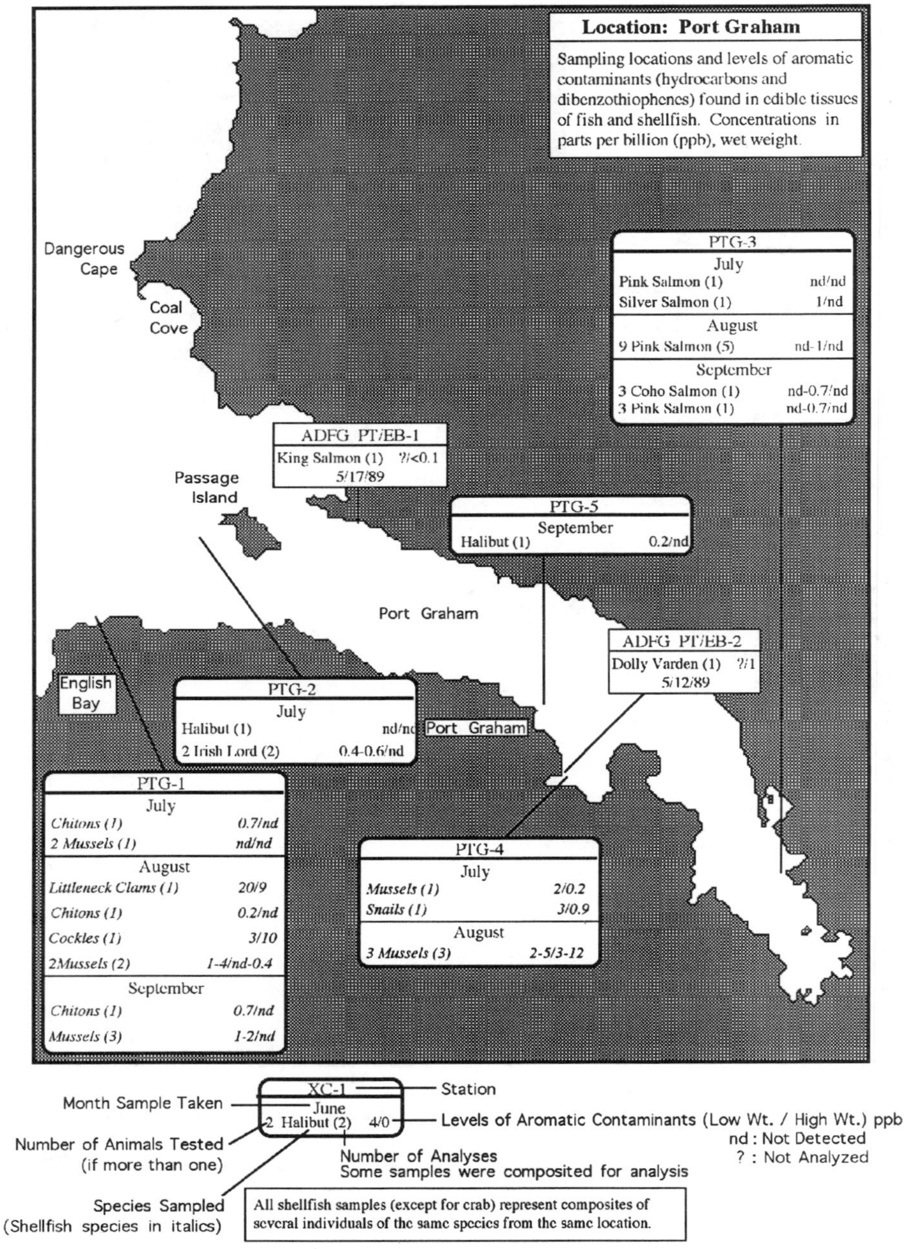

1989 Subsistence Fish & Shellfish Studies

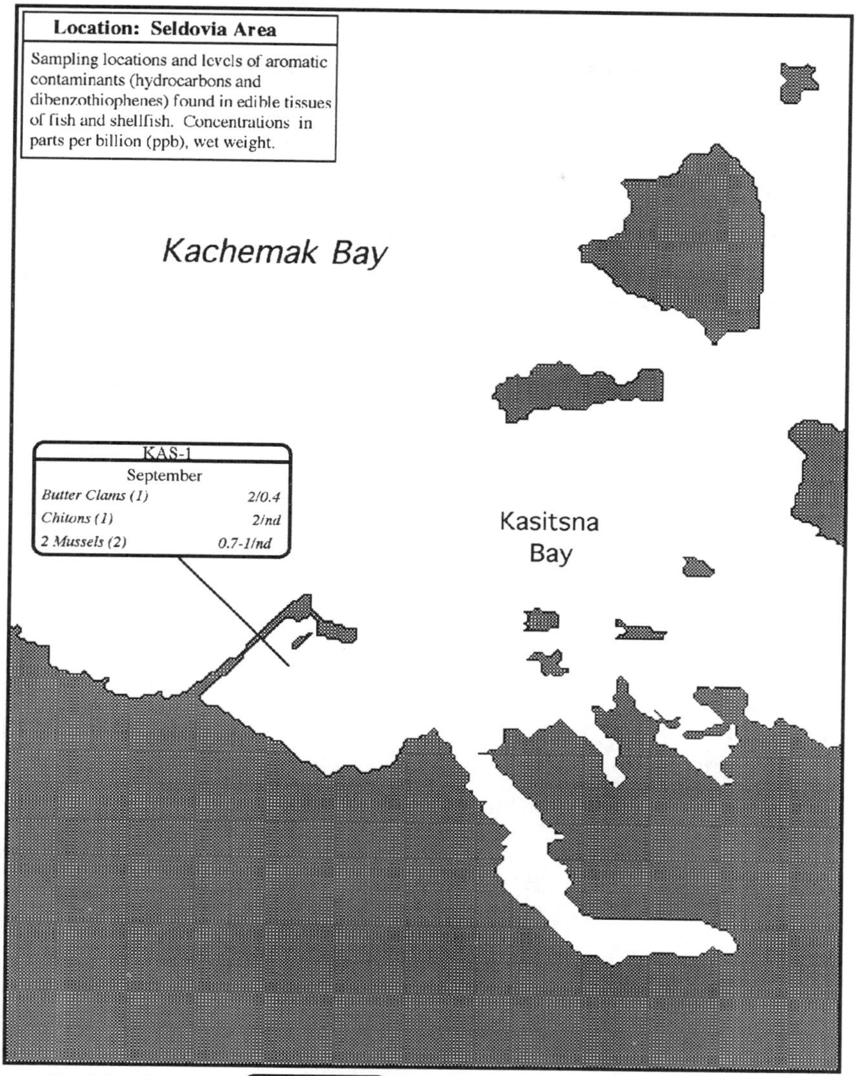

Key to the sample box (example: XC-1, June, 2 Halibut (2), 4/0):

- XC-1 — Station
- June — Month Sample Taken
- 2 — Number of Animals Tested (if more than one)
- Halibut — Species Sampled (Shellfish species in italics)
- (2) — Number of Analyses. Some samples were composited for analysis
- 4/0 — Levels of Aromatic Contaminants (Low Wt. / High Wt.) ppb
  - nd : Not Detected
  - ? : Not Analyzed

All shellfish samples (except for crab) represent composites of several individuals of the same species from the same location.

1989 Subsistence Fish & Shellfish Studies

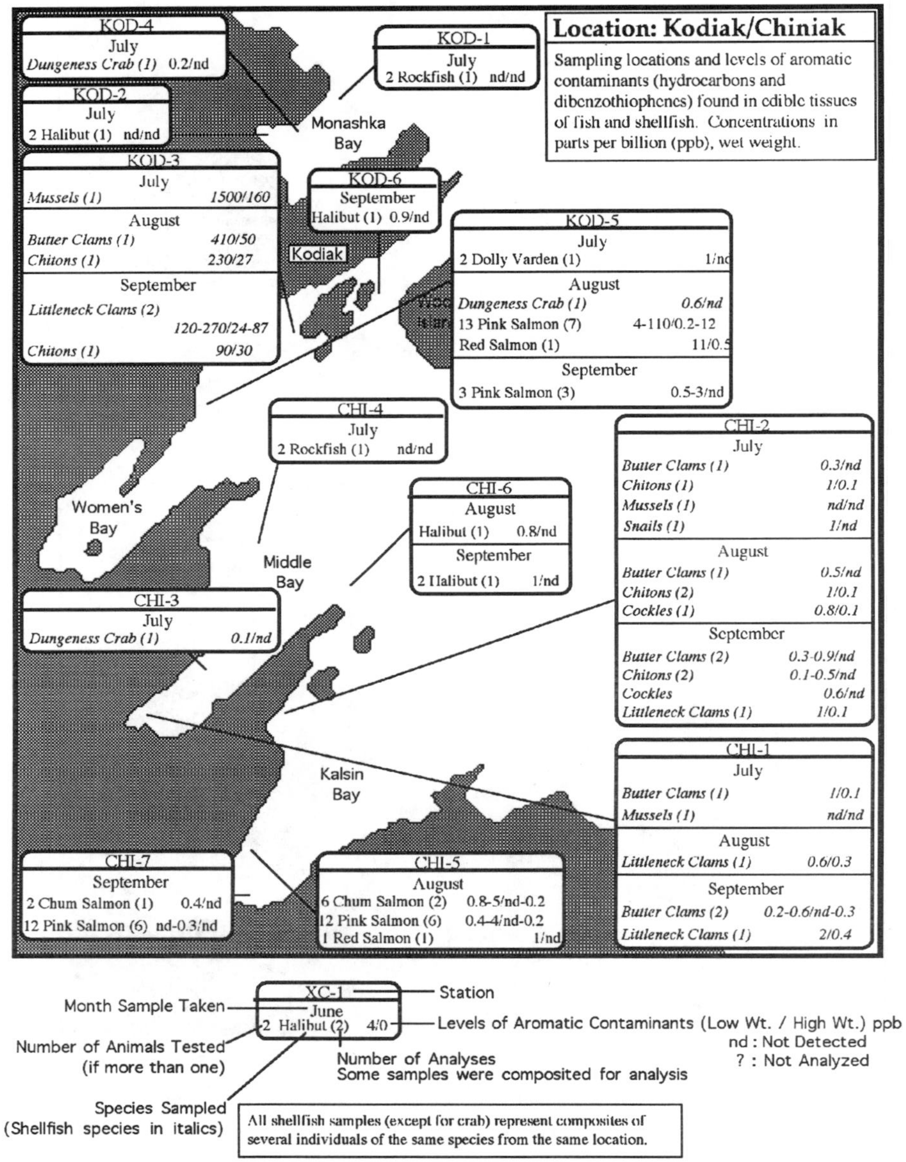

1989 Subsistence Fish & Shellfish Studies

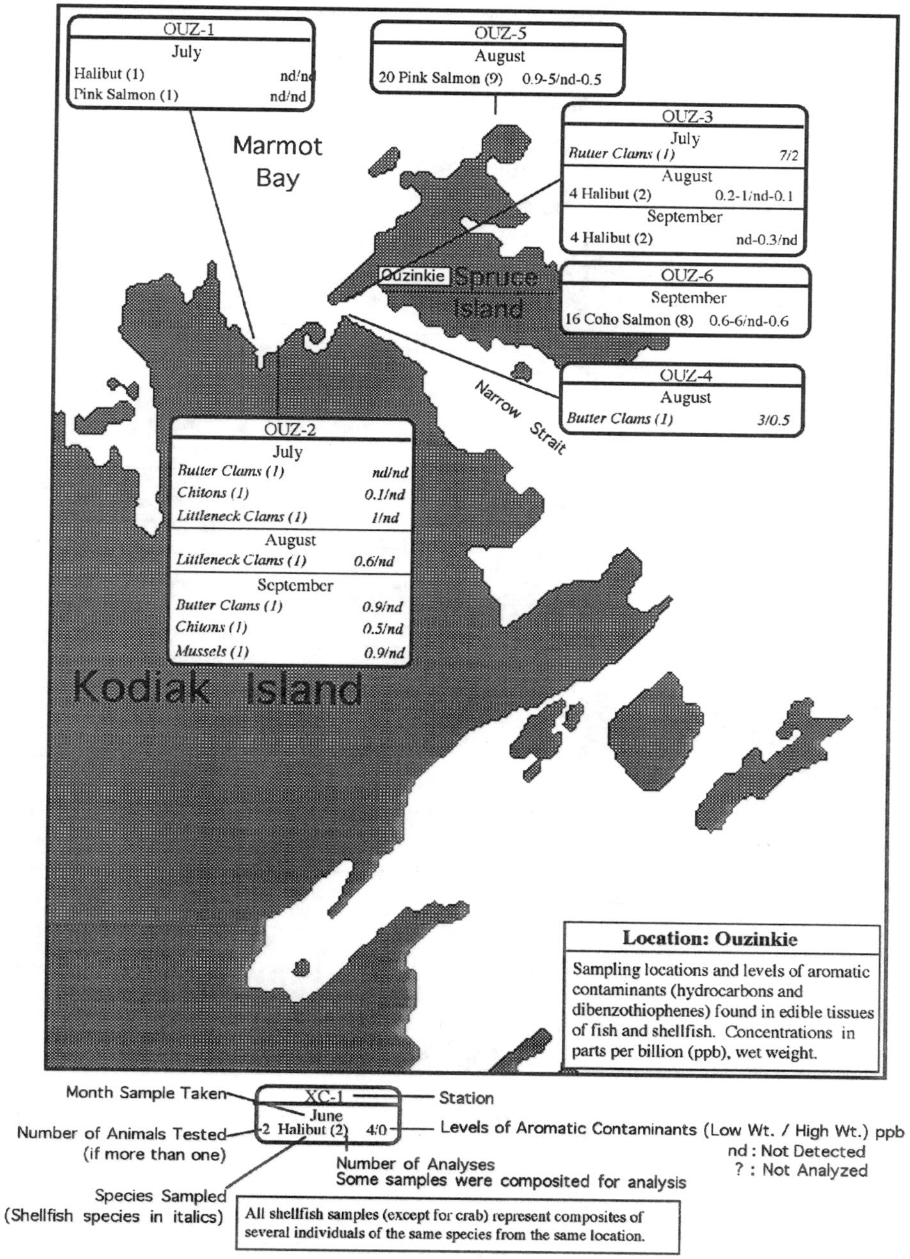

1989 Subsistence Fish & Shellfish Studies

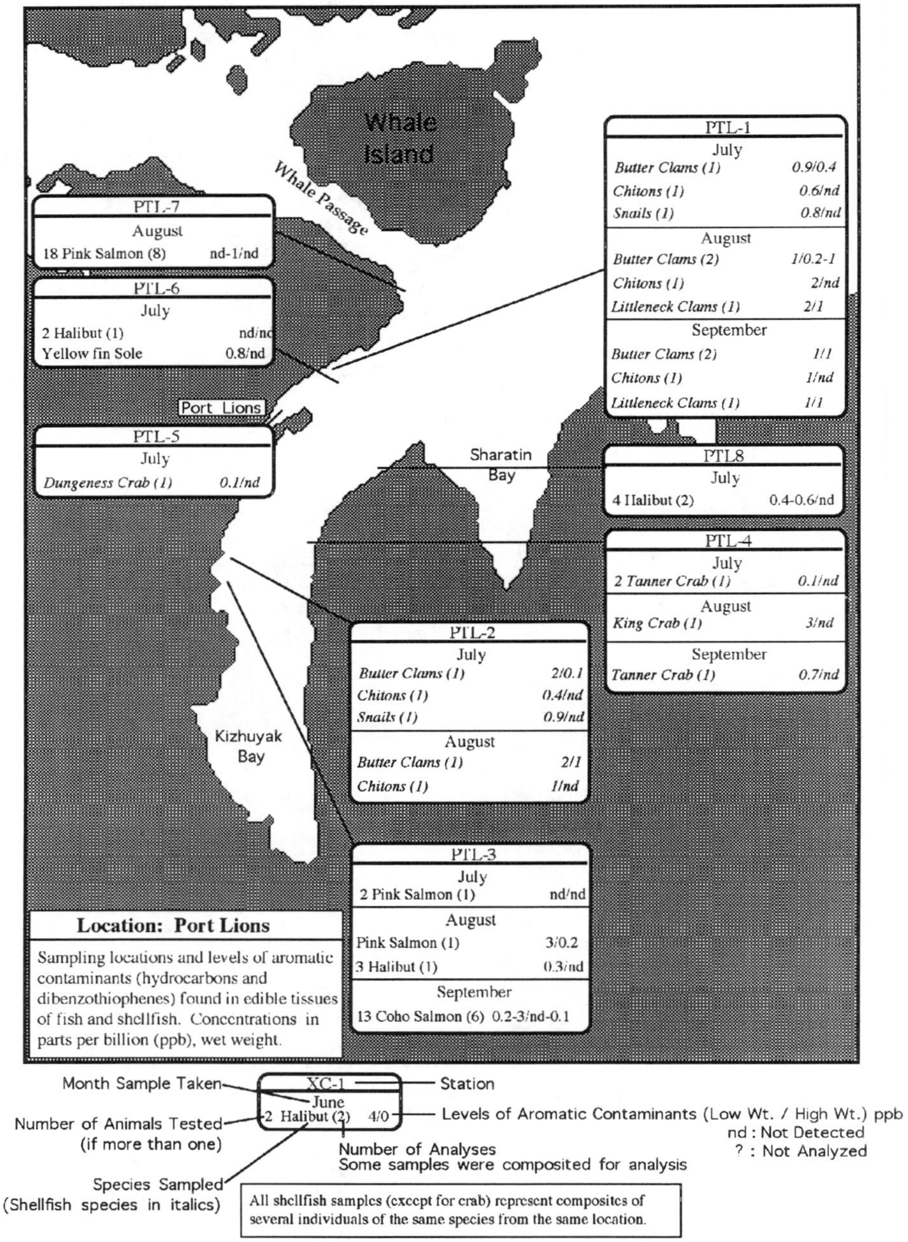

1989 Subsistence Fish & Shellfish Studies

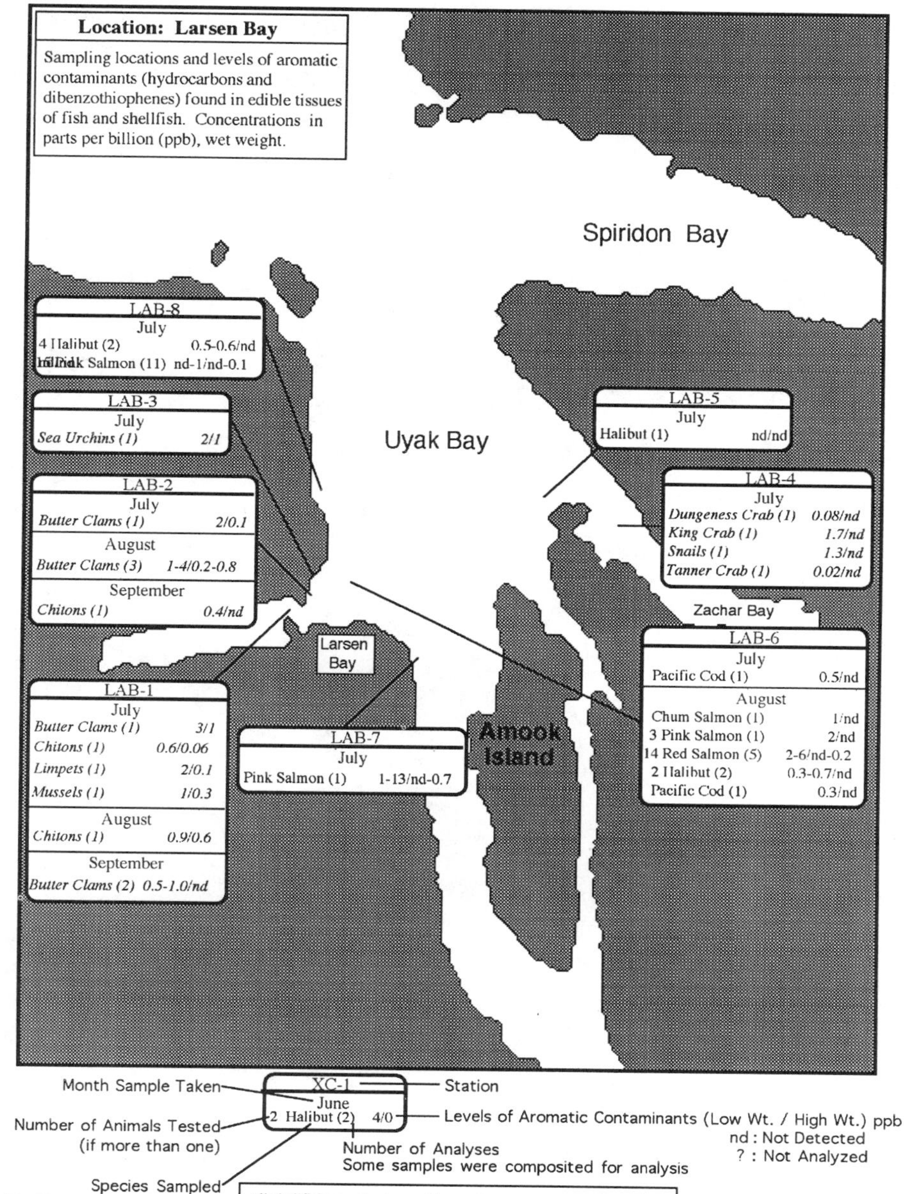

All shellfish samples (except for crab) represent composites of several individuals of the same species from the same location.

1989 Subsistence Fish & Shellfish Studies

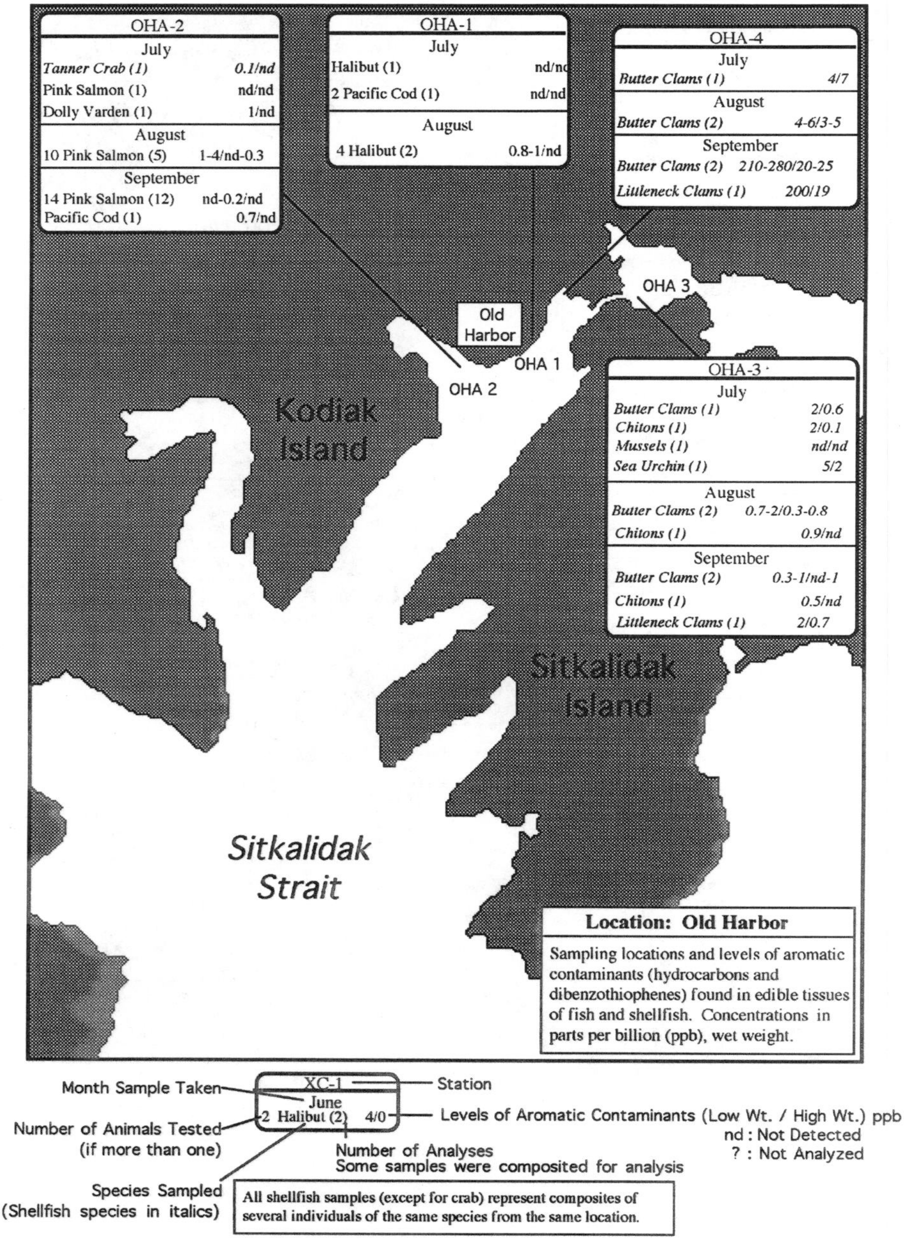

1989 Subsistence Fish & Shellfish Studies

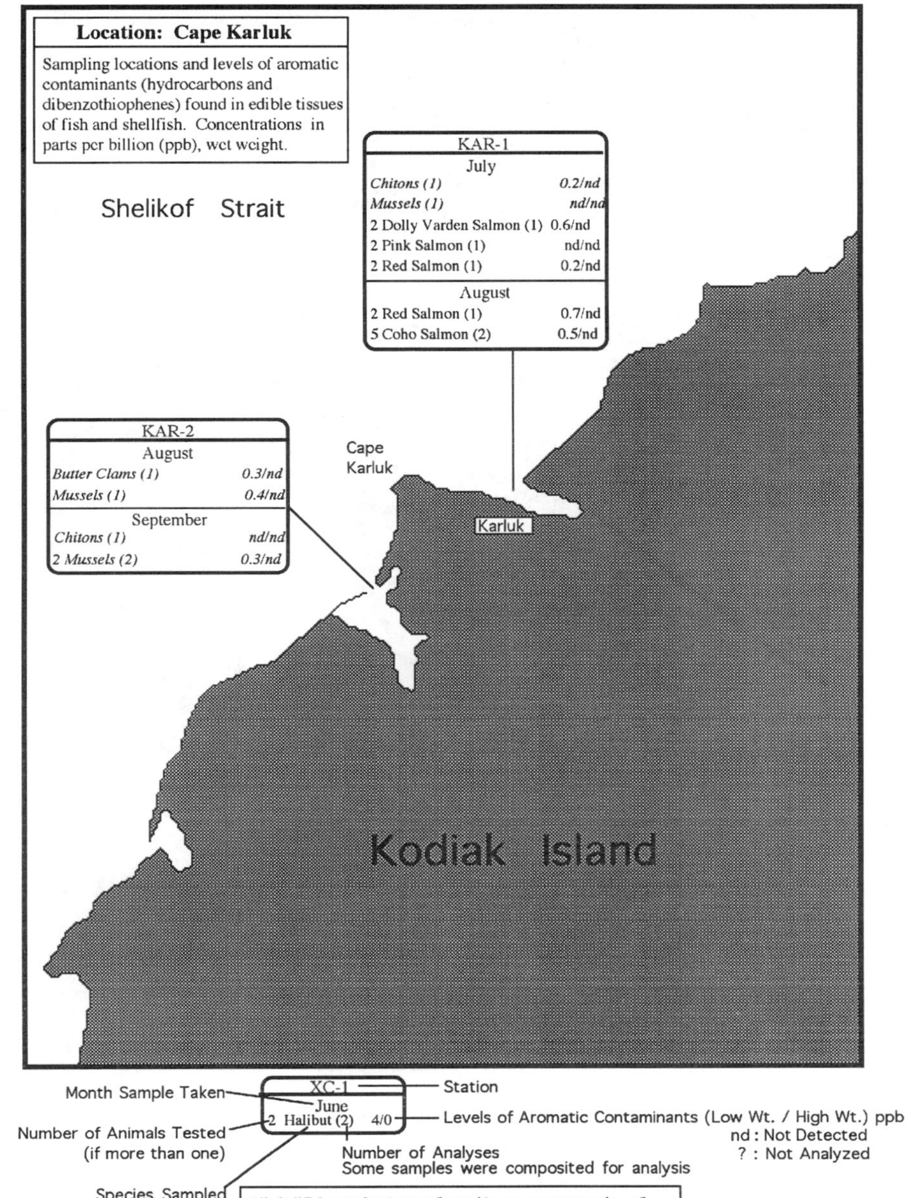

All shellfish samples (except for crab) represent composites of several individuals of the same species from the same location.

1989 Subsistence Fish & Shellfish Studies

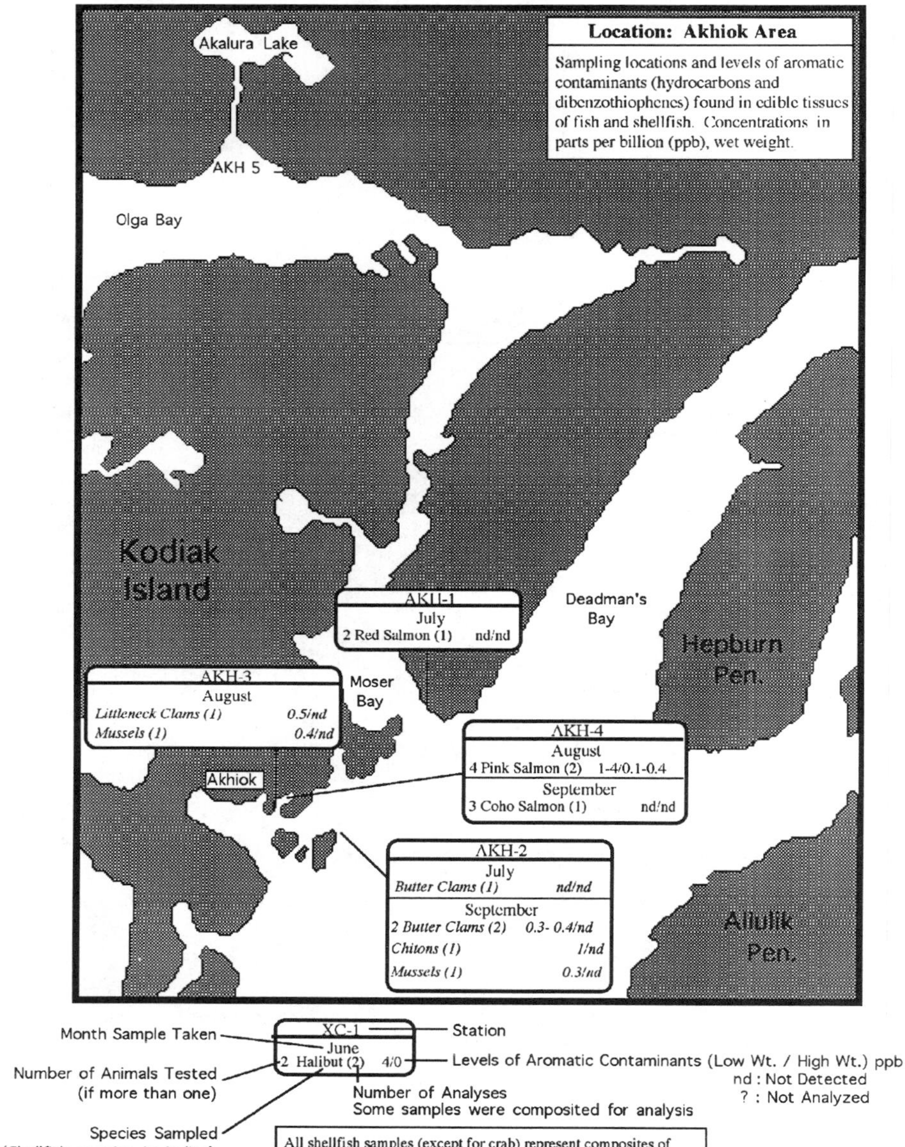

All shellfish samples (except for crab) represent composites of several individuals of the same species from the same location.

Appendix 5

Memorandum of Understanding between National Oceanic and Atmospheric Administration and Exxon related to the Sampling and Analysis of Subsistence Food Resources

[Dated 19 July 1989]

Exxon Company, USA (Exxon) and the National Oceanic and Atmospheric Administration (NOAA) hereby enter into an agreement with regard to the collection and analysis of biota for petroleum hydrocarbon/metabolites from subsistence use areas in Prince William Sound, Lower Cook Inlet, and Kodiak, Alaska. Sampling will be conducted in accordance with the Dames & Moore study plan entitled, "Subsistence Food Resource Sampling for Petroleum Contaminants." Sampling will be conducted in July, August and September, 1989 and may continue in 1990 pending results from 1989. A NOAA biologist will accompany Dames & Moore personnel during field sampling. Samples will be transferred as quickly as possible from the field to NOAA's National Marine Fisheries Service (NMFS), Environmental Conservation Division, in Seattle. Normal chain of custody procedures will be followed.

NOAA/NMFS laboratories will perform analyses of 800 bile and 120 edible tissues for petroleum hydrocarbons/metabolites on a prioritized basis following each monthly round of sampling. Turnaround is estimated at four weeks, however initial results may be available within two weeks. An additional 120 edible tissue samples/round will be analyzed after completion of the 1989 field season. Methodology will be in accordance with NOAA Tech. Memo. NMFS F/NWC-102 - Standard Analytical Procedures of the NOAA National Analytical Facility, 1986: Metabolites of Aromatic Compounds in Fish Bile; and NOAA Tech. Memo. NMFS/NWC-153 – Standard Analytical Procedures of the NOAA National Analytical Facility, 1988: New HPLC Cleanup and Revised Extraction Procedures for Organic Contaminants. Target PAH compounds will be as per SOP EV89-2. Since bile metabolite levels have been shown to be far more sensitive than muscle tissue levels, bile fluid will be used to screen fish samples. If metabolites are detected in bile samples, selected tissues corresponding to high bile values will be analyzed (20%). To provide additional confidence that failure to detect metabolites in bile indicates nondetectable levels in tissue, 5% of edible tissue from fish with "clean" bile will be analyzed. All invertebrate tissues will be analyzed as composites. For the first round of sampling, all tissues will be analyzed in addition to bile screenings.

  ISBN 1-880611-29-5

Results of analyses will be placed in the public domain and made immediately available to all interested parties. Costs for analyses are estimated at $266,000 per month (complete sampling round), but will be based on actual analyses. Costs for analyses will be $100 per bile sample and $750 per tissue sample. Total costs for 1989 are estimated at $800,000, recognizing that sampling success will be less than optimal in the first and last sampling rounds.

Appendix 6

Chronology of Events Related to the Work of the Oil Spill Health Task Force

Date	Event
24 March 1989	The Exxon Valdez hits Bligh Reef
11 April 1989	Teleconference on "Food Safety/Health Effects" of the oil spill; issues raised regarding acute and chronic effects of oil on subsistence foods
24 April 1989	First meeting of the OSHTF, Anchorage
5 May 1989	First ADHSS Bulletin regarding subsistence food safety
May & June 1989	Division of Subsistence, ADF&G, conducts pilot study
8 June 1989	Zero-tolerance policy regarding commercial fisheries announced by ADF&G and ADEC
15 June 1989	NMFS releases report on analysis of halibut from spill area
21 June 1989	NOAA attends its first OSHTF meeting
July 1989	Agreement between NOAA and Exxon signed
July 1989	Cycle I of Exxon Collection Program
12 July 1989	Exxon attends first OSHTF meeting to describe its program
14 July 1989	Second ADHSS Bulletin
30 July 1989	Meeting of OSHTF in Seattle, in conjunction with the first National Forum on the EVOS
August 1989	Cycle II of Exxon Collection Program
21 August 1989	Release of findings from ADF&G pilot study by USFDA
28 August 1989	Release of findings from Exxon Cycle I by NOAA
September 1989	Cycle III of Exxon Collection Program; final round of sample collection in 1989
14 September 1989	First meeting of the Expert Toxicological Committee, Seattle
22 September 1989	Third ADHSS Bulletin, reporting recommendations from Expert Committee
September & October 1989	First round of OSHTF-sponsored village meetings
2 October 1989	Release of findings from Exxon Cycle II by NOAA
13 October 1989	Fourth ADHSS Bulletin
18 October 1989	At AFN meeting, State commits to funding collection of subsistence samples
25 October 1989	At OSHTF meeting, Exxon announces it will fund more collections, based on meeting between T. Nighswander, J. Meidinger, and O. Harrison of 16 October 1989
13 November 1989	NOAA releases results from Cycle III of Exxon sample collection
7 February 1990	NOAA releases its summary report on Cycles I–III of the Exxon sample-collection program
21–22 February 1990	Second meeting of the Expert Toxicological Committee, Seattle
28 February 1990	Final ADHSS Bulletin regarding subsistence food safety
February 1990	ADF&G, Division of Subsistence, begins second year of sample collection
February 1990	First issue of The Oil Spill Health Task Force Newsletter produced
February 1990	Exxon begins its second year of sample collection

Date	Event
June 1990	First results on seals released
June 1990	Video "Oil Spill: Threat to Subsistence" released by ADF&G
27 July 1990	First results on ducks and deer released
14–15 August 1990	Review workshop, Queenstown, Maryland
21 August 1990	Release of USFDA risk assessment
September 1990	Risk Communication Workshop (sponsored by the OSHTF), Anchorage
March 1991	USFWS releases, for the first time, selected results of government damage-assessment studies
April & June 1991	First round of third year of sample collection
August 1991	Second round of third year of sample collection
September 1991	Final Oil Spill Health Task Force newsletter (continued as the "Subsistence Restoration Project Newsletter")
12 June 1992	State and federal on-scene coordinators declare that the oil-spill cleanup is over
June 1992	Second, final round of village meetings sponsored by OSHTF takes place in Chenega Bay, Tatitlek, Nanwalek, Port Graham, and Kodiak
2–5 February 1993	Exxon Valdez Oil Spill Symposium, Anchorage; first public discussion of results of government damage-assessment studies
April 1993	Results of damage-assessment studies conducted by Exxon reported at the Third Symposium on Environmental Toxicology and Risk Assessment, Atlanta, Georgia
June & July 1993	Round of sample collection, funded by the EVOS Trustee Council
16 August 1993	NOAA releases its final report on the testing of subsistence seafood from 1989 through 1991
25 August 1993	Last meeting of the Oil Spill Health Task Force, Anchorage
27 August 1993	Community representatives visit the NOAA lab in Seattle; a second group visited the lab on September 22, 1994
September 1993	Round of sample collection, funded by EVOS Trustee Council
November 1993	First Subsistence Restoration Newsletter
February 1994	Subsistence Restoration Project Newsletter reports findings from 1993 round of sample collections
June & July 1994	Round of sample collection, funded by EVOS Trustee Council
August & September 1994	Final round of sample collection, funded by EVOS Trustee Council
August 1995	Penultimate Subsistence Restoration Newsletter reports results from 1994 rounds of sample collection
April 1996	Last Subsistence Restoration Newsletter
March 1999	10th Year Symposium: The Legacy of An Oil Spill, Anchorage; subsistence remains listed as an injured natural resource service

Abbreviations

AC	aromatic compounds/contaminants
ADEC	Alaska Department of Environmental Conservation
ADF&G	Alaska Department of Fish and Game
ADHSS	Alaska Department of Health and Social Services
ADPH	Alaska Division of Public Health
AFN	Alaska Federation of Natives
AH	aromatic hydrocarbon
ATSDR	Agency for Toxic Substances and Disease Registry
B[a]P	benzo[a]pyrene
B[a]PE	benzo[a]pyrene equivalency
C1NPH	C1-substituted naphthalene
C2NPH	C2-substituted naphthalene
C2PHN	C2-substituted phenanthrenes
CDC	Center for Disease Control
CERCLA	Comprehensive Environmental Response, Compensation, and Liability Act of 1980
EVOS	*Exxon Valdez* oil spill
FAC	fluorescent aromatic compounds
GC CS	gas chromatography calibration solution
GC I-Std	gas chromatography internal standard
GC/MS	gas chromatography/mass spectroscopy
HAC	high molecular weight aromatic compounds/contaminants
HPLC	high pressure liquid chromatography

HPLC CS	high pressure liquid chromatography calibration solution
HPLC I-Std	high pressure liquid chromatography internal standard
IRA	Indian Reorganization Act
KANA	Kodiak Area Native Association
LAC	low molecular weight aromatic compounds/contaminants
MMTAP	Marine Mammal Tissue Archival
MOU	Memorandum of Understanding
NRDA	Natural Resource Damage Assessment
NIOSH	National Institute for Occupational Safety and Health
NMFS	National Marine Fisheries Service
NOAA	National Oceanic and Atmospheric Administration
NPH	naphthalene
NWFSC	Northwest Fisheries Science Center
OR&R	Office of Response and Restoration
OSHTF	Oil Spill Health Task Force
PAH	polycyclic aromatic hydrocarbons
PBCO	Prudhoe Bay crude oil
PCB	polychlorinated biphenyl
PHN	phenanthrenes
PSP	paralytic shellfish poisoning
QA	quality assurance
QRAC	Quantitative Risk Assessment Committee

RC	reference compound
RSD	relative standard deviation
SAP	Sampling and Analysis Plan
SEQ	Social Effects Questionnaire
SSC	Scientific Support Coordinators
SSIM	sequenced selected-ion monitoring
S-Std	surrogate standard
USCG	U.S. Coast Guard
USFDA	U.S. Food and Drug Administration
VHS	viral hemorrhagic septicemia

Index

Bold typeface denotes figures or tables.

C

D

E

G

H

I

U

V

W

Y

Z